The Complete E.C. Segar Popeye

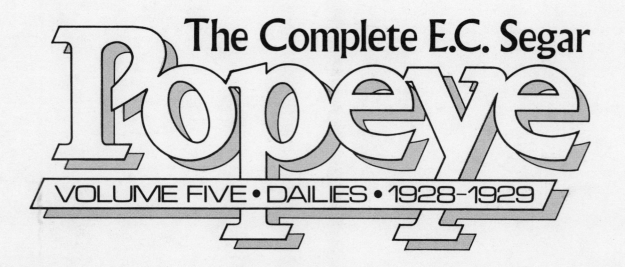

VOLUME FIVE • DAILIES • 1928–1929

the nemo bookshelf

Rick Marschall, Series Editor

The Complete E.C. Segar Popeye

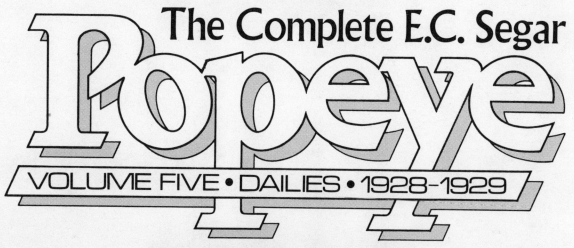

VOLUME FIVE • DAILIES • 1928-1929

Foreword by Bobby London

Edited and with an Introduction by Rick Marschall

WELL, BLOW ME DOWN
SEGAR

FANTAGRAPHICS BOOKS

FANTAGRAPHICS BOOKS
4359 Cornell Road
Agoura, CA 91301

With special thanks to Bob Jones, Bob Woodworth, and Rick Marschall for providing the artwork used in this volume.

Design and art direction by Dale Crain.
Production assistance and color separations by Teresa Moore.
Typesetting by Linda M. Gorell. Logo by Kevin Nowlan.

First Fantagraphics Books edition: January, 1987.
10 9 8 7 6 5 4 3 2 1

ISBN (soft): 0-930193-29-6
ISBN (hard): 0-930193-30-X

Library of Congress Catalog Number: 84-81462

Printed in the U.S.A.

Foreword by Bobby London

Popeye the Sailor Man was one of the most beloved anti-heroes of the Great Depression. He ate hot dogs, throttled Olive Oyl, and shot craps. He also murdered the English language but when he growled "I yam what I yam" he became Jean-Paul Sartre on steroids. Then, suddenly, children flocked around him and he became a role model; from then on he had to behave and tell the youngsters to eat their spinach.

When Hollywood made Popeye a movie star, everything about him was boiled down to a simple formula. The mustachioed con-artists who menaced his comic strip world, scoundrels who could make G. Gordon Liddy look like Santa Claus, were replaced on film by big, bad Bluto. Olive Oyl, once a violent femme who carried the torch for women's suffrage by crowning her lovers with living-room furniture, was reduced to a mere damsel in distress. Olive's brother Castor Oyl disappeared completely. Castor was the infamous, bald-headed little jazz-age hustler who discovered Popeye on a sea voyage. He was like Jonas Salk on a bad day.

When Popeye's creator died in 1938, the old salt must have seriously considered settling down, marrying his anorexic sweet-patootie, and retiring to the life of a sea-food restauranteur on Catalina Island but cooler heads prevailed and he was kept in harness. The best artists and writers money could buy were called in to keep the curtain up at Thimble Theatre. It was business as usual for twenty years when, just as Popeye's career was about to segue peacefully into the Swinging 'Sixties, things began to fall apart. Syndicate bosses sent Olive Oyl to the Carol Doda Clinic for a face lift and breast implants but she broke down hours before the operation; doctors in Palm Springs put Wimpy on a mysterious diet of lentils and Indian hemp until they found him one day holding up a Bob's Big Boy in Fresno; Bluto joined the Rosicrucians, changed his name to Brutus and ran away to Memphis where he worked for years as an Elvis impersonator, the victim—it is said—of too many lost battles. Just as all was thought lost, E.C. Segar's original assistant, Bud Sagendorf, was brought in to nurse the old comic strip back to health although on television you couldn't tell the difference between Popeye and Huckleberry Hound.

Happily, the original Popeye is still with us, more or less. He may be a bit more subdued these days but then, so is the country that made him a national hero. His ugly mug still adorns an unending supply of merchandise reminding all of us that trends in humor may come and go but a great comic character can live forever provided he becomes a growth industry.

Bobby London
New York, 1986

ED. NOTE: Bobby London, winner of the 1978 Yellow Kid Award for his comic strip Dirty Duck, *is now the artist-writer of the* Popeye *daily syndicated feature.*

Introduction by Rick Marschall

LET THE SHOW BEGIN!

The daily comic strip format barely 10 years old when Elzie Crisler Segar began *Thimble Theatre.* And it was as a daily strip that *Thimble Theatre* shone, before Popeye entered the strip in 1929 (those earlier strips are better than fans could imagine), and, especially, after.

The Sunday pages were masterpieces of comedy, but with a few, short, notable exceptions, they were independent, single-gag entities (See Volumes 2-3 of this series for the Sea Hag saga, and the latter part of Volume 3 for a sequence with the cast out West).

Viewed from the perspective of the 1980s, the average comic-strip reader might assume that the function of daily humor strips has always been to provide a daily dose of humor, period—each day's strip having little connection with the previous day's or the next day's appearance.

In fact for much of the history of the comic strip—mostly during what today is commonly called the Golden Age—these daily appearances were called installments, for they were indeed scenes in a longer story. Then, dailies were episodes; now they are vignettes.

We should marvel at these technicians of the past, for they labored under the dual obligations to be funny and maintain a continuity. . . simultaneously. It was no easy feat, but once the cartoonists collectively sat down at their drawing boards and accepted the challenge, some remarkable things happened. The humor was wonderful, and the story quality was at a high level.

A strip like *Just-Kids,* which was a poorly drawn, insipid Sunday page, actually was a respectable humor-and-adventure daily strip appealing to children and adults alike. And in strips like *Barney Google* and *Moon Mullins,* the scheming, Dickensian personalities of the principal characters could never, never have been developed if their showcases had been truncated vignettes of three or four panels each.

Enough of the Good-Old-Days harangue. Let us just feel fortunate that geniuses like Segar and DeBeck and Willard and Capp came along when they did during the span of comics history. And of course we are just addressing ourselves here to humor strips, setting aside, in this consideration, geniuses like Harold Gray and Milton Caniff.

It would seem that the continued-story daily strip would have had its genesis in adventure/suspense/realistic features, but this is not so. Actually, most of the standard histories of the form point to the first week of January, 1929, as the time when comic-strip continuity (or at least adventure) began: The debuts of *Buck Rogers* and *Tarzan* occurred on the same day—Jan. 1929. With Popeye introducing himself in the third week of the very same month and year, the temptation is great to erect a monument to that assertion.

But—like the accepted history about the birth of the Yellow Kid—myths have more durable, and more accessible, than facts. Continuity in strips is almost as old as the form itself, and adventure certainly predated 1929.

Happy Hooligan and the Katzenjammer Kids each went on 'round-the-world cruises, with continuing stories spanning the weekly pages, in the first few years of the century. Alphonse and Gaston engaged in mock cliffhangers that brought the readers back each week, around 1903. Also in the first decade, there was Little Nemo, whose dreams continued from week to week, and Feininger's Kin-Der-Kids, whose dream-like (and sometimes nightmarish) adventures where parts of a continuing sequence. In the 'teens there was Everrett Lowry's Binnacle Jim, whose weekly adventures were parts of a larger whole and whose humor was subordinated to adventure elements; and a 1917 sequence of

Our Friend by Ad Carter, in which the kids met up with very threatening pirates. *Our Friends Mush,* by the way, changed its title to *Just Kids* in a few years.

In the 1920s, two strips that began in 1924, *Little Orphan Annie* and *Wash Tubbs,* almost immediately engaged in continuity, specializing in melodrama and adventure, respectively. Within a few years each was a certified story strip, eschewing self-contained daily episodes. In 1925, George Storm began *Phil Hardy*, a story with a dramatic overtones, and the next year created *Bobby Thatcher,* a remarkably violent strip. Interestingly, *Annie, Tubbs, Hardy,* and *Thatcher,* whatever their realistic elements, were all drawn at first in a semi-comic style.

The 1920s were also replete with a myriad of adaptations of classic novels—all drawn realistically—and parodies of movie serials, which, *pro forma,* involved continuing stories and cliffhangers.

It was into this state of comic-strip affairs—astoundingly vital and plastic—that E.C. Segar became a strip cartoonist. As touched on in various introductory pieces in previous volumes of this series, Segar's first professional work was drawing the *Charlie Chaplin* comic strip—mandating a consideration of movie-like plot elements, although the storyline was not continued from day to day. His first assignment with a major syndicate (Hearst's King Features) was to imitate—frankly—Ed Wheelan's *Midget Movies* upon that cartoonist's departure for another organization the strip was itself a parody of movie serials and cliff-hangers.

Thimble Theatre was initially a strip about a repertory company of actors. Their one-day skits were announced, titled, and preceded by a cast list, with "actors'" "real" names and their character names for that day. But unlike Wheelan and Chester Gould (whose *Fillum Fables* indicated that Hearst liked to plug holes in his dyke with several fingrs), Thimble Theatre consisted of daily "blackout" gags, vaudeville style. But not for long.

Begun in 1919, *Thimble Theatre* within a few years featured longer stories. The "hook" of a parody rep company and satirical movie bits was reduced to the running titles and "teasers" about the next day's episodes. Otherwise, by 1922, Segar had fashioned a full-fledged, independent, totally integrated, and intrinsically mature continuity strip.

Olive Oyl and her dippy suitors, Ham Gravy chief amongst them, were relegated to the Sunday page, and Castor Oyl, one of the comics' greatest rogue heroes, took over the dailies with epics of mendacity, adventure, intrigue, deception, violence—all with humor and a daily laugh, of course—as well as sports-related epics and travel to bizarre locales. An astonishing cast of good guys and bad guys, fighters and promoters, people and animals, rushed through *Thimble Theatre* in a dizzying array, with equal parts of comedic and episodic baggage.

The continuity comic strip—being adopted with increasing frequency by cartoonists but never more adroitly than by Segar—was now more than a commercial exploitation of cinematic forms. It had even outgrown the aspects of homage. The comic strip, born almost at the same moment as the motion picture, and borne of similar cultural and dramatic impulses, was now its own being.

And when the latecomers *Buck Rogers* and *Tarzan* came on the scene in that first week of January, 1929, Elzie Crisler Segar was waiting for them. The cartoonist was one character short of propelling his modest strip into a commercial and cultural colossus; that character, of course, was the unprepossessing sailor with one eye. At first, we sense, even Segar didn't know Popeye for his full import; introduced as an incidental character, he then leaves.

But he comes back, into *Thimble Theatre,* and into America's consciousness. And—blow me down!—into the hallowed literary and artistic echelons of history.

In a *comic strip*?? About as likely as a theater the size of a thimble. □

THIMBLE THEATER
NOW SHOWING—A FRIEND IN A PINCH.
Tomorrow—Pants, Don't "Dessert Him."

HAM I WANT YOU TO BRACE UP AND BE A MAN-SURE I WANT TO HELP! I'M GOING TO BUY YOU SOME CLOTHES
WE'LL HOP INTO THIS SECOND HAND STORE AND SEE WHAT WE CAN FIND
YEAH, FIX 'IM UP GOOD
H-M- I WILL MAKE FROM HIM A "BO BUMMEL"
AND GLOOK AT DE CLOT IN DEM PANTS! FOR TWICE AS MUCH IT'S A GIVE-AWAY
NOW— DON'T SAY I NEVER DID ANYTHING FOR YA
SECOND HANDED STORE
SEGAR

THIMBLE THEATER
NOW SHOWING—PANTS, DON'T "DESSERT" HIM.
Tomorrow—Taking No Chances.

IT WAS NICE OF CASTOR TO BUY ME CLOTHES BUT I NEED SOMETHING ON THE INSIDE ALSO
MISTER, I'M HUNGRY AND BROKE, WILL YOU GIVE ME A COUPLA HOT DOGS FOR MY COAT?
SURE
HOT DOGS
YEP, I HELPED A POOR MISGUIDED SOUL! HE'LL NEVER FORGET THE GOOD DEED I DONE 'IM
I KNOW HE APPRECIATES THE CLOTHES I BOUGHT FOR HIM
I WONDER HOW MUCH PIE I COULD GET FOR MY PANTS?
?
LUNCH
SEGAR

THIMBLE THEATER
NOW SHOWING—TAKING NO CHANCES.
Tomorrow—A Boy in Love.

CASTOR BOUGHT ME NEW CLOTHES BUT I HAD TO EAT SO I TRADED MY COAT FOR HOT DOGS, AND MY SHIRT FOR COFFEE
AND I GOT A HAMBURGER FOR MY VEST
AND I TRADED MY COLLAR, TIE AND HAT FOR PIE - NOW ALL I'VE GOT LEFT IS MY TROUSERS
GEE - HERE'S A LUNCH STAND - OH, BOY. BUT I'M HUNGRY
?
FOR HEAVENS SAKE TAKE THIS DOLLAR!
DOGS HAMBOIGER CHIZ- COFEY MILCH SODY-POP!
SEGAR

THIMBLE THEATER
NOW SHOWING—A BOY IN LOVE.
Tomorrow—The Fisherman.

TURTLE DOVE WANTS MATE APPLY- 1928 GOOF ST
!
I'M NOT THINKING OF GETTING MARRIED. BUT I'LL ANSWER THE AD ANYWAY
SHE MIGHT TREAT ME TO A SQUARE MEAL AND BELIEVE ME I'M INTERESTED IN FOOD
TURTLE DOVE. SHE MUST BE A LITTLE DOLL!
I'M THE DOVIE YOU CAME TO SEE- WONT YOU HAVE DINNER WITH ME?
SURE I WILL
YOU ARE A PERFECT EXAMPLE OF MODERN MANHOOD- A NICE CLEAN YOUNG MAN. I CAN TELL THAT- MY DREAM BOY- NOW WHAT DO YOU THINK OF ME?
YOU'RE A GOOD COOK
SEGAR

THIMBLE THEATER
NOW SHOWING—THE FISHERMAN.
Tomorrow—The "Unclosed" Chapter.

HAM ANSWERED A HUSBAND WANTED AD— "TURTLE DOVE WANTS MATE" AND HERE IS THE DOVE. HE HAD NO INTENTION OF MARRYING BUT BEING ON THE ROCKS FINANCIALLY HE SAW A CHANCE OF GETTING AN INVITE TO DINNER
NOW THAT I'VE HAD MY EATS I MUST MAKE SOME EXCUSE AND GET OUT OF HERE
COMING TO SEE ME IN YOUR UNDER SHIRT MERCY! YOU CERTAINLY ARE A STRANGE MAN
YEAH I DO THE FUNNIEST THINGS- OH! BY THE WAY I HAVE A DATE WITH MY DENTIST- I MUST GO RIGHT NOW!
AW THAT'S TOO BAD
SAY THOSE ARE FINE PEARLS YOU HAVE ON YOUR EARS
YOU LIKE THEM? THEY WERE LAID BY MY PRIVATE OYSTERS I HAVE QUARTS OF THEM
QUARTS OF OYSTERS, OR PEARLS ?
PEARLS, SILLY, REAL PEARLS
COME, SIT DOWN, YOU INTEREST ME STRANGELY
TEE HEE
SEGAR

THIMBLE THEATER
NOW SHOWING—THE "UNCLOSED" CHAPTER.
Tomorrow—It's a Gift.

AND YOU REALLY HAVE QUARTS OF PEARLS LIKE THOSE ON YOUR EARS?
OH, MY YES, GALLONS OF THEM
BUT ENOUGH OF THAT- LET'S TALK ABOUT SOMETHING ELSE
NOW, TELL ME—WHY DID YOU COME TO SEE ME IN YOUR UNDER-SHIRT?
THERE ARE MILLIONS AND MILLIONS OF UNANSWERED QUESTIONS- AND YOU HAD TO ASK THAT
WELL- I TRADED MY COAT VEST AND SHIRT FOR HOT DOGS- I'M BROKE! I'VE GONE WITHOUT FOOD FOR MONTHS!
!
SNIFF
BOOOOOO
STOP! YOU'RE BREAKING MY HEART

THIMBLE THEATER

NOW SHOWING—IT'S A GIFT.

Tomorrow—A Narrow Escape.

FOR DAYS, WEEKS, MONTHS, YEARS ! I HAVE GONE WITHOUT FOOD" DOWN IN THE SLUMS
SNIFF
BAW! YOU HAVE TOUCHED MY HEART!!
IT MAKES ME SHUDDER TO THINK OF IT! DOWN IN THE SLUMS! DOWN WHERE THE SEA OF LIFE IS ALWAYS AT LOW TIDE!
SNIFF
MY GOSH!
!
CLINK CLINK
HERE! GO BUY YOURSELF SOME CLOTHES
7-27
SEGAR

THIMBLE THEATER

NOW SHOWING—A NARROW ESCAPE.

Monday—Fashion-Plated.

CERTAINLY- TAKE THIS MONEY AND BUY SOME CLOTHES
I MUST ACT AS THOUGH I DON'T WANT TO TAKE IT- I'LL REFUSE IT A FEW TIMES
OH, MY NO! I WOULDN'T THINK OF IT NO! I CAN'T! IT WOULDN'T BE RIGHT!
WELL IF YOU WON'T TAKE IT YOU WON'T - I'M NOT GOING TO FORCE IT UPON YOU
HEY- JUST A MINUTE!
7-28
SEGAR

THIMBLE THEATER

NOW SHOWING—FASHION-PLATED.

Tomorrow—Weak Hearts

HE'S A NICE YOUNG MAN- I'M GLAD I GAVE HIM MONEY TO BUY CLOTHES
OH BABY! WILL I BUY CLOTHES!
HELLO, SIS- SEEN YOUR SWEETY LATELY?
YOU MEAN HAM GRAVY? HE'S NOT MY SWEETY - I'M OFFA HIM
I'M TELLING YOU, CASTOR- HE'S A BUM AT HEART- HE HAS LOST ALL SELF RESPECT
SURE, HE HAS, YOU'RE RIGHT ABOUT THAT
AH, GOOD EVENING, EVERYBODY- PLEASANT WEATHER- EH, WHAT?
7-30
SEGAR

THIMBLE THEATER

NOW SHOWING—WEAK HEARTS.

Tomorrow—A Woman's Intuition.

SEE WHAT YOU DID BY COMING AROUND HERE ALL DOLLED UP—SHE'S FAINTED! THE SHOCK WAS TOO MUCH FOR HER
SHE'S BEEN ACCUSTOMED TO SEEING YOU LOOKIN' LIKE A BUM—TOO MUCH OF A SURPRISE!
YOU GOTTA BE CAREFUL ABOUT SURPRISING PEOPLE. THE HUMAN HEART IS NONE TOO STRONG AT BEST
BY-THE-WAY, CASTOR HERE'S THE TEN I BORROWED FROM YOU FIVE YEARS AGO
P L O P
7-31
SEGAR

THIMBLE THEATER

NOW SHOWING—A WOMAN'S INTUITION.

Tomorrow—"Rolled" Hose Are a "Sockcess."

HAM YOU LOOK SWELL IN YOUR NEW CLOTHES. WHERE DID YOU GET THE MONEY ?
HAM, DARLING, CAN'T WE BE SWEET HEARTS AGAIN ?
HE DIDN'T SAY YES AND HE DIDN'T SAY NO!
I DON'T THINK HE LOVES ME ANYMORE
IF HE FALLS FOR SOME OTHER WOMAN I'LL BUY A GUN AND END MYSELF!
AH, MY DREAM BOY—YOU ARE HANDSOME
SEGAR
8-1

THIMBLE THEATER

NOW SHOWING—"ROLLED" HOSE ARE A "SOCKCESS."

Tomorrow—A Concealed Map.

DOGGONIT! I WONDER IF THERE'S SOMEBODY ELSE? HE MAKES ME FEEL LIKE A COLD POTATO
HELLO-HELLO! HELLO HAM! HEY! I SAID HELL-O
OH, ALL RIGHT—HELLO!
NOW I KNOW THERE'S SOMEBODY ELSE! I KNOW IT! I KNOW IT! I KNOW IT! I KNOW IT! I KNOW IT
WHY MISS PHIZ WHAT'S THE MATTER ?!
NOT A THING, I'M GOING SHOPPING AND THIS IS HOW I CARRY MY HUNDRED DOLLAR BILLS
WHAT A BEAUTIFUL PAIR OF LIMBS! NO FOOLIN'!
FLATTERER
Great Britain rights reserved
© 1928 by King Features Syndicate, Inc.
8-2
SEGAR

THIMBLE THEATER
NOW SHOWING—A CONCEALED MAP.
Tomorrow—Behind the Scene.

I'M GOING TO FIND OUT IF SOME OTHER DAME HAS STOLEN HAM'S HEART—I'LL FIND OUT
I'VE BEEN TRYING TO DISCOVER WHO BOUGHT HIM THOSE SWELL CLOTHES- BUT I'VE FAILED - HAM'S FOXY
BROTHER, I'M A NATURAL BORN "SHE DETECTIVE" LEND ME YOUR POCKET KNIFE - I WANT TO MAKE A QUICK DISGUISE
I USED THIS DISGUISE ABOUT FIVE YEARS AGO- IT'S O.K.
BUT CUTTING THREE HOLES IN YOUR SKIRT DOESN'T MAKE A DISGUISE, SILLY!
SURE IT DOES! WATCH!
?
!
SEGAR
8-3

THIMBLE THEATER
NOW SHOWING—BEHIND THE SCENE.
Monday—Just an Old-Fashioned Girl.

SAY, HAM- HAVE YOU GOT ANOTHER SWEETY- TELL ME, WILL YA?
I'LL TELL YA NOTHIN'
THINK YOU'RE SMART DONTCHA? WELL I'LL FIND OUT!
HE DIDN'T NOTICE THE THREE HOLES IN MY SKIRT
AND HE DOESN'T KNOW THAT I'M A NATURAL BORN "SHE" DETECTIVE
MY DISGUISE IS PERFECT I CAN TRAIL HIM ANYWHERE AND HE'LL NEVER KNOW ME
SEGAR
8-4

THIMBLE THEATER
NOW SHOWING—JUST AN OLD-FASHION GIRL.
Tomorrow—A Friend of Great Value.

WHAT DO YOU THINK OF MY DISGUISE MRS. KNIP? YOU'D NEVER KNOW I WAS OLIVE OYL, WOULD YOU? ALL I DID WAS CUT THREE HOLES IN MY SKIRT AND HOIST IT UP! YOU SEE I WANT TO SHADOW HAM GRAVY
HEAVENS! HOW SHOCKING!
WHAT'S SHOCKING ABOUT THIS?
WHY- GOING ABOUT IN YOUR PETTICOAT!
SURE- THAT'S TERRIBLE
H-M-M-M
8-6
SEGAR

THIMBLE THEATER

NOW SHOWING—A FRIEND OF GREAT VALUE.

Tomorrow—Verified Suspicions.

STRANGE ABOUT HAM- A FEW DAYS AGO HE WAS A BUM-AND NOW HE WEARS SWELL CLOTHES AND SEEMS TO HAVE MONEY
HELLO, CASTOR, SEEN HAM TO-DAY?
NO, I HAVEN'T, SIS- HAVE YOU FOUND OUT ANYTHING YET?
NO- BUT WITH THE AID OF THIS PERFECT DISGUISE I EXPECT TO TRACK HIM DOWN
MISS PHIZ-WHAT'S THE IDEA IN BEING SO GOOD TO ME? BUYING ME CLOTHES AND GIVING ME CASH?
I'M SO KIND-HEARTED AND GENEROUS I HAD TO HELP YOU- I JUST LOVE TO GIVE MONEY AWAY
SAY— YOU AND ME ARE GONNA BE GREAT FRIENDS! SURE WE ARE
8-7
SEGAR

THIMBLE THEATER

NOW SHOWING—VERIFIED SUSPICIONS.

Tomorrow—Stung, That's All.

THERE HE GOES! I'LL FOLLOW HIM AND SEE IF HE MEETS SOME GIRL
AND WITH THIS UNIQUE DISGUISE HE'LL NEVER KNOW ME
AH, GOOD EVENING, JOSEPHINE
HOW'S MY DREAM BOY THIS EVE?
O-K.
JUST AS I THOUGHT. HE'S GOT ANOTHER SWEETY!
THUMP
THUMP
CRACK
8-8
SEGAR

THIMBLE THEATER

NOW SHOWING—STUNG, THAT'S ALL.

Tomorrow—What a Question.

HAM, AND HIS NEW SWEETY, NOT SO SWEET, BUT OH, BOY, IS SHE RICH!
AND I AM THE WOMAN SCORNED. HE SCORNED ME UP AND DOWN!
CRASH
HOLD'ER, MA! HOLD'ER!
WHAT DO YOU RECKON'S EATIN' THE CHILD PAW?!
G-R-R.
G-R-R
8-9
SEGAR

THIMBLE THEATER
NOW SHOWING—WHAT A QUESTION.
Tomorrow—Moon-Mad.

SNAP OUT OF IT! SNAP OUTTA IT!
G-R-R
GOL DING IT, MAW! COME HOLD'ER AWHILE. I'M ALL SHOT
WHAT AILS HER, PAW? WHATCHA'SPOSE AILS HER?
FLOP
FLOP
I'LL BE WHOOPED IF I KNOW!
IT MUST BE SOME SORT OF MADNESS! SOMETHING'S GONE WRONG
PLOP
8-10
DID YOU EVER LOVE ANY OTHER GIRL, HAM?
WHO ME? WHY, JOSEPHINE, HOW YOU TALK!
SEGAR

THIMBLE THEATER
NOW SHOING—MOON MAD.
Monday—Get an Anchor.

GOOD GOSH, PAW! GET THE DOCTOR!
PLOP
FOR CRYIN' OUT LOUD, DOC! COME ON OVER
H-M-M-M
H-M-M IS RIGHT!
M.D.
A VERY, VERY GRAVE CASE! "LUNAPHOBIA" YES-A BAD CASE OF "LUNAPHOBIA"!!
LUNAPHOBIA?
LUNAPHOBIA?
YES-
LUNAPHOBIA
GOOCH!
GLORX
SEGAR 8-11

THIMBLE THEATER
NOW SHOWING—"GET AN ANCHOR!
Tomorrow—Dangerous Symptoms.

IT'S "LUNAPHOBIA"-A VERY HAYWIRE CONDITION-A SORT OF ANGRY MADNESS SO TO SPEAK
BUT, DOCTOR, WHAT IS IT CAUSED FROM?
YEAH, WHAT?
WOPF!
M.D.
LUNAPHOBIA IS CAUSED FROM-SHOCK, RAGE OR JEALOUSY OR A COMBINATION OF ALL THREE
MAKE SURE, DOC. BETTER EXAMINE'R
I WILL IF SHE'LL LIGHT SOME PLACE
!
8-13
AND YOU'VE NEVER KISSED A GIRL IN ALL YOUR LIFE
ONLY MY MOTHER, YEAH, THAT'S RIGHT
SEGAR

THIMBLE THEATER

NOW SHOWING—DANGEROUS SYMPTOMS.
Tomorrow—He's Convinced—Almost.

HOW DID OLIVE HAPPEN TO GET "LUNAPHOBIA"? I CAN'T DOPE IT OUT
HELLO, FATHER DEAR
WHY, I BELIEVE SHE'S GETTING BETTER
HOW'S MY DEAR SWEET DADDY?
GLOP!
!
SOMETHING'S GOT TO BE DONE ABOUT THIS!
TWEET!!
8-14
SEGAR

THIMBLE THEATER

NOW SHOWING—HE'S CONVINCED—ALMOST.
Tomorrow—It May Be the Wrong Combination.

LUNAPHOBIA, ME EYE! SHE LOOKS ALL RIGHT TO ME- YOU'RE GOOFY, DAD
SHE'S O-K NOTHING WRONG WITH HER!
GLOP!
WELL-WHAT THU-!?
BLOP!
BLIP!
SAY, DAD- I BELIEVE THERE IS SOMETHING WRONG WITH HER
!
SEGAR 8-15

THIMBLE THEATER

NOW SHOWING—MAY BE WRONG COMBINATION
Tomorrow—Ham'll Pay Later.

SEE YOU LATER, DREAM BOY
O.K., JOSEPHINE S'LONG
SAY, HAM- DID YOU KNOW THAT YOU'RE THE CAUSE OF SIS HAVING LUNAPHOBIA?
WHAT'S LUNAPHOBIA?
IT'S A SORT OF MADNESS CAUSED FROM JEALOUSY AND ANGER- YOU SEE, SHE SAW YOU WITH ANOTHER WOMAN
!
I'M SORRY, BUT I'VE GOT MYSELF A REAL SWEETY NOW! RICH AND LIBERAL-WHAT MORE COULD I ASK?
RICH AND LIBERAL- BY GOLLY! THAT'S A GREAT COMBINATION, I'LL SAY IT IS!
THE POOR FOOL TAKES ME FOR AN EASY MARK! BUT JUST WAIT TILL WE'RE MARRIED JUST WAIT!
8-16
SEGAR

THIMBLE THEATER
NOW SHOWING—HAM'LL PAY LATER.
Tomorrow—Paw's the Patient.

GLOP
SUPPOSE HAM GRAVY CAME BACK TO OLIVE- WOULDN'T THAT CURE HER OF "LUNAPHOBIA"?
NO CHANCE. HAM'S GOT GOOD SENSE
HIS NEW SWEETY. WHOEVER SHE IS - IS BOTH RICH AND LIBERAL. A VERY, VERY HARD COMBINATION TO BEAT
HEAVEN FACE, I SURE COULD MAKE USE OF A HUNDRED BUCKS
WHY, CERTAINLY. DREAM BOY. I'LL GET IT FOR YOU RIGHT NOW
JUST LIKE BEING NIGHT WATCHMAN IN A MINT
HA! HA! JUST WAIT TILL WE'RE MARRIED
8-17

THIMBLE THEATER
NOW SHOWING—PAW'S THE PATIENT
Tomorrow—Framed.

GLOP!
OLD HER, PAW. I'LL GET THE DOCTOR
UMPH!
PLOP!
WHERE IS THE PATIENT?
!!
RIGHT HERE, DOC.
SEGAR 8-18

THIMBLE THEATER
NOW SHOWING—FRAMED.
Tomorrow—Speech Is Golden.

THERE IS STILL MUCH TO BE LEARNED ABOUT THE STRANGE MADNESS, "LUNAPHOBIA". NOW I WANT TO TRY A LITTLE EXPERIMENT
GET A PICTURE OF HER SWEETY AND SHOW IT TO HER- I WILL WATCH AND SEE WHAT HAPPENS
O.K. DOC.
!
HEY, DAUGHTER, LOOK
!
KNOW ANYMORE TRICKS? YOU BUM QUACK!
8-20

THIMBLE THEATER

NOW SHOWING—SPEECH IS GOLDEN.

Tomorrow—Mines, But No Mind.

SHE'S AN AWFUL LOOKIN' THING-BUT SHE'S RICH
WHAT I MUST DO IS FIND OUT HOW RICH
OH, BY THE WAY, JOSEPHINE, ER-AH-NOT THAT IT MATTERS-BUT HOW MUCH ARE YOU WORTH?
ABOUT FIFTY MILLION DOLLARS
YES, I'M VERY RICH, BUT I'M NOT PRETTY ENOUGH FOR A HANDSOME MAN LIKE YOU
DON'T SAY THAT, HEAVEN FACE-WHY, YOU'RE THE MOST BEAUTIFUL WOMAN ON EARTH! WHEN YOU'RE AROUND, THE ROSES LOSE THEIR CHARM, NO KIDDIN'!
OH, DREAM BOY, YOU MAKE ME FEEL SO FOOLISH!
8-21
SEGAR

THIMBLE THEATER

NOW SHOWING—MINES, BUT NO MIND.

Tomorrow—A Genuine Crop.

DOGGONIT! EVEN AT FIFTY MILLION SHE'S STILL A HAYWIRE DAME
THE MORE I THINK OF HER THE PUNKER SHE SEEMS
STILL, FIFTY MILLION IS FIFTY MILLION
I SUPPOSE YOU HAVE YOUR FIFTY MILLION TIED UP IN REAL ESTATE
OH, MY NO! IT'S IN CASH-
AND I HAVE TEN OIL WELLS-ONE SILVER MINE
FIVE GOLD AND SIX DIAMOND MINES-AND A COUPLA PEARL-BEARING OYSTERS
YOU MAY KISS ME, JOSEPHINE
8-22
SEGAR

THIMBLE THEATER

NOW SHOWING—A GENUINE CROP.

Tomorrow—Misleading Crockery.

JOSEPHINE PHIZ! IS SHE YOUR NEW SWEETY? WHY SHE'S OLD ENOUGH TO BE YOUR GRANDMOTHER
SHE TOLD ME TWENTY SIX-SURE-SHE'S GOT BLACK HAIR
YEAH? WELL, SHE'S WEARING A WIG THEN
I'LL FIND OUT
I'LL GO PULL IT OFF
BUT DREAM BOY, WHAT DO YOU WANT ME TO STAND LIKE THIS FOR?
JUST BECAUSE
HELP!
WHAT ARE YOU TRYING TO DO?!
YOU SEE, HEAVEN FACE, ER- I LOVE YOU SO MUCH I FEEL LIKE TEARING YOU TO PIECES! SURE I DO! GULP!
LISTEN WORM-ONE MORE CRACK ABOUT MY SWEETY AND I'LL PUT YA OUT!
8-23
SEGAR

THIMBLE THEATER

NOW SHOWING—MISLEADING CROCKERY.

Tomorrow—An Adhesive Toupee.

YOU SAY YOU'RE ONLY TWENTY SIX YEARS OLD?
YES- I'LL BE TWENTY SEVEN MY NEXT BIRTHDAY
I KNOW A WAY OF FINDING OUT HOW OLD SHE IS
LEMME SEE YOUR TEETH!
!?
FIFTY - SIXTY - SEVENTY FIVE YEARS OLD - GOOD NIGHT
YOU CAN'T TELL THAT WAY!!
SURE I CAN!! I WAS A HORSE DOCTOR
SMARTY!! THESE ARE FALSE TEETH!
8-24
SEGAR

THIMBLE THEATER

NOW SHOWING—AN ADHESIVE TOUPEE.

Monday—Methuselah's Rival.

TWENTY SIX YEARS OLD ME EYE - HAM'S BEING DECEIVED THAT'S WHAT!
LISTEN, HAM - MY DAD KNEW JOSEPHINE PHIZ WHEN HE WAS A KID - AND SHE WAS THIRTY THEN
SHE CAN'T BE THAT OLD CASTOR
SHE'S GOT BLACK HAIR
I'LL BET IT'S A WIG - I'LL BET ON THAT
IT'S NOT A WIG!
YOU KNOW I GRABBED HER BY THE HAIR AND YANKED WITH ALL MY MIGHT - SHE'S NOT WEARING A WIG
THIS IS JOSEPHINE PHIZ SPEAKING - PLEASE SEND UP A BOTTLE OF THAT EXTRA STRONG WIG GLUE - THE KIND I ALWAYS GET

THIMBLE THEATER

NOW SHOWING—METHUSELAH'S RIVAL

Tomorrow—The Cradle Snatcher

DARN IT, JOSEPHINE! I WOULDN'T MARRY ANY WOMAN WITHOUT KNOWING HER AGE - REGARDLESS OF WEALTH
HOW MANY TIMES MUST I TELL YOU? I'M TWENTY SIX "26"
WHAT AM I WORRYING ABOUT? I'LL BET SHE IS ONLY "26" AT THAT - AND SHE'S RICH! I THINK I'LL MARRY HER
HEY THERE, YOUNG FELLER, YOU KEEP AWAY FROM JOSEPHINE PHIZ -
?
SHE'S MY SWEETY! YOU'RE TRYING TO CUT ME OUT!
!
8-27
SEGAR

THIMBLE THEATER

NOW SHOWING—THE CRADLE SNATCHER

Tomorrow—Kindergarten's Over

YOU HEARD ME! SHE'S BEEN MY SWEETY FOR YEARS — NO FOOLIN'
MISTER, DON'T THINK YOU CAN PULL THAT KIND OF STUFF ON ME AND GET BY WITH IT
HA! HA! JOSEPHINE PHIZ IS TOO YOUNG FOR YOU
SON— YOU CAN'T TELL A WOMAN'S AGE BY HER TONGUE!
ALWAYS REMEMBER THAT
SHE IS FIVE YEARS OLDER THAN ME
HOLD EVERYTHING !!!!
SEGAR 8-28

THIMBLE THEATER

NOW SHOWING—KINDERGARTEN'S OVER

Tomorrow—*For the Love o' Castor*

I'LL FIND OUT RIGHT NOW IF YOU'RE LYING TO ME!
GO TO IT, SON!
HEY, JOSEPHINE - I'VE HEARD PLENTY ABOUT YOU! NOW I WANT THE TRUTH
WHAT IS YOUR AGE? COME— SPEAK THE TRUTH!
ALL RIGHT DREAM BOY— I THOUGHT YOU SUSPECTED SOMETHING WHEN YOU TRIED TO PULL MY WIG OFF— YOU SEE I HAD IT GLUED ON THAT DAY
I'M EIGHTY SIX YEARS OLD- TAKE A GOOD LOOK
HEH! HEH!
COME ON HENRY- WE'LL GET MARRIED AT ONCE- I'M THROUGH WITH INFANTS
O.K. JOSEPHINE
8-29
SEGAR

THIMBLE THEATER

NOW SHOWING—FOR THE LOVE O' CASTOR

Tomorrow—Actions Speak Louder Than Words

THERE'S ONLY ONE THING TO DO- AND THAT IS- GO BACK TO OLIVE OYL MY FIRST LOVE
MR. OYL- I'VE MADE A MISTAKE- YOUR DAUGHTER IS THE GIRL FOR ME— I LOVE ONLY HER
ALL RIGHT HAM- I'LL CALL HER. BUT PREPARE YOURSELF! DON'T BE SURPRISED AT ANYTHING
COME IN DAUGHTER- HERE'S A GENTLEMAN TO SEE YOU
SHE'S GOT LUNAPHOBIA HAM, IT'S A SORT OF MADNESS- SHE GOT THAT WAY WHEN SHE SAW YOU WITH ANOTHER SWEETY
WHAT THU-!
SEGAR

THIMBLE THEATER
NOW SHOWING—ACTIONS SPEAK LOUDER THAN WORDS

Tomorrow—Is There a Cage in the Audience?

MAYBE I CAN CURE OLIVE OF LUNAPHOBIA BY MENTAL SUGGESTION. I'LL TRY IT!
LISTEN, YOU HAVEN'T GOT LUNAPHOBIA - YOU HAVEN'T! GET ME?!
THAT'S RIGHT - KEEP SAYING O.K. - I BELIEVE SHE'S BETTER ALREADY
O.K. O.K.
NOW GO OVER AND SIT DOWN ON THAT CHAIR - KEEP SAYING "I'M O.K."
I'M O.K. O.K. O.K. O.K. O.K. I'M O.K.!!
8-31

THIMBLE THEATER
NOW SHOWING—IS THERE A CAGE IN THE AUDIENCE

Monday—It Won't Be Long Now

I'LL TAKE HER FOR A WALK - THE FRESH AIR MAY BE GOOD FOR HER LUNAPHOBIA
HEY! COME BACK HERE! WHERE DO YOU THINK YOU'RE GOING?!
!
CLICK
DON'T YOU KNOW IT'S AGAINST THE LAW TO SOCK COPS!? SHAME ON YOU!
LISTEN COP - YOU CAN'T DO THAT TO MY SWEETY EVEN IF YOU ARE A POLICEMAN
ZAT SO?
AW - SHUT UP
GLOP!
SEGAR
9-1

THIMBLE THEATER
NOW SHOWING—IT WON'T BE LONG NOW.

Tomorrow—Bring on the Mustard.

MRS. OYL, I'VE BROUGHT A HOT DOG SANDWICH FOR OLIVE - SHE USED TO BE GOOFY OVER 'EM
SHE STILL IS - IF YOU'RE GOOD TO HER, HAM, YOU MAY CURE HER OF "LUNAPHOBIA"
MORE HOT DOGS
THAT'S ALL THERE IS, THEY'RE ALL GONE
I TELL YOU THERE ISN'T ANY MORE HOT DOGS, AND I WANT YOU TO STOP LOOKING AT MY NOSE LIKE THAT
NOW THAT HAM HAS COME BACK TO HER, SHE MAY GET OVER HER MADNESS
YEH, SHE MAY
HOT DOG!
HELP! HELP! SOMEBODY DO SOMETHING
9-3
SEGAR

THIMBLE THEATER

NOW SHOWING—BRING ON THE MUSTARD.

Tomorrow—It's No Picnic for Ham.

WHAT ARE YOU SHOVING ME INTO THE KITCHEN FOR, OLIVE?
OF COURSE SHE'LL GET OVER IT, BUT IT WILL TAKE TIME — MERCY! LUNAPHOBIA CERTAINLY IS A STRANGE AFFLICTION
YOU SAID IT!
BREAD
SHE'S GETTING A BUN OUT OF THE BREAD BOX - WHAT THE DICKENS IS SHE UP TO?
HOT DOG!
!
9-4
SEGAR

THIMBLE THEATER

NOW SHOWING—IT'S NO PICNIC FOR HAM.

Tomorrow—A Slip of the Tongue.

COME HERE !!
I'M GETTING TIRED OF HUMORING HER
HEY, MAW - I KNOW LUNAPHOBIA IS A SERIOUS THING, BUT THIS IS HOT
WHAT, PAW?
WHY, OLIVE INSISTS UPON PLAYING LUNCH ROOM WITH HAM — HA! HAW!
COME INTO THE KITCHEN
PICKLE OR ONION, DAD?
LISTEN, LET'S PLAY SOME OTHER GAME!
MUSTARD
I'LL TAKE THE SAME AND A CUPA' COFFEE
ONION
SEGAR 9-5

THIMBLE THEATER

NOW SHOWING—A SLIP OF THE TONGUE.

Tomorrow—Paw Gives 'Til It Hurts.

H-M-M- IT DOESN'T LOOK REAL TO ME
GLIP!
GLOP
!
I SURE GET A LOT OF SYMPATHY BY ACTING LIKE I HAD "LUNAPHOBIA"
I'M GONNA TELL- HEY- PAW!! OLIVE'S FAKIN'! OLIVE'S FAKIN'!
GOOD HEAVENS! I GAVE MYSELF AWAY!
9-6
SEGAR

THIMBLE THEATER

NOW SHOWING—PAW GIVES 'TIL IT HURTS.

Tomorrow—The Seat of the Trouble.

YEAH, DAD, SHE DIDN'T KNOW I WAS AROUND, AND SHE WAS TALKING TO HERSELF - SAID SHE WAS FAKING "LUNAPHOBIA" FOR SYMPATHY TO MAKE HAM COME BACK TO HER
DAUGHTER!
OH, BOY, THIS IS GONNA BE GOOD
WHAT'S COMING OFF?
SAY!
WHAT'S GOING ON?
FAKIN' FOR SYMPATHY! GOSH DARN IT! YOU'RE GONNA NEED SYMPATHY BEFORE I FINISH
WHOP
OUCH PAW!! THIS HURTS ME MORE'N IT DOES YOU!
SURE IT DOES-IF IT DIDN'T I'D QUIT
WHOP
9-7
SEGAR

THIMBLE THEATER

NOW SHOWING—THE SEAT OF THE TROUBLE.

Monday—Here's One Cold Storage Didn't Get.

HEY, 'SIS, HOW'D THAT SPANKING FEEL? THAT'S WHAT YOU GET FOR ACTING LIKE YOU HAD "LUNAPHOBIA"
IT SERVES YOU RIGHT
SURE IT DOES
IT DIDN'T HURT A BIT - NOT A BIT!
YOU SEE I WAS PREPARED!
A BIG ROUGH BOARD
GOOD NIGHT! HOW'D YOU GET THE SPLINTERS?
I DON'T KNOW MAW, LOOKS LIKE I'D BEEN SPANKIN' A HOBBY HORSE
9-8
SEGAR

THIMBLE THEATER

NOW SHOWING—HERE'S ONE COLD STORAGE DIDN'T GET.

Tomorrow—A Sex Problem Solved.

HELLO, THERE, UNCLE LUBRY, WHEN DID YOU GET IN TOWN?
WELL, IF IT ISN'T UNCLE LUBRY FROM AFRICA!
SURE ENOUGH
HELLO, FOLKS!
YEP ALL THE WAY FROM AFRICA, I NEEDED A VACATION
LUBRY KENT OYL
HEY, UNCLE - WHATCHA GOT IN THAT BOX? PRESENTS?
IN THIS BOX IS THE STRANGEST BIRD THAT EVER HAPPENED - NO HUMAN OR ANY OTHER ANIMAL HAS EVER BEEN ABLE TO KILL OR CAPTURE ONE
HEY, LISTEN, IF THEY JUST CAN'T BE CAPTURED. HOW COME YOU'VE GOT ONE?
YOU FORGET THAT I, LUBRY KENT OYL AM AN UNUSUALLY SMART AND RESOURCEFUL MAN ——
I RAISED IT FROM A EGG
9-10
SEGAR

THIMBLE THEATER

NOW SHOWING—A SEX PROBLEM SOLVED.
Tomorrow—An Illusive Dame.

YES, IT'S A BIRD OF THE WHIFFIS FAMILY
WHY DON'T YOU OPEN THE BOX UNCLE? WHAT'S HIS NAME?
BERNICE
BERNICE, A SHE, EH?
CERTAINLY, A FEMALE
INFACT THERE ARE NO MALE WHIFFLE HENS
!
YOU DON'T MEAN THAT, UNCLE - YOU DON'T MEAN THAT!
SURE I DO-
THE MALES ARE WHIFFLE ROOSTERS
9-11
SEGAR

THIMBLE THEATER

NOW SHOWING—AN ILLUSIVE DAME.
Tomorrow—A Champion "Boxer."

YOU SAY IT'S A STRANGE SORT OF BIRD
SHE IS EXACTLY THAT
WELL, COME ON - OPEN THE BOX AND GIVE US A LOOK
SHE ISN'T IN THE BOX
UNCLE, ARE YOU TRYING TO KID ME?
I PUT HER IN THIS BOX AND NAILED THE LID ON JUST BEFORE I LEFT AFRICA
AND THE BOX HAS NOT BEEN OPENED SINCE - STILL I'M SURE THE BIRD ISN'T IN IT
FICTION!
WHAT ARE YOU TRYING TO HAND US UNCLE?
YOU MIGHT GET BY WITH THAT IN AFRICA. BUT NOT HERE!
IT'S NO JOKE
9-12
TO BE CONTINUED
SEGAR

THIMBLE THEATER

NOW SHOWING—A CHAMPION "BOXER."
Tomorrow—"Nailed" for Ten.

YOU SAY YOU NAILED THE BIRD IN THIS BOX WHEN YOU LEFT AFRICA - AND THAT THE BOX HAS NEVER BEEN OPENED?
NEVER
WHIFFLE
AND YOU ALSO SAY THAT WHEN THE BOX IS OPENED IT WILL BE EMPTY - ARE YOU TRYING TO KID SOMEBODY?
I AM NOT!
WHIFFLE
UNCLE LUBRY, I'M GOING TO SHOW YOU UP - I'LL BET TEN BUCKS THAT THE BIRD IS IN THE BOX - I KNOW SHE IS BECAUSE I HEAR HER SAYING "WHIFFLE"
WHIFFLE
THIS'LL BE THE SOFTEST "TEN" I EVER MADE! HA! HA! I STILL HEAR HER
IT'LL BE EMPTY
WHIFFLE
GOOD GOSH IT IS EMPTY!
COMPARED TO THIS BIRD PERPETUAL MOTION WOULD BE A CINCH TO FIGURE OUT - BERNICE IS A STRANGE BIRD
SEGAR
9-13

THIMBLE THEATER

NOW SHOWING—"NAILED" FOR TEN.
Tomorrow—The Whiffle o' the Wisp.

YOU GOOFY LOOKIN' BIRD, HOW DID YOU DO IT? I HEARD YOU IN THE BOX AND I BET TEN DOLLARS YOU WERE INSIDE - THEN WHEN I OPENED IT, IT WAS EMPTY!
WHIFFLE
BERNICE IS AN AFRICAN WHIFFLE BIRD - BETTER KNOWN AS THE AFRICAN ESCAPE HEN - NOW NAIL THE BOX UP
THERE, UNCLE, THE BOX IS NAILED UP TIGHT - WHAT'S THE IDEA?
NOW I'LL BET YOU ANOTHER TEN THAT BERNICE IS INSIDE
SURE, I'LL COVER YOUR TEN - AND I'LL WIN THIS TIME TOO - BECAUSE I LOOKED IN THE BOX BEFORE I NAILED DOWN THE LID
ALL RIGHT - OPEN IT - AND PLEASE REMEMBER THE BET
AS I'VE SAID BEFORE - BERNICE IS A VERY UNUSUAL BIRD
WELL I'LL BE POP-EYED!
WHIFFLE
9-14
SEGAR

THIMBLE THEATER

NOW SHOWING—THE WHIFFLE O' THE WISP.
Monday—A Guy's Money's Never Safe.

HEY, SIS, WHAT DO YOU THINK OF BERNICE? UNCLE SAYS SHE'S AN AFRICAN ESCAPE HEN
WHERE IS SHE?
GONE!
!?
THERE SHE IS - HIDING UNDER THE TABLE CLOTH!
QUICK! LET'S CATCH HER
WHIFFLE
TALK ABOUT SPEED! LOOK - HERE SHE IS UNDER THE RUG
IT'S UNCANNY
YOU HAVEN'T SEEN ANYTHING YET
WHIFFLE
9-15
SEGAR

THIMBLE THEATER

NOW SHOWING—A GUY'S MONEY'S NEVER SAFE.
Tomorrow—Bernice, the Home Wrecker.

SAY, CASTOR, I'LL BET YOU "FIVE" THAT BERNICE IS IN THIS VASE
THINK I'M CRAZY? YOU KNOW SHE'S IN THERE
WELL, THEN I'LL BET YOU THE SAME AMOUNT THAT SHE ISN'T IN IT
UNCLE, THERE'S ONLY ONE BET THAT I'LL MAKE WITH YOU - I'VE GOT TEN BERRIES THAT SAYS YOUR AFRICAN ESCAPE HEN IS NOT IN THIS SAFE
I'LL TAKE YOU UP ON THAT - GO AHEAD - UNLOCK THE SAFE
PAY ME
WHIFFLE

THIMBLE THEATER

NOW SHOWING—BERNICE, THE HOME WRECKER.
Tomorrow—She Knows Her Ammunition.

UNCLE, DID YOU MEAN IT WHEN YOU SAID YOU'D GIVE ME ONE THOUSAND DOLLARS IF I SUCCEEDED IN KILLING BERNICE?
SURE I DID
BETTER MEN THAN YOU HAVE TRIED AND FAILED TO KILL AN AFRICAN ESCAPE HEN
THAT'S A LOTTA FICTION
HA!! SOUND ASLEEP-OH BABY, ONE THOUSAND SMACKERS!
BAM
CRASH
SMASH
POW
CRASH
COME ON, BERNICE
JUST WHAT IN THE GOOD GOSH A'MIGHTY HECK'R YOU TRYING TO DO?! WHAT'SA IDEA?!!
WHIFFLE
9-18
SEGAR

THIMBLE THEATER

NOW SHOWING—SHE KNOWS HER AMMUNITION.
Tomorrow—The Fruit of His Labor.

MOTHER, WHY DO YOU SUPPOSE UNCLE OFFERED CASTOR A THOUSAND DOLLARS IF HE SUCCEEDED IN KILLING "BERNICE" HIS AFRICAN ESCAPE HEN?
MAYBE THE BIRD CAN'T BE KILLED
AH-HA! SOUND ASLEEP
BANG
WHIFFLE
!
9-19
SEGAR

THIMBLE THEATER

NOW SHOWING—THE FRUIT OF HIS LABOR.
Tomorrow—The Eternal Woman.

UNCLE SAYS YOU CAN'T KILL AN AFRICAN ESCAPE HEN- WE'LL SEE - I'VE DIPPED THIS NICE RED APPLE IN POISON ONE PECK AT IT AND SHE'LL BE DEAD
HERE, BERNICE, OLD KID - LOOK AT THE NICE RED APPLE I BRUNG YOU
WHIFFLE
WHERE THE HECK IS SHE TAKING IT?
WELL I'LL BE DOGGONED! SHE'S WASHING OFF THE POISON !!
9-20
SEGAR

THIMBLE THEATER

NOW SHOWING—THE ETERNAL WOMAN.
Tomorrow—The Cannon Reported But So Did Bernice.

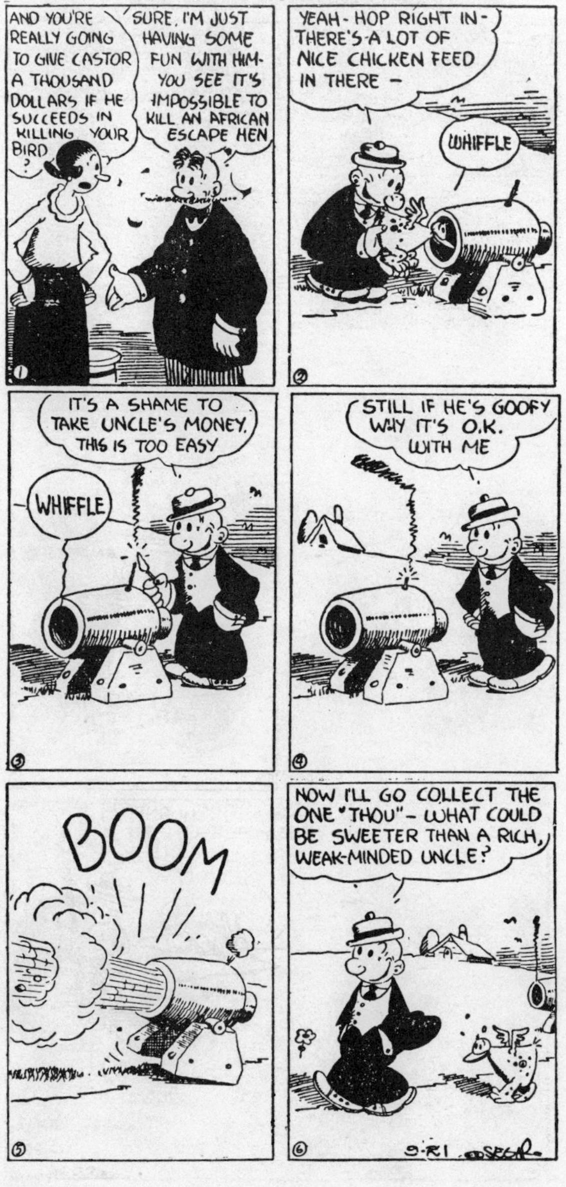
AND YOU'RE REALLY GOING TO GIVE CASTOR A THOUSAND DOLLARS IF HE SUCCEEDS IN KILLING YOUR BIRD ?
SURE, I'M JUST HAVING SOME FUN WITH HIM- YOU SEE IT'S IMPOSSIBLE TO KILL AN AFRICAN ESCAPE HEN
YEAH- HOP RIGHT IN- THERE'S A LOT OF NICE CHICKEN FEED IN THERE -
WHIFFLE
IT'S A SHAME TO TAKE UNCLE'S MONEY. THIS IS TOO EASY
WHIFFLE
STILL IF HE'S GOOFY WHY IT'S O.K. WITH ME
BOOM
NOW I'LL GO COLLECT THE ONE "THOU" - WHAT COULD BE SWEETER THAN A RICH, WEAK-MINDED UNCLE?

THIMBLE THEATER

NOW SHOWING—THE CANNON REPORTED BUT SO DID BERNICE
Monday—It's No Bluff.

MAW, DO YOU THINK THAT LUBRY'S PET WHIFFLE HEN REALLY IS UNKILLABLE?
IF BERNICE COULD BE KILLED, UNCLE WOULDN'T OFFER CASTOR $1000. FOR HER FUNERAL
RICH AND TIGHT, THAT'S LUBRY KENT OYL
HEY, UNCLE, COME ACROSS I JUST KILLED YOUR AFRICAN ESCAPE HEN - GIMME THAT THOUSAND!
I CERTAINLY AM HAVING A LOT OF FUN WITH CASTOR
HOW'D YOU KILL BERNICE ?
I PUT HER INTO A CANNON AND BLEW HER INTO LESS THAN NOTHING! I SURE DID!!
WELL WHAT THE ?!
WHIFFLE
I STILL SAY THAT NO HUMAN BEING CAN KILL BERNICE, TRY AGAIN, CASTOR

THIMBLE THEATER

NOW SHOWING—IT'S NO BLUFF.
Tomorrow—The Wings of an "Angel."

UNCLE'S HAVING A LOT OF FUN WITH ME - SAID HE'D GIVE ME $1000.00 IF I SUCCEED IN KILLING BERNICE, HIS AFRICAN ESCAPE HEN. HE HAS AN IDEA THAT IT'S IMPOSSIBLE TO KILL HER
THERE SHE IS STANDING ON THE EDGE OF A THOUSAND FOOT CLIFF! NOW'S MY CHANCE
SHE CAN'T ESCAPE - I'LL TAKE A QUICK RUN AND PUSH HER OFF
!
WHIFFLE

THIMBLE THEATER

NOW SHOWING—THE WINGS OF AN "ANGEL."

Tomorrow—A Pullet and Bullets

YES, I TOLD CASTOR I'D GIVE HIM $1000.°° IF HE SUCCEEDED IN KILLING MY AFRICAN ESCAPE HEN AND I'M HAVING A LOT OF FUN WATCHING HIS ATTEMPTS
SHE MUST BE A DARN SMART BIRD
WELL, BERNICE, I HATE TO DO IT - BUT I NEED THAT THOUSAND BUCKS. YOU'RE GOING TO PASS OUT
I'LL DROP HER OFF OF THIS THOUSAND FOOT CLIFF-
IN ABOUT A MINUTE SHE'LL BE JUST A GREASE SPOT ON THE ROCKS BELOW
GOOD NIGHT! I DIDN'T KNOW SHE COULD FLY
WHIFFLE

THIMBLE THEATER

NOW SHOWING—A PULLET AND BULLETS.

Tomorrow—You Can't Rock Bernice to Sleep.

BANG
@x!!
BAM!
BANG
WHIFFLE
AW SHUT UP!!

THIMBLE THEATER

NOW SHOWING—YOU CAN'T ROCK BERNICE TO SLEEP

Tomorrow—Thanks for the Bath.

CAN'T BE KILLED EH? HA! HA! BERNICE YOU'RE JUST THE SAME AS DEAD RIGHT NOW
I'LL BRING UNCLE HERE. I WANT HIM TO SEE THIS, HE THINKS HIS BIRD IS UNKILLABLE
WHIFFLE
I'VE GOT A ROCK TIED AROUND HER NECK, UNCLE -
SURE I'M GOING TO DUMP HER INTO THE OCEAN AND DROWN'ER TO DEATH
HA! HA! YES YOU WILL!!
WHIFFLE
DIDN'T I TELL YOU SHE WAS AN ESCAPE HEN?

THIMBLE THEATER

NOW SHOWING—THANKS FOR THE BATH.

Tomorrow—Fowl, Not "Fish."

WELL, UNCLE, YOU'LL HAVE TO ADMIT DEFEAT. I'M GOING TO DROWN BERNICE AND PROVE THAT AN AFRICAN ESCAPE HEN CAN BE KILLED
IF YOU SUCCEED, I'LL GIVE YOU A THOUSAND BUCKS!
THAT'S THAT!
SPLASH
COME ACROSS UNCLE, GIVE ME THE THOUSAND!
9-28
SEGAR

THIMBLE THEATER

NOW SHOWING—FOWL, NOT "FISH."

Monday—Undermining Castor's Work.

CASTOR HAS TRIED A DOZEN TIMES TO KILL YOUR WHIFFLE BIRD WITHOUT ANY SUCCESS AT ALL-
HE SAYS HE WON'T GIVE UP
I TOLD HIM I'D GIVE HIM A THOUSAND DOLLARS IF HE KILLED BERNICE - BUT MY MONEY IS SAFE - THIS STRANGE AFRICAN ESCAPE HEN CAN'T BE KILLED
HE'S BEEN IN THE NEXT ROOM FOR AN HOUR TRYING TO FEED A WORM TO YOUR PET
S'FUNNY, BERNICE LIKES WORMS
EAT NICE WORM!
LET'S GO SEE WHY SHE WON'T EAT IT
SURE- SEE NICE FAT WORM- OPEN YOUR MOUTH- SURE IT'S A WORM!
WHIFFLE
SEGAR
9-29

THIMBLE THEATER

NOW SHOWING—UNDERMINING CASTOR'S WORK.

Tomorrow—"Stringing" Castor Along.

BERNICE, YOUR GOOSE IS COOKED - I'M GOING TO BURY YOU - I'LL SHOW UNCLE THAT AN AFRICAN ESCAPE HEN CAN BE KILLED
WHIFFLE
I'LL ADMIT SHE'S A TRICKY BIRD BUT SHE'LL NEVER GET OUT OF THIS
EASY!
AS SOON AS I'M SURE SHE'S DEAD I'LL DIG HER UP AND SHOW THE REMAINS TO UNCLE
WHIFFLE
SEGAR
10-1

THIMBLE THEATER

NOW SHOWING—"STRINGENG CASTOR ALONG.

Tomorrow—A "Tied" Score.

I'LL WRAP THIS COIL OF ROPE AROUND YOU SO YOU CAN'T POSSIBLY GET LOOSE
THEN OVER THE CLIFF INTO THE OCEAN! I'LL PROVE TO MY UNCLE THAT AFRICAN ESCAPE HENS CAN BE KILLED
I DON'T CARE WHAT ANYONE SAYS—I SAY THERE ISN'T ANYTHING IN THE WORLD THAT COULD GET OUT OF THIS MESS OF ROPE
SHE MAY BE A BRAINY BIRD, BUT I'VE GOT A FEW UNDER THE HAT MYSELF
WHIFFLE
!!X?!! XXm!
FLYING BACKWARDS IN ORDER TO DODGE STONES
Great Britain rights reserved.
by King Features Syndicate, Inc.
10-2
SEGAR

THIMBLE THEATER

NOW SHOWING—A "TIED" SCORE.

Tomorrow—A "Jonah" and a Whale.

WHY DON'T YOU GIVE UP, CASTOR? YOU'LL NEVER KILL MY AFRICAN ESCAPE HEN-
YOU SAID YOU'D GIVE ME A THOUSAND DOLLARS IF I SUCCEEDED IN CROAKING BERNICE - AND I WON'T GIVE UP
YEP, I'M GOING TO STRING YOU UP- #1,000, OH, BABY!!
TA-TA BERNICE, OLD DEAR!
I'LL LET HER HANG THERE FOR A COUPLA WEEKS - SHE'LL BE GOOD AND DEAD BY THEN
WHIFFLE
SEGAR
10-3

THIMBLE THEATER

NOW SHOWING—BERNICE IS NEVER NAPPING.

Tomorrow—Bernice Is Never Napping.

WHEN A SHARK COMES UP TO GRAB THIS BAIT, I'LL THROW HER RIGHT DOWN HIS THROAT
THERE BY GOLLY, THAT'S THE END OF THE "SO CALLED" UNKILLABLE AFRICAN ESCAPE HEN
I'M THE ONLY PERSON WHO EVER KILLED A WHIFFLE HEN - THAT'S BECAUSE UP UNDER THE HAT IS SOMETHING
!
WELL, DOGGONE! A SHARK'S TONSIL!!
10-4
SEGAR

THIMBLE THEATER

NOW SHOWING—BERNICE IS NEVER NAPPING.

Tomorrow—You Can't Keep a Good Woman Down.

HEY THERE, MISTER
I'LL GIVE YOU FIVE DOLLARS IF YOU'LL KILL THIS BIRD
YOU'RE EITHER RICH OR CRAZY
I'LL FIND A CAN, AND MAKE HEN SOUP
ATTA' BOY
I HIRED A YEGG TO KILL YOUR ESCAPE HEN - AND HE'LL DO IT TOO — OH. WHAT A TOUGH BABY!
NO HE WON'T
I'VE LOST A LOT OF SLEEP THE LAST FEW WEEKS TRYING TO THINK UP A WAY TO KILL BERNICE - BUT THAT'S ALL SETTLED NOW - SO I'LL HIT THE QUILTS EARLY TO-NIGHT
!
WHIFFLE
SEGAR

THIMBLE THEATER

NOW SHOWING—YOU CAN'T KEEP A GOOD WOMAN

Monday—A Wise Dame.

I'LL PILE ROCKS ON HER, SHE CAN'T GET OUT FROM UNDER A BUNCH OF ROCKS
WHIFFLE
I'LL LET HER STAY THERE TILL SHE STARVES!
UNCLE IS ALL WRONG IF HE THINKS HIS ESCAPE HEN CAN OUTWIT ME
AND I'LL TELL THAT TO THE POPEYED WORLD
WHIFFLE
10-6
SEGAR

THIMBLE THEATER

NOW SHOWING—A WISE DAME.

Tomorrow—A Popcorn Recipe.

I'LL LAY THIS HEAVY STEEL TRAP RIGHT HERE —
NOW I'LL BLINDFOLD HER AND LEAD HER INTO IT
COME ON, BERNICE, FOLLOW ME - RIGHT THIS WAY -
COME ON, BERNICE!
YOU MUST HAVE A HECK OF A LOT OF INSTINCT — WOMAN'S INTUITION OR SOMETHING
WHIFFLE
10-8
SEGAR

THIMBLE THEATER

NOW SHOWING—A POPCORN RECIPE.

Tomorrow—She Knows Her Currents.

THIS IS A MEAN TRICK TO PLAY ON BERNICE – BUT UNCLE SAID IT WASN'T POSSIBLE TO KILL HER – I'M GOING TO PROVE THAT HE'S WRONG
DYNAMITE
DYNAMITE
EAT NICE CORN!! WHERE YOU GOING?
HEY, COME BACK HERE AND EAT YOUR CORN – SURE – DON'T BE SILLY LIKE THAT—
DYNAMITE
BANG
WHIFFLE
WHIFFLE! WHIFFLE!
10-9 SEGAR

THIMBLE THEATER

NOW SHOWING—SHE KNOWS HER CURRENTS.

Tomorrow—She "Weights" for No Man.

CASTOR WON'T GIVE UP UNCLE – HE SAYS HE'LL PROVE YOU'RE WRONG AND THAT BERNICE WILL PASS OUT BEFORE NIGHT
NOBODY CAN KILL A WHIFFLE HEN
HE'S GOING TO ELECTROCUTE HER
YEAH? HA! HA!
!?
OH, YOU !! GODD GOSH DARN !
WHAT'S THE MATTER WITH YOU, CASTOR?
HERE I'VE GONE TO A LOT OF TROUBLE AND EXPENSE – BUILT A NICE COMFORTABLE ELECTRIC CHAIR –
AND SHE WON'T SIT IN IT!!
WHIFFLE
10-10 SEGAR

THIMBLE THEATER

NOW SHOWING—SHE "WEIGHTS" FOR NO MAN.

Tomorrow—A Dry-Eyed Gal.

BERNICE IS VERY FOND OF DOUGH – SO I'VE MADE HER A BUNCH OF DOUGH BALLS AND I PUT A BUCK SHOT INTO EACH ONE
NOW I'LL TAKE HER TO THE MIDDLE OF THE LAKE AND DUMP HER IN I KNOW SHE CAN'T SWIM WHEN SHE'S FULL OF LEAD
HA! HA!
AT LAST I HAVE SUCCEEDED IN KILLING AN "UNKILLABLE" WHIFFLE HEN
WHIFFLE!
AW, WHAT'S THE USE!!
SEGAR 10-11

THIMBLE THEATER
NOW SHOWING—A DRY-EYED GAL.
Tomorrow—A Case of Mistaken Identity.

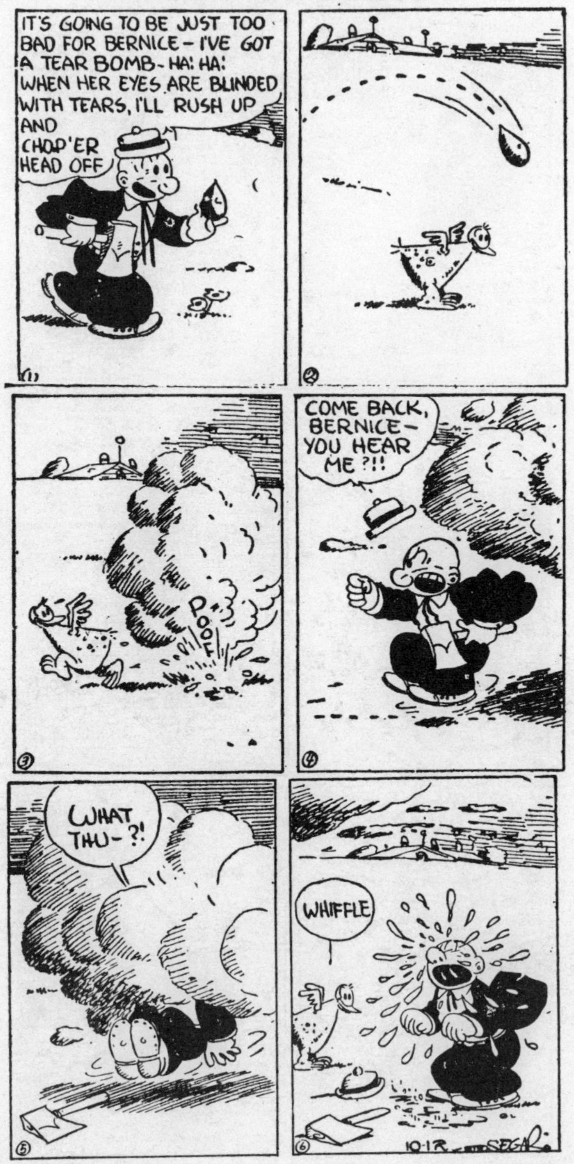
IT'S GOING TO BE JUST TOO BAD FOR BERNICE - I'VE GOT A TEAR BOMB - HA! HA! WHEN HER EYES ARE BLINDED WITH TEARS, I'LL RUSH UP AND CHOP 'ER HEAD OFF
POOF
COME BACK, BERNICE - YOU HEAR ME ?!!
WHAT THU - ?!
WHIFFLE
10-12
SEGAR

THIMBLE THEATER
NOW SHOWING A CASE OF MISTAKEN IDENTITY.
Monday—A Missed Miss.

SOME NERVE! BERNICE WALKED RIGHT INTO THIS STRANGER'S HOUSE. I'LL GO IN AND GET HER
SAY, LADY, DID YOU KILL THAT HEN JUST NOW ?
SURE I DID!
YOU SEE I WANT TO PROVE TO MY UNCLE THAT A WHIFFLE HEN CAN BE KILLED, SO I'LL GIVE YOU TEN DOLLARS FOR HER
I DON'T KNOW WHAT YOU'RE TALKING ABOUT BUT I'M WILLING
SAY! I THOUGHT YOU KILLED BERNICE
I KILLED A HEN OUT OF MY OWN COOP
WHIFFLE
WHY SHOULD I GIVE YOUR "TEN" BACK? BEAT IT!
WOP
WHIFFLE
SEGAR
10-13

THIMBLE THEATER
NOW SHOWING—A MISSED MISS.
Tomorrow—Trapped.

THIS ARROW HAWK IS THE MEANEST BIRD ON EARTH HE COST ME $25.00 BUT HE'LL FIX UNCLE'S WHIFFLE HEN
THAT'S THE STUFF - FLY 'WAY UP IN THE AIR AND THEN DART DOWN ON HER HEAD
Z-Z-Z
WHIFFLE
10-15
SEGAR

THIMBLE THEATER

NOW SHOWING—TRAPPED.

Tomorrow—Thanks for the Ride.

YOU'RE SUPPOSED TO BE THE MEANEST BIRD ON EARTH- NOW I WANT YOU TO PUT ALL YOUR STRENGTH INTO ONE PECK AND LAND ON THAT ESCAPE HEN'S HEAD
GORK
COME HERE, BERNICE
WHIFFLE
COME ON, OLD ARROW HAWK SPEAR HER ON THE BEAN- WHAT'S SHE DOING WITH THAT BLOCK OF WOOD IN HER MOUTH?
!
?
?
SEGAR 10-16

THIMBLE THEATER

NOW SHOWING—THANKS FOR THE RIDE.

Tomorrow—Then He Will Always Be Alone.

I STILL HAVE FAITH IN THIS "ARROW HAWK" EVEN IF HE DID FAIL TWICE
ALL RIGHT- GO AHEAD. ALL YOU'VE GOT TO DO IS EXTERMINATE HER COMPLETELY
GORK
IF THAT ARROW HAWK IS AS BAD AS THEY SAY HE IS - IT'LL BE CURTAINS FOR BERNICE
!
WHIFFLE
SEGAR 10-17

THIMBLE THEATER

NOW SHOWING—THEN HE WILL ALWAYS BE ALONE.

Tomorrow—A Fearful Shock.

WELL, CASTOR, I'M GOING BACK TO AFRICA AND I'LL HAVE TO TAKE BERNICE WITH ME - SHE'S A VALUABLE BIRD
LUBRY KENT OYL
AFRICA
I TOLD YOU I'D GIVE YOU A THOUSAND DOLLARS IF YOU SUCCEEDED IN KILLING HER AND YOU FAILED, AS I KNEW YOU WOULD- THAT PROVES SHE'S UNUSUAL
GOOD-BYE, CASTOR
SO LONG, UNCLE
WHIFFLE
WELL, THANK HEAVEN I'LL NEVER SEE THAT SILLY LITTLE ESCAPE HEN AGAIN! SHE HAD MY GOAT COMPLETELY
IT SURE WAS TOUGH TO BE OUTWITTED BY A BIRD- FROM NOW ON I'M NOT GOING TO ASSOCIATE WITH ANYTHING THAT'S SMARTER THAN I AM
10-18
SEGAR

THIMBLE THEATER
NOW SHOWING—A FEARFUL SHOCK.
Tomorrow—Living Up to Its Reputation.

WELL SIS-UNCLE LEFT FOR AFRICA AND TOOK BERNICE ALONG-I'M HAPPY AS HECK OVER IT
BELIEVE ME, I'M SURE GLAD TO GET RID OF THAT AFRICAN ESCAPE HEN
ARE YOU SURE YOU'RE RID OF HER?
ABSOLUTELY! I SAW UNCLE PUT HER IN HIS SUITCASE
WELL, WHAT'S THAT BEHIND YOU?
MEANING WHICH, HUH?
LOOK AND SEE
I WON'T LOOK! IF IT'S BERNICE THE SHOCK WOULD BE TOO MUCH FOR ME-I'D PASS OUT
WHIFFLE !
10-19
SEGAR

THIMBLE THEATER
NOW SHOWING—LIVING UP TO ITS REPUTATION.
Monday—Such a Playful Bird.

WHIFFLE!
IT'S HER! IT'S BERNICE! AND I THOUGHT I WAS RID OF HER!
GET OUTTA HERE!! YOU—
I'M GOING TO TAKE YA' APART RIGHT THIS MINUTE
NOW I'VE GOT YOU, —!!
10-20
SEGAR

THIMBLE THEATER
NOW SHOWING—JUST A PLAYFUL BIRD
Tomorrow—An Egg Shampoo

SAY, CASTOR, BERNICE GOT AWAY-DID SHE COME BACK TO YOU?
LUBRY KENT OYL, AFRKA
YES, HERE SHE IS-GEE, I'M GLAD YOU CAME FOR HER-I HATE THE SIGHT OF HER!
IT WOULD BE USELESS FOR ME TO TAKE HER AWAY AGAIN. SHE'D COME RIGHT BACK TO YOU, BECAUSE SHE LIKES YOU
LIKES ME!! WHY, I'VE TRIED TO KILL HER A HUNDRED TIMES!
THAT'S THE REASON— SHE THINKS YOU'RE PLAYING WITH HER, YEAH, A VERY PECULIAR BIRD
WHIFFLE!
SEGAR
10-22

THIMBLE THEATER
NOW SHOWING—AN EGG SHAMPOO
Tomorrow—Quit Your Kidding

UNCLE GAVE BERNICE TO CASTOR BEFORE HE SAILED FOR AFRICA
CASTOR HATES THE GROUND SHE WALKS ON
I SAID, STOP FOLLOWING ME! BEAT IT! CAN'T YOU UNDERSTAND ENGLISH?
THAT WHIFFLE HEN HAS GOT ME ALL BURNED UP!
EGG
WHAT A LIFE!
SPLAT
WHIFFLE
WHY, YOU LOW DOWN-
10-23
SEGAR

THIMBLE THEATER
NOW SHOWING—QUIT YOUR KIDDING
Tomorrow—The Adding Machines

I SUPPOSE THERE'S NO WAY OF GETTING RID OF BERNICE - WHAT A PEST! TAGS AFTER ME ALL DAY LONG
DO YOU SEE WHAT I SEE? OR ARE MY EYES PLAYING TRICKS? THAT LOOKS LIKE AN AFRIC WHIFFLE HEN!
IT'S A WHIFFLE HEN! I KNOW !!!
IT IS - STILL IT CAN'T BE - IT CAN'T POSSIBLY BE!
SON, HOW MUCH DO YOU WANT FOR YOUR HEN?
TEN CENTS. CASH OR CREDIT!!
DO NOT JEST, YOUNG MAN, WE ARE SERIOUS
HE PROBABLY MEANS TEN MILLION DOLLARS, BUT WE CAN PAY NO SUCH PRICE
10-24
CONTINUED
SEGAR

THIMBLE THEATER
NOW SHOWING—THE ADDING MACHINES
Tomorrow—Another Sleeping Powder, Please

WHY ARE THESE TWO STRANGERS SO INTERESTED IN CASTOR'S WHIFFLE HEN?
NO DOUBT ABOUT IT!
SURE IT IS!
SAY - WHAT ARE YOU FELLOWS TALKING ABOUT?
SHALL I MAKE HIM AN OFFER?
BY ALL MEANS DO THAT
YOUNG MAN, WILL YOU TAKE TWO THOUSAND DOLLARS FOR YOUR WHIFFLE HEN?
STOP! MY CONSCIENCE WOULD HURT THE REST OF MY LIFE -
LET'S GIVE HIM FOUR THOUSAND
WHY NOT MAKE IT FIVE THOUSAND WHILE WE'RE ABOUT IT?
10-25
SEGAR

THIMBLE THEATER

NOW SHOWING—ANOTHER SLEEPING POWDER, PLEASE

Tomorrow—That Gal's Got a Good "Figure"

LISTEN, DO YOU GENTS WANT TO BUY MY WHIFFLE HEN, OR NOT?
SURE-WE WANT TO BUY HER! CERTAINLY!
WE'RE TRYING TO DECIDE ON HOW MUCH TO GIVE YOU
WE OUGHT TO GIVE HIM AT LEAST $5,000.00
LET'S GIVE HIM $6,000.00
?!
AW, LET'S MAKE IT SEVEN
HOW ABOUT EIGHT?
?
DO YOU THINK SHE'S WORTH NINE THOUSAND?
YES, AND THEN SOME, I THINK WE SHOULD OFFER HIM TEN OR MAYBE ELEVEN THOUSAND
WHO CARES ABOUT BREAKFAST, I HOPE I NEVER WAKE UP!
SEGAR 10-26

THIMBLE THEATER

NOW SHOWING—THAT GAL'S GOT A GOOD "FIGURE"

Monday—Bernice Grows "Grander"

LET'S SETTLE THIS THING. SUPPOSE WE GIVE HIM ELEVEN THOUSAND DOLLARS?
WE'LL GIVE HIM TWELVE THOUSAND. WHAT DO YOU SAY?
OH, I KNOW! I SEE IT ALL NOW- THEY'RE A COUPLE OF COO-KOOS- THAT'S WHAT THEY ARE
THEIR KEEPER WILL BE ALONG SOON- GEE- THEY HAD ME ALL EXCITED FOR A FEW MINUTES
HEY!
"HEY" ME EYE! YOU'RE A PAIR OF GOOFS- YEAH, ALL WET UNDER THE HAT!
HEAVENS! HE THINKS WE'RE CRAZY!
WE'LL GIVE $15,000.00
MAKE IT "SIXTEEN"
10-27 SEGAR

THIMBLE THEATER

NOW SHOWING—BERNICE GROWS "GRANDER."

Tomorrow—Anxious to "Shell Out."

DON'T LET THAT WHIFFLE HEN GET AWAY- WE MUST HAVE HER AT ANY COST
STOP! STOP! $17,000.00 WE OFFER YOU!
G'WAN- YOU'RE ALL DAMP IN THE HEAD! QUIT FOLLOWING ME!
I'LL BET THEIR KEEPER IS LOOKIN' FOR 'EM RIGHT NOW
YOUNG MAN! YOU MUST NOT TALK TO US LIKE THAT!
IF YOU DON'T LIKE IT, SUE ME!
NOW LISTEN, HOW MUCH DO YOU WANT FOR YOUR AFRICAN WHIFFLE HEN?
TEN CENTS, I TOLD YOU!
HE'S JESTING WITH US AGAIN. OFFER HIM EIGHTEEN THOUSAND
WE'LL GIVE YOU NINETEEN THOUSAND DOLLARS
TWENTY THOUSAND! NO MORE! HOW ABOUT TWENTY ONE THOUSAND?
MEAT ON THE TABLE FOR ANY SQUIRREL
10-29 SEGAR

THIMBLE THEATER

NOW SHOWING—ANXIOUS TO "SHELL OUT."

Tomorrow—Merely Chicken Feed.

THESE TWO STRANGERS OFFERED CASTOR $21,000. FOR BERNICE. CASTOR, NATURALLY THINKS THEY'VE ESCAPED FROM SOME ASYLUM— BUT NOT SO— THEY'D PAY THAT AMOUNT AND MORE
ANYONE THAT WOULD PAY MORE THAN "FOUR BITS" FOR THIS BIRD IS ALL DAMP BETWEEN THE EARS
HE WON'T SELL
WE HAVE FAILED
DON'T BOTHER ME ANY MORE GO ON BACK TO YOUR PADDED CELLS
I SUPPOSE THE REASON HE THINKS WE'RE CRAZY IS BECAUSE WE ONLY OFFERED HIM $21,000.
THANK GOODNESS I'M RID OF THOSE TWO BOZOS
AS I LIVE!! AN AFRICAN WHIFFLE HEN! I WILL PAY $10,000.
WHAT! ANOTHER NUT?
10-30
SEGAR

THIMBLE THEATER

NOW SHOWING—MERELY CHICKEN FEED.

Tomorrow—A Higher Bid.

I WILL PAY TEN-TWELVE-FOURTEEN-TWENTY THOUSAND FOR THE AFRICAN WHIFFLE HEN
G'WAN!
GOOD NIGHT! ARE ALL THE GOOFS IN THE WORLD RUNNING LOOSE AROUND HERE!
JUST A MINUTE !!
STOP CHASING ME - IF YOU WANT TO BUY THIS BIRD SHOW ME THE CASH
ALL RIGHT HERE'S $20,000
MY GOSH! YOU MEAN THAT?
!
!
I'LL PAY THIRTY THOUSAND
SEGAR
10-31

THIMBLE THEATER

NOW SHOWING—A HIGHER BID.

Tomorrow—A Bird of a Sale.

QUIT HORNING IN, I OFFERED $20,000. FOR HIS WHIFFLE HEN!
AND I'M OFFERING $30,000
LET'S GO HOME, BERNICE — IF THEY'RE WILLING TO PAY THAT MUCH THEY'LL PAY MORE
AND I WANT TO FIND OUT WHY YOU'RE SO VALUABLE. A FEW DAYS AGO I WOULD HAVE SOLD YOU FOR A THIN DIME
FOLKS, I'VE BEEN OFFERED THIRTY THOUSAND DOLLARS FOR BERNICE
WAKE UP!
YOU'RE SICK
P-S-T- I'LL PAY $31,000.00
!
SEGAR
11-1

THIMBLE THEATER

NOW SHOWING—A BIRD OF A SALE.
Tomorrow—He Can Bank on That.

HERE'S $31,000. CASH FOR YOUR AFRICAN WHIFFLE HEN- WHAT DO YOU SAY?
TAKE 'IM UP ON THAT, SON, GRAB THE MONEY, QUICK!
HURRY, CASTOR, BEFORE HE CHANGES HIS MIND
O-K
SHE'S YOURS, MISTER
HOO-RAY! $31,000.00
HOO-RAY!
HOO-RAY
HOO-RAY!! WHOOPEE!! BARGAIN!
SEGAR 11-2

THIMBLE THEATER

NOW SHOWING—HE CAN BANK ON THAT.
Monday—Dollars and Sense.

BERNKE- YOU ARE MINE- ALL MINE!
HE PAID $31,000. FOR THAT SILLY LOOKING WHIFFLE HEN - AND HE SEEMS TO BE HAPPY OVER IT
SON- I'LL BET THE MONEY HE PAID YOU IS COUNTERFEIT- NOBODY'D GIVE THAT MUCH FOR A DUMB BIRD
I'LL TAKE IT TO THE BANK AND FIND OUT
IS IT ANY GOOD?
IT'S WORTH A HUNDRED CENTS TO THE DOLLAR
BURGLARS KEEP OUT
THE CASHIER SAID 'SWORTH A HUNDRED CENTS TO THE BUCK! THIRTY ONE THOUSAND IN REAL MONEY— I'M A MILLIONAIRE!!
WE OUGHT TO MAKE HIM PAY BOARD MA
SURE YOU ARE
11-3 SEGAR

THIMBLE THEATER

NOW SHOWING—DOLLARS AND SENSE.
Tomorrow—Every Man for Himself.

OH, BABY- $31,000. FOR THAT NO GOOD- GOOD FOR NOTHING WHIFFLE HEN— WHAT I MEAN, THAT'S GOOD BUSINESS
THINK OF SELLING THAT CRAZY BIRD FOR SO MUCH MONEY! CASTOR SURE IS LUCKY
YOU SAID A CAR LOAD, NO FOOLIN'!
A BUCK WOULD'A BEEN FOUR BITS TOO MUCH-
SAY- DID YOU SELL YOUR WHIFFLE HEN TO THAT GUY FOR $31,000.?
YES- WHY?
FOOL-SAP-BOOB-DUMB-BELL-MORON FAT HEAD-HALF WIT-FLY-BRAINED NINCOMPOOP!
I'DA GIVEN YOU FIFTY THOUSAND DOLLARS
SEGAR 11-5

THIMBLE THEATER

NOW SHOWING—EVERY MAN FOR HIMSELF.
Tomorrow—Aladdin and His Lamp.

IT'S HARD TO BELIEVE BUT I REALLY OWN HER! WHOOPS! SHE'S MINE
TRY THAT ON YOUR DICTIONARY!! HE'S THE GUY WHO BOUGHT BERNICE
MINE! MINE! ALL MINE!
OUW WHAT A WOLLOP
BOP
!
?
SHE'S MINE! WHOOPEE!
AFTER PUTTING TWO AND TWO TOGETHER IT'S STILL A MYSTERY!
SEGAR 11-6

THIMBLE THEATER

NOW SHOWING—ALADDIN AND HIS LAMP.
Tomorrow—No Xmas "Sock" for Castor.

I GOT $31,000.⁰⁰ FOR BERNICE AND IT'S A LOT OF MONEY, SURE I KNOW THAT——
BUT SOMETHING TELLS ME I GOT SWINDLED
RIGHT AFTER I'D SOLD HER ANOTHER FELLOW SAID HE WOULD'A GIVEN FIFTY THOUSAND FOR HER
WHY SHE'S SO VALUABLE IS A MYSTERY TO ME! I CAN'T DOPE IT!
I WISH NOW THAT I HADN'T SOLD HER! WISH I HAD HER BACK
BERNICE!
WHIFFLE
11-7 SEGAR

THIMBLE THEATER

NOW SHOWING—NO XMAS "SOCK" FOR CASTOR.
Tomorrow—Numbered Hours.

HELLO, CASTOR. SAY WHAT'S THIS I HEAR ABOUT YOU SELLING THE WHIFFLE HEN YOUR UNCLE GAVE YOU? OLIVE SAID YOU GOT $31,000. FOR HER
WHIFFLE
THAT'S RIGHT HAM- SEE- HERE'S THE MONEY- I'M TAKING IT TO THE BANK
BUT THE FUNNY PART IS—— BERNICE CAME BACK AND NOW I'VE GOT THE MONEY AND HER ALSO
HAW! HAW THAT'S HOT!
GOOD BUSINESS
SAY YOU BIG BUM! WHO YOU HITTIN' LIKE THAT?! YOU HEARD ME!!
THINK I'M SANTA CLAUS?!
11-8 SEGAR

THIMBLE THEATER

NOW SHOWING—NUMBERED HOURS.
Tomorrow—A Bad "Egg."

WHY PAY GOOD MONEY FOR THIS WHIFFLE HEN? STEALING
IF THAT LITTLE NITWIT KNEW HER VALUE HE'D GUARD HER WITH HIS LIFE
ACCORDING TO THOSE STRANGERS YOUR WHIFFLE HEN IS WORTH THOUSANDS OF DOLLARS - AND YOU SAY SHE'S BEEN STOLEN?
WHAT I CAN'T DOPE OUT IS THE GOOFY SMILE ON YOUR FACE - WHY AREN'T YOU WORRYING?
SHE'LL COME BACK, SURE SHE WILL
'LO BERNICE OLD KID
WHIFFLE
THERE'S SOMETHING UNCANNY ABOUT THIS BIRD - AND THEY KNOW MORE ABOUT HER THAN CASTOR DOES
SO YOU'VE GOT HER TRAINED TO COME BACK TO YOU - EH? WELL GET THIS - IF YOU WERE DEAD SHE WOULDN'T COME BACK TO YOU - HA! SHE'D STAY WITH ME THEN! G-R-R- YOU MAY NOT LIVE MANY MORE DAYS!
HUH! YOU MEAN ME!!
11-9 SEGAR

THIMBLE THEATER

NOW SHOWING—A BAD "EGG."
Monday—A Glutton for Punishment.

AS I SAID BEFORE YOUR DAYS ARE NUMBERED
I WOULDN'T BE IN YOUR SHOES FOR A MILLION - YOU'RE OUT OF LUCK, CASTOR
WHY DOES HE WANT TO CROAK YOU?
BECAUSE BERNICE WON'T STAY WITH ANYONE BUT ME -
AND HE THINKS THAT IF I'M "BUMPED OFF" SHE'LL STAY WITH HIM
WHAT'S HE WANT WITH AN AFRICAN WHIFFLE HEN? WHY'S SHE SO VALUABLE?
HOW THE HECK DO I KNOW!
SHE'S THE ONLY WHIFFLE HEN IN CAPTIVITY - IT IS IMPOSSIBLE TO CAPTURE A WILD ONE - HIS UNCLE RAISED HER FROM AN EGG - HOW HE FOUND THE EGG I CAN'T UNDERSTAND - I HUNTED TWENTY YEARS FOR A WHIFFLE HEN EGG
11-10 SEGAR

THIMBLE THEATER

NOW SHOWING—A GLUTTON FOR PUNISHMENT.
Tomorrow—In Training.

AW, COME ON, CASTOR, OLD BOY - CHEER UP
BUT I'M WORRIED, HAM - THAT STRANGER SAID HE WAS GOING TO KILL ME
HE WAS ONLY BLUFFING, SURE HE WAS
YA' THINK SO? GEE - MAYBE HE WAS BLUFFING
SURE!
HA! HA! I'LL BET HE WAS BLUFFING! I'LL BET THAT'S JUST WHAT HE WAS DOING
YOU'LL PASS OUT INSIDE OF ONE MONTH
AW COME ON, CASTOR, CHEER UP
SAY! WILL YOU PLEASE GET THE HECK OUTTA HERE AND LET ME WORRY
11-12 SEGAR

THIMBLE THEATER
NOW SHOWING—IN TRAINING.
Tomorrow—The Process of Elimination.

GOOD NIGHT!
!
REMEMBERRR-R-R- YOU'RE GOING TO DIE!!
STOP TALKING LIKE THAT!! YOU MAKE ME FEEL TERRIBLE
BERNICE, YOU'RE THE CAUSE OF ALL THIS - THAT FOREIGNER WANTS YOU AND HE'LL DO MURDER TO GET YOU - WHY ARE YOU SO VALUABLE? THERE'S SOMETHING WE DON'T KNOW
OH, BY THE WAY MOTHER — HOW'S THAT PRAYER GO I USED TO SAY WHEN I WAS A KID?
?
!
11-13
SEGAR

THIMBLE THEATER
NOW SHOWING—THE PROCESS OF ELIMINATION.
Tomorrow—Henpecked.

LISTEN, HAM - YOU KNOW MY LIFE'S IN DANGER - AND I WANT YOU TO HELP ME - TAKE THIS GUN AND BE MY BODY GUARD
HEY! I DON'T WANT TO GET MIXED UP IN THIS MESS
DON'T BE SILLY - 'SALL RIGHT! 'SABSOLUTELY ALL RIGHT
DO YOU THINK THERE'S ANY DANGER?
NO! COME ON
AS LONG AS I'VE GOT A BODY GUARD I'M NOT AFRAID. NOT A BIT!
WHIFFLE
SEGAR 11-14

THIMBLE THEATER
NOW SHOWING—HENPECKED.
Tomorrow—A Dog's Life.

I'M THROUGH BEING YOUR BODY GUARD RIGHT NOW - THAT FELLOW BEANED ME GOOD - IF HE WANTS TO "BUMP YOU OFF" THAT'S YOURS AND HIS BUSINESS, NOT MINE
WE'RE PALS AIN'T WE? CANTCHA HELP A PAL?
WELL, ALL RIGHT - I'LL LOOK OUT FOR MYSELF - I'M NO COWARD WHAT THERE IS OF ME IS HOT STUFF - I'M JAKE - O.K. UP AND DOWN! I'M THE BERRIES!
JUST A MOMENT PLEASE!!
WHO ME?
YOU MAY MEAN SOMEBODY BUT YOU DON'T MEAN ME!
STOP! ARE YOU AFRAID OF A WOMAN?
I DIDN'T KNOW YOU WERE A WOMAN - QUIT HANGIN' ON ME - LAY OFF
WELL I AM A WOMAN - A BEAUTIFUL WOMAN - TWENTY MEN HAVE DIED FOR ME
IF YOU WANT SPEECH WITH ME MAKE IT SNAPPY BECAUSE I'M GONNA START RUNNING AGAIN REAL SOON
11-15 CONTINUED
SEGAR

THIMBLE THEATER

NOW SHOWING—A DOG'S LIFE.
Tomorrow—An "Unshiverless" Son.

IT'S IMPORTANT! YOU MUST LISTEN TO ME - MUST! MUST!!
PLEASE GO 'WAY- DON'T TAG AFTER ME! IN ABOUT A MINUTE I'M GOING TO FAINT! I'VE HAD TOO MUCH MYSTERY THE LAST FEW WEEKS ANYWAY
GOOD HEAVENS I'M BEING FOLLOWED!
MAYBE IT'S A GAME
WHO WAS THAT WOMAN I SAW YOU WITH?
SURE!! SAY. DON'T BE LIKE THAT, MISTER- FOR CRYIN' OUT LOUD DON'T BE LIKE THAT!
IF THAT'S "RENA" IT MEANS JUST ONE THING-THE "KING'S" IN AMERICA
ANYTHING YOU SAY IS RIGHT, MISTER! NO FOOLIN'
AND IF YOU GIVE THAT WHIFFLE HEN UP TO ANYONE BUT ME- G-R-R- I'LL STICK YOU LIKE A PIG - YOU DOG!
WOOF! WOOF!
11-16
SEGAR

THIMBLE THEATER

NOW SHOWING—AN "UNSHIVERLESS" SON.
Monday—"Mail" and Female.

MYSTERY! MUCH MYSTERY! AND ALL ON ACCOUNT OF THAT FUNNY LOOKIN' LITTLE AFRICAN WHIFFLE HEN— WHY IS BERNICE IN SUCH DEMAND? AND WHO IS THIS?
THERE'S THAT BLACK GHOST BEHIND A TREE
HOME, FEET! HOME!
WHEW! OH, BOY! OH BOY!
COME!
DAD, OLD BOY, WILL YOU DO ME A BIG FAVOR? GO SHUT THAT WINDOW I FEEL A DRAFT!!
YA MEAN THAT!?
SEGAR
11-17

THIMBLE THEATER

NOW SHOWING—"MAIL" AND FEMALE.
Tomorrow—An International Disguise.

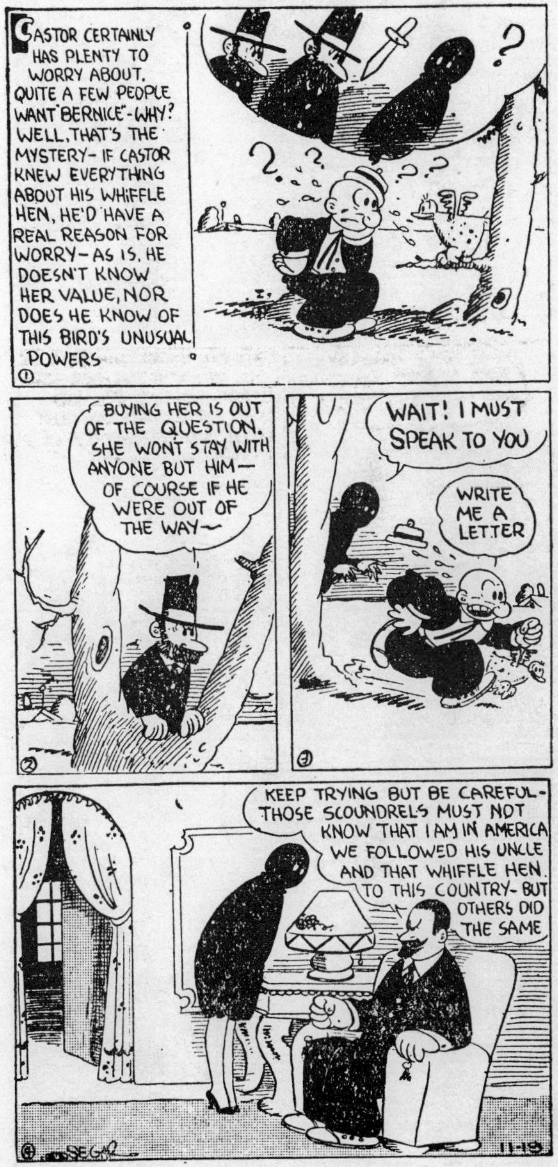
CASTOR CERTAINLY HAS PLENTY TO WORRY ABOUT. QUITE A FEW PEOPLE WANT "BERNICE"-WHY? WELL, THAT'S THE MYSTERY- IF CASTOR KNEW EVERYTHING ABOUT HIS WHIFFLE HEN, HE'D HAVE A REAL REASON FOR WORRY- AS IS, HE DOESN'T KNOW HER VALUE, NOR DOES HE KNOW OF THIS BIRD'S UNUSUAL POWERS
BUYING HER IS OUT OF THE QUESTION. SHE WON'T STAY WITH ANYONE BUT HIM— OF COURSE IF HE WERE OUT OF THE WAY—
WAIT! I MUST SPEAK TO YOU
WRITE ME A LETTER
KEEP TRYING BUT BE CAREFUL- THOSE SCOUNDRELS MUST NOT KNOW THAT I AM IN AMERICA WE FOLLOWED HIS UNCLE AND THAT WHIFFLE HEN TO THIS COUNTRY- BUT OTHERS DID THE SAME
SEGAR
11-18

THIMBLE THEATER

NOW SHOWING—IT WON'T BE LONG NOW.

Tomorrow—Tuning In on Heaven.

WE'RE SAFE NOT A SOUL SAW US. DUMP HIM IN THE SHACK
FEW PEOPLE COME INTO THESE HILLS
HELP
THAT'S THAT
GO RENA- GO THIS INSTANT- FIND OUT WHERE THEY HAVE TAKEN HIM AND HIS WHIFFLE HEN
IF WE "BUMP HIM OFF" THE BIRD WILL STAY WITH US - BUT AS LONG AS HE'S ALIVE WE'RE OUT OF LUCK
SHALL WE USE A GUN OR JUST LET HIM STARVE?
WHIFFLE
© 1928, by King Features Syndicate, Inc. Great Britain rights reserved.

THIMBLE THEATER

NOW SHOWING—TUNING IN ON HEAVEN.

Monday—Dangerous "Carves" Ahead."

I WAS A KNIFE THROWER ONCE - HANG UP THIS TARGET, I WANT TO PRACTICE
WHY WOULDN'T THAT BE AN IDEAL WAY OF CROAKING THE RUNT?
EXACTLY! THAT'S WHAT I WAS THINKING
THE BEST OF STEEL AND A SKILLED HAND AH- THERE IS NOTHING MORE DEADLY
PRETTY GOOD, EH? HAW! HAW!
YOU DONT NEED ANY PRACTICE
WHIFFLE
© 1928, by King Features Syndicate, Inc. Great Britain rights reserved.
SEGAR 11-24

THIMBLE THEATER

NOW SHOWING—DANGEROUS "CARVES" AHEAD.

Tomorrow—Some Drop!

YOU'RE A KNIFE-THROWER LET'S GET IT OVER! GO ON GET RID OF HIM!
RIGHT!
DO YOUR STUFF!
CURSES! I CUT THE ROPE!!
?
!
!
G-R-R-R
HELP! HELP! SOMEBODY DO SOMETHING!
G-R-R
SEGAR 11-26

THIMBLE THEATER

NOW SHOWING—SOME DROP!

Tomorrow—Wisdom Teeth.

I'VE GOT THE UPPER HAND NOW! G-R-R-R
STOP! HAVE YOU NO HEART !!!?
DID YOU HAVE A HEART A FEW MINUTES AGO? YOU TRIED TO MURDER ME!
LOOK! YOU'RE STANDING ON A RATTLE SNAKE!
WHO ME?!
G'WAN. I AM NOT!
DROP IT!
!
DROP THAT KNIFE! DROP IT! DROP IT! DROP IT! DROPIT! DROPIT! DROPIT! DROPIT! DROPIT!
I WON'T
WHIFFLE
11-27
SEGAR

THIMBLE THEATER

NOW SHOWING—WISDOM TEETH.

Tomorrow—He's Gotta Grip But He's Not Traveling.

IT LOOKS BAD FOR CASTOR! VERY BAD - GRAPPLING WITH A MAN TWICE HIS SIZE
DROP THAT KNIFE!
NO!
DROP IT! DROPIT!
OUW! LEGGO!
PLEASE LET GO OF MY FINGER! THAT'S NO WAY TO FIGHT
LET GO OF MY FINGER THIS INSTANT OR I'LL DROP YOU OVER THE CLIFF
WHIFFLE
NO!
11-28
SEGAR

THIMBLE THEATER

NOW SHOWING—HE'S GOTTA GRIP BUT HE'S NOT TRAVELING.

Tomorrow—The Meat Lover.

THAT'S NO WAY TO FIGHT- LET GO OF MY FINGER- PLEASE OPEN YOUR MOUTH
OUCH!
AND ONE OF THEM THREW A KNIFE AT HIM-IT MISSED AND CUT THE ROPES WHICH BOUND HIM-HE GRABBED THE KNIFE AND CHASED ONE OF THE BRUTES INTO THE HILLS-I LOST THEIR TRAIL
GO, RENA, HELP HIM IF YOU CAN - AND BRING HIM AND HIS WHIFFLE HEN TO ME
I OUGHTA ITE YOUR HINGER OFF AND TEACH YOU A LESSON
11-29
SEGAR

THIMBLE THEATER

NOW SHOWING—THE MEAT LOVER.

Tomorrow—The Call of the Wild.

CASTOR ISN'T LICKED YET- HE STILL HAS THE KNIFE AND THE SCOUNDREL WHO TRIED TO MURDER HIM IS PLAINLY WORRIED
LET GO OF MY FINGER
I WON'T
LEAVE GO! SAY I'M GONNA BUST YOU IN A MINUTE
JUST TRY IT AND I'LL ITE IT OFF
THIS IS A FINE MESS! I'VE LOOKED ALL OVER THESE HILLS BUT I CAN'T FIND THEM
WE HAD THINGS OUR OWN WAY BUT OF COURSE SOMETHING HAD TO HAPPEN. DARN THAT PARTNER OF MINE!
HAVE A CHEW OF TOBACCO, SON COME ON LET'S BE SOCIABLE.
THINK I'M A SAP? I CAN SEE THROUGH YOUR TRICKS
WHIFFLE
Great Britain rights reserved.
© 1928, by King Features Syndicate, Inc.
SEGAR
11-30

THIMBLE THEATER

NOW SHOWING—THE CALL OF THE WILD.

Monday—The Traveling Men.

WHY DOESN'T MY PARTNER COME AND HELP ME? SAY I'LL GIVE YOU A HUNDRED DOLLARS IF YOU'LL LEAVE GO
OUCH!
NO
I'VE LOOKED HIGH AND LOW! 'SMIGHTY FUNNY!
YOO-HOO! YOO-HOO!
ANSWER HIM AND I'LL ITE IT OFF
WHERE ARE YOU PARTNER? YOO-HOO
CURSES! CURSES! OUCH!
WHIFFLE
Great Britain rights reserved.
SEGAR
12-1

THIMBLE THEATER

NOW SHOWING—THE TRAVELING MAN.

Tomorrow—The Swimming Instructor.

THIS IS NO WAY TO FIGHT! LEAVE LOOSE! BE A MAN AND FIGHT FAIR
THERE YOU'RE FREE- BUT I WARN YOU- ADVANCE ONE TENTH OF AN INCH AND YOUR GOOSE IS COOKED
HELLO, PARTNER, YOU'RE JUST IN TIME TO SAVE ME
HUH?!
YOU'RE SEEING THINGS MISTER THERE'S NO ONE NEAR HERE
NO! NO! NOT THAT!
I'M GOING TO THROW YOU OVER THE CLIFF
LET GO OF MY NOSE
I ALWAYS LIKE COMPANY ON A LONG JOURNEY
Great Britain rights reserved
© 1928, by King Features Syndicate, Inc.
SEGAR
12-3

THIMBLE THEATER
NOW SHOWING—THE SWIMMING INSTRUCTOR.
Tomorrow—Ignorance Is Bliss.

THE VILLAIN SUCCEEDED IN THROWING CASTOR OVER THE CLIFF-BUT CASTOR GRABBED HIS NOSE AND IS TAKING HIM ALONG
SPLASH
HELP! I CAN'T SWIM
I'LL TELL YOU HOW- JUST DUCK YOUR HEAD, OPEN YOUR MOUTH AND TAKE A LONG BREATH- THAT'S ALL THERE IS TO IT
12-4
SEGAR

THIMBLE THEATER
NOW SHOWING—IGNORANCE IS BLISS.
Tomorrow—Clock Watchers.

WELL, I GUESS THAT'S THE END OF THE BRUTE HE FELL INTO THE BAY AND COULDN'T SWIM
BOP
I MANAGED TO CRAWL OUT! AND NOW, YOUNG MAN, I'LL SETTLE WITH YOU- GIMME THAT KNIFE!
STOP- COME ONE SIXTEENTH OF AN INCH NEARER AND I'LL PUT YA OUT!
NOW JUST BE CAREFUL- I'M THE BOSS OF THIS SITUATION- GET THAT? UNDERSTAND?
© 1928, by King Features Syndicate, Inc. Great Britain rights reserved
12-5
SEGAR

THIMBLE THEATER
NOW SHOWING—CLOCK WATCHERS.
Tomorrow—Out But Not Down.

DON'T TRY ANY OF YOUR TRICKS. ONE MOVE AND I'LL STICK YOU
SOCK
TICK-TOCK TICK-TOCK BONG-BONG-BONG CU-KOO-CU-KOO-CU-KOU
HA! HA! HE THINKS HE'S A CLOCK
HE'LL DROP IN A MINUTE, NO HUMAN HEAD COULD STAND A CRACK LIKE THAT
© 1928, by King Features Syndicate, Inc. Great Britain rights reserved
SEGAR
12-6

THIMBLE THEATER
NOW SHOWING—OUT BUT NOT DOWN.
Tomorrow—The Miracle Man.

TWEET! TWEET TWEET TWEET-TWEET
DON'T WORRY. HE'LL FLOP IN A MINUTE- HE'S JUST ABOUT READY TO SINK
TRA-LA-LA-LA-LE-LA' SAID THE BIRD ON NELLIE'S HAT
MANY BRAVE HEARTS ARE ASLEEP IN THE DEEP SO BEWARE-BE BE—WARE BEEE- WOR—WARE
BRAVO! BRAVO! MORE OF THAT! MORE! MORE- ENCORE!
I BOPPED HIM HARD ENOUGH TO KNOCK OVER AN ELEPHANT. HE'LL DROP SOON
CLAP CLAP CLAP CLAP CLAP
SEGAR

THIMBLE THEATER
NOW SHOWING—THE MIRACLE MAN.
Monday—Burying Their Troubles.

THE BLOW WAS A TERRIFIC ONE BUT STILL HE STANDS A BIT DELIRIOUS BUT ON HIS FEET NEVER-THE-LESS
I'LL HAVE THE RENT TO-MORROW! GO NOW-AND RETURN NO MORE I'LL MAIL IT TO YOU SURE TO-MORROW
I CAN'T BELIEVE MY EYES- HE'S STILL ON HIS FEET
'SMIGHTY STRANGE
SO THIS IS PARIS!
ONE TABLE DE HOT A-LA-MOOD GARCON
HEH! HEH! HEH!
HEY! PULL UP TO THE CURB YOU NITWIT! S-S-SAY! NOW LISTEN-SHUT UP! OH, IZZ ZAT SO! YAS YOU!
YOU AIN'T GOT A GUN HAVE YOU?
NO
NO I AIN'T GOT NO GUN, AIN'T YOU?
© 1928, by King Features Syndicate, Inc. Great Britain rights reserved.
SEGAR

THIMBLE THEATER
NOW SHOWING—BURYING THEIR TROUBLES.
Tomorrow—A Tardy Mourner.

CRACK
THAT SHOT GOT HIM!
BERNICE- WHEN YOUR MASTER WAS ALIVE YOU WOULD STAY WITH NO ONE BUT HIM- BUT HE'S OUT NOW SO YOU'D JUST AS WELL STAY WITH US. WE ARE YOUR NEW MASTERS
GO UP TO THE SHACK AND GET A SHOVEL. LET'S GET THIS THING OVER
WHIFFLE
12-10
© 1928, by King Features Syndicate, Inc. Great Britain rights reserved.
SEGAR

THIMBLE THEATER

NOW SHOWING—A TARDY MOURNER.

Tomorrow—A Grave Situation.

?
THE GROUND'S TOO HARD - I CAN'T GO OVER EIGHT INCHES DEEP
O-K
WHIFFLE
THAT'S THAT
COME ON, BERNICE
WHIFFLE
SEGAR 12-11

THIMBLE THEATER

NOW SHOWING—A GRAVE SITUATION.

Tomorrow—A Voice from the Sod.

WHERE'S BERNICE ?
I THOUGHT SHE WAS FOLLOWING US
BERNICE - WHERE ARE YOU ?
OH, SO THAT'S IT!
WHIFFLE
FORGET HIM - UNDERSTAND! YOU BELONG TO US NOW - YOU'LL NEVER SEE HIM AGAIN
FRIENDS, ROMANS, COUNTRYMEN - PULL IN YOUR EARS - TRA LA LE - LA - WHOPEE!!
12-12 SEGAR

THIMBLE THEATER

NOW SHOWING—A VOICE FROM THE SOD.

Tomorrow—Hot Air Artists.

DO YOU THINK WE PLANTED HIM DEEP ENOUGH?
STOP WORRYING, PARTNER, WE'VE GOT THE WHIFFLE HEN AND EVERYTHING IS ROSY
HE WON'T CRAWL OUT, YOU CROWNED HIM A COUPLA' GOOD ONES
WE'LL CLEAN UP A FORTUNE WITH BERNICE! HA! HA! THE ONLY WHIFFLE HEN IN CAPTIVITY AND WE'VE GOT HER
WHAT HAVE THEY DONE WITH CASTOR OYL?
STEP UP GENTS - I'M BUYING — COO-KOO — COO-KOO — COO-KOO
HEY! WHO'S STANDING ON MY CHEST ?
12-13 SEGAR

THIMBLE THEATER
NOW SHOWING—HOT AIR ARTISTS
Tomorrow—Two of a Kind.

MURDERER!
HUH !
GOOD HEAVENS WHO SAID THAT?!
WE'RE DISCOVERED! SOMEBODY YELLED "MURDERER" AT ME!
WHAT! YOU MEAN THAT?
THEY CAN'T DO NOTHIN' WITH ME! I'M INNOCENT! YOU SMACKED HIM WITH A CLUB - I DIDN'T DO A THING
YOU DUG THE HOLE. YOU THREW DIRT IN HIS FACE!
SOMEBODY OPEN A WINDOW 'STOO STUFFY IN HERE: NO AIR
12-14
SEGAR

THIMBLE THEATER
NOW SHOWING—TWO OF A KIND
Tomorrow—The Planted Blooms Again

THERE'S NO DOUBT ABOUT IT - WE'VE BEEN DISCOVERED - WHEN I WAS WALKING THROUGH THE WOODS SOMEONE YELLED MURDERER AT ME!
THAT'S JUST WHAT YOU ARE. BUT I AM INNOCENT
YOU SMACKED HIM WITH THE CLUB - I DIDN'T DO NOTHIN' - WHY I WOULDN'T HARM A FLY - I'M A GOOD MAN
TRYIN' TO MAKE YOURSELF FEEL GOOD, AINTCHA ?
MURDERERS!
PLURAL! GOOD HEAVENS! I DIDN'T DO NOTHIN' YOU DID IT: YOU DID IT
STOP KIDDING YOURSELF DIDN'T YOU DIG THE HOLE AND THROW DIRT IN HIS FACE?
OXYGEN! GIMME OXYGEN! WHERE'S THE AIR? WHO TOOK THE AIR?
12-15
SEGAR

THIMBLE THEATER
NOW SHOWING—THE PLANTED BLOOMS AGAIN.
Tomorrow—Out of His Mind But on Ma's.

WHERE'S THE AIR? WHO TOOK THE AIR? - GET OFF MY CHEST!
SOMEBODY'S WATCHING THIS SHACK - DO YOU THINK HE SAW US BUMP HIM OFF?
WHAT DO YOU MEAN "US"? YOU BOPPED HIM!
DON'T NEVER MAKE THAT MISTAKE AGAIN - REMEMBER "US" DIDN'T DO IT - YOU DID IT - I'M A GOOD MAN, I WOULDN'T KILL A GERM EVEN! I GOT THE KINDEST HEART
MAKIN' YOURSELF FEEL GOOD, AINTCHA?
KIDDIN' ALWAYS KIDDIN' YOUR CONSCIENCE! A GOOD MAN! BAH! A LOWDOWNER CROOK THAN YOU NEVER LIVED
OH! HOW YOU TALK!
ALL I DID WAS DIG THE HOLE AND COVER HIM UP - IT WAS A GOOD DEED WHAT I DONE! I DIDN'T WANT THE BUZZARDS TO GET HIM
WELL, IF THEY CATCH US THERE'LL BE HEMP AROUND YOUR NECK TOO
SHIP AHOY! AHOY! OY! OY! OY! LET ME IN THE LIFE BOAT FIRST! AIN'T I THE CAPTAIN?
Great Britain rights reserved.
© 1928, by King Features Syndicate, Inc.
12-17
SEGAR

THIMBLE THEATER

NOW SHOWING—OUT OF HIS MIND BUT ON MA'S.
Tomorrow—Busting Up the Combination.

WHAT HAVE YOU DONE WITH HIS BODY?
DID YOU HEAR THAT?! SOME ONE KNOWS WE CROAKED HIM!
DON'T SAY WE - YOU SOCKED HIM!
WHAT A NIGHT! MATE - SEE IF THE MEN IN THE FO'CASTLE ARE COMFORTABLE
THE RAIN WAS POURING AND I WAS WET - WAS WET FROM MY NECK TO MY TOES - THE WAVES DASHED OVER THE ROTTEN SHIP AND THE WIND WAS BLOWING MY NOSE!
BRAVO!
WONDER WHY CASTOR DOESN'T COME HOME? DO YOU THINK SOMETHING HAS HAPPENED TO HIM?
OF COURSE NOT, MAW, STOP WORRYING
MUTINY, EH? SO IT'S MUTINY! I'LL SHOOT THE FIRST MAN WHO TOUCHES THAT HELM - PUT 'IM IN IRONS - THROW 'IM TO THE ANCHOVIES!
Great Britain rights reserved.
© 1928, by King Features Syndicate, Inc.
12-18
SEGAR

THIMBLE THEATER

NOW SHOWING—BUSTING UP THE COMBINATION.
Tomorrow—Bernice, the Bloodhound.

I SOCKED HIM, BUT YOU BURIED HIM - YOU'RE IN THIS AS MUCH AS ME - AND DON'T SAY YA AIN'T!
I AIN'T!
SAY - YOU CAN'T BUST ME ON THE ABDOMEN LIKE THAT
SMOCK
WHO YOU SOCKIN' ON THE NOSE ?!
YOU! THA'S WHO YOU!
WHY GET THE DUST PAN? JUST SWEEP IT UNDER THE SINK
12-19
SEGAR

THIMBLE THEATER

NOW SHOWING—BERNICE THE BLOODHOUND.
Tomorrow—Through the Fog.

THINK THAT OVER!
NOW I'M GONNA UNCORK ONE!
G-R-R
KLINK
HITTIN' A PAL LIKE THAT!!! WHERE'S YOUR HOSPITALITY?
THE WHIFFLE HEN! SHE'S NOT IN THE ROOM - BERNICE IS GONE!
WHAT A CUTE LITTLE DOG! WOOF-WOOF
WHIFFLE!
12-20
SEGAR

THIMBLE THEATER

NOW SHOWING—THROUGH THE FOG.

Tomorrow—Three of a Kind.

WE DID MURDER TO GET THAT WHIFFLE HEN- AND NOW SHE'S LEFT US! WE'RE COMPLETELY OUT OF LUCK
AND ON TOP OF THAT SOMEBODY'S WATCHING THIS SHACK- CRIME DOESN'T PAY- WISH I'DA BEEN BRUNG UP DIFFERENT
MURDERERS! WHERE'S THE WHIFFLE HEN? AND WHAT HAVE YOU DONE WITH CASTOR OYL'S BODY?
THERE'S THAT VOICE AGAIN!
THIS IS A FINE MESS I'M AFRAID WE'RE COOKED!
I CAN FEEL THE STEELY CLUTCHES OF THE LAW CLOSING UPON ME —ARF!!
THEY CAN'T HANG A WEAK-MINDED GUY- AND BELIEVE ME FROM NOW ON I'M GOING TO BE GOOFY!
YOUR FACE SEEMS FAMILIAR. SAY- HAVEN'T I SEEN YOU SOME PLACE BEFORE?
WHIFFLE
12-21
SEGAR

THIMBLE THEATER

NOW SHOWING—THREE OF A KIND.

Monday—An Interrupted Departure.

MAYBE IT'S A DETECTIVE WATCHING THIS SHACK!
IT'S AGAINST THE CONSTITUTION TO HANG COO-KOO'S - AND I'M AWAY OFF
YOU'RE A FAKE - THAT'S WHAT YOU ARE- AND THE BIGGEST COWARD THAT EVER LIVED!
MURDERERS! IT WON'T BE LONG NOW
I'M NOT RESPONSIBLE FOR MY ACTS
ME EITHER!
WHIFFLE, ME EYE ANSWER MY QUESTION! ARE YOU A DOG OR A SQUIRREL? DON'T BE LIKE THAT- SPEAK UP!
WHIFFLE
12-22
SEGAR

THIMBLE THEATER

NOW SHOWING—AN INTERRUPTED DEPARTURE.

Tomorrow—The Uninvited Guest.

WHO COVERED ME WITH DIRT? SOMEBODY BURIED ME ALIVE- OH, YES- A WHISKERED GUY BEANED ME WITH A CLUB- I SUPPOSE HE THOUGHT HE'D KILLED ME
WHIFFLE
HAVENT SEEN A RABBIT ALL DAY- GEE BUT I'M TIRED AND THIRSTY
WE CAN'T STAY IN THIS SHACK FOREVER - WE'VE GOT TO LEAVE THE COUNTRY BECAUSE IF WE'RE CAUGHT WE'LL HANG
HOWDY GENTS, GOT ANY DRINKIN' WATER?
SH-SURE!
SH-SH SURE!
WHAT'S YOUR HAND SHAKIN' LIKE THAT FOR, MISTER?
IT AIN'T S-SH-SHAKIN' SH-SHERIFF- IT AIN'T SH-SHAKIN
IT AIN'T SH-SH-SH-SHAKIN'!
SEGAR
12-24

THIMBLE THEATER
NOW SHOWING—THE UNINVITED GUEST.
Tomorrow—A Guilty Conscience.

THE SHERIFF AFTER A TIRESOME AND UNSUCCESSFUL RABBIT HUNT, STOPS AT THE SHACK FOR A DRINK OF WATER THE CROOKS ARE VERY NERVOUS VERY - VERY NERVOUS
THANKS FOR THE WATER — WELL I'LL HAVE TO TRAVEL NOW, GENTS
GOOD BYE SH-SHERIFF
BYE-BYE-TA-TA-SO-LONG-ADIOS GOOD BYE!
WHEW
WHEW
I SEE IT ALL NOW - THEY BUSTED ME WITH A CLUB, AND BURIED ME THINKING I WAS DEAD, HA! BUT THEY UNDERESTIMATED THE THICKNESS OF MY SKULL
WHIFFLE
SAY - YOU'RE A COUPLA PERTY NICE FELLOWS, I THINK I'LL STAY AND HAVE COFFEE WITH YOU
SURE - GOOD BYE - GOOD BYE, I MEAN, SIT DOWN SH-SHERIFF - WE'RE HA-HOSSS-SPITABLE HAVE A CH-CH-CHAIR!
QUICK MAKE SOME COFFEE!
SEGAR 12-25
Great Britain rights reserved. © 1928, by King Features Syndicate, Inc.

THIMBLE THEATER
NOW SHOWING—A GUILTY CONSCIENCE.
Tomorrow—The Diving Act.

CONTROL YOURSELF! HE'S OUT RABBIT HUNTING AND JUST DROPPED IN FOR A CUP OF COFFEE. HE DON'T KNOW A THING ABOUT US
NO! NO! NO! HE'S WISE TO US! HE'S GETTIN' READY TO ARREST US I CAN'T STAND IT!!
IT'S A GOOD THING I'VE GOT A HARD HEAD! WHAT A SOCK! AND THEY HAD ME BURIED
WHIFFLE
I'LL HAVE A TOUGH TIME GETTING HOME - EVERY BONE IN MY HEAD HURTS
I-I-YI-YI-YI-DIDN'T DO IT! I DIDN'T KILL 'IM - I DIDN'T KILL 'IM! I DIDN'T KILL 'IM!!
KILL WHO? SAY - HAS SOMEBODY BEEN KILLED?!
HEY, SHUT UP!
SEGAR 12-26

THIMBLE THEATER
NOW SHOWING—THE DIVING ACT.
Tomorrow—The Hooded Lady.

YOU FOOL - YOU SPILLED THE BEANS - IT'LL BE CURTAINS FOR US IF WE'RE CAUGHT
AND I LET 'EM GET AWAY. WHY THE HECK DIDN'T I OPEN FIRE ON THOSE BIRDS?!!
THE SHERIFF WILL NEVER FIND US IN THIS ROUGH COUNTRY WE'RE SAFE
GHOST!
FIVE HUNDRED FEET TO THE BAY BELOW - IF THEY SURVIVE LET'S HOPE THEY'VE LEARNED A LESSON - IF THEY'RE DEAD —— LET 'EM BE DEAD
12-27 SEGAR

THIMBLE THEATER
NOW SHOWING—THE HOODED LADY.
Tomorrow—The Prodigal Son.

THOSE TWO WHISKERED CROOKS DIVED OVER THE CLIFF WHEN THEY SAW ME THOUGHT I WAS A GHOST- MORE PROOF THAT CRIME DOESN'T PAY
IT'S GOING TO BE TOUGH GETTING HOME. I'M WEAK AS A JELLY FISH AND MY HEAD IS SPLITTING
THERE HE IS — AND THE BIRD TOO — I THOUGHT THEY'D KILLED HIM!
WAIT A MINUTE, LISTEN TO ME!
GOOD NIGHT! I THOUGHT MY TROUBLES WERE OVER
FAINTED!
12-28
SEGAR

THIMBLE THEATER
NOW SHOWING—THE PRODIGAL SON.
Monday—A Royal Menu.

MOTHER, WHAT DO YOU SUPPOSE COULD HAVE HAPPENED TO CASTOR?
I DON'T KNOW, HE MAY POP UP ANY MINUTE-AND- AND- WE MAY NEVER SEE HIM AGAIN
I'D BET A MILLION DOLLARS OF ANYBODY'S MONEY THAT BERNICE IS THE CAUSE OF ALL THIS - SOME FOREIGNERS WANT THAT WHIFFLE HEN BAD
I'M BECOMING A LITTLE BIT WORRIED MYSELF. STILL HE'S ALWAYS IN SOME SORT OF A MESS.
FAINTED WHEN HE SAW ME - HE MUST BE IN A VERY WEAKENED CONDITION
I HEAR FOOT-STEPS - IT MUST BE RENA- IF SHE HAS THE WHIFFLE HEN MY DREAMS HAVE COME TRUE —
12-29
SEGAR

THIMBLE THEATER
NOW SHOWING—A ROYAL MENU.
Tomorrow—The Marathon's Over.

I HAVE BOTH OF THEM!
I KNEW YOU WOULD SUCCEED, RENA
AND HERE'S THE WHIFFLE HEN- AH- A GENUINE AFRICAN WHIFFLE HEN!
THE MOST VALUABLE BIRD IN THE WORLD- TO ANYONE WHO UNDERSTANDS AND KNOWS HOW TO USE HER STRANGE POWERS
HE'S BEEN UNCONSCIOUS FOR ABOUT FOUR HOURS. FAINTED DEAD AWAY WHEN HE SAW ME - I DO WISH IT WASN'T NECESSARY FOR ME TO WEAR THIS HOOD
WHIFFLE
I HOPE YOU ENJOY THIS ANGEL FOOD CAKE, BERNICE. I'D FEED YOU DIAMONDS IF YOU WANTED THEM
12-31
SEGAR

THIMBLE THEATER

NOW SHOWING—THE MARATHON'S OVER.
Tomorrow—Caged Birds.

AH, HE HAS COME TO, AT LAST!
WHERE AM I?
WHIFFLE
© 1929, King Features Syndicate, Inc., Great Britain rights reserved.
HELP!! GO 'WAY- YOU BLACK GHOST!
DON'T BE AFRAID I WON'T HURT YOU
SEE-I AM ONLY A WOMAN
AND I'VE BEEN RUNNING AWAY FROM YOU FOR WEEKS!— STICK AROUND 'SALL RIGHT- GEE, YOU'RE SWELL
SAY, WHAT DO YOU COVER YOURSELF UP LIKE THAT FOR ?
IT'S A GOOD DISGUISE
AND ALSO — MY EMPLOYER HAS A GREAT DEAL OF THINKING TO DO - AND I AM SO BEAUTIFUL THAT UNLESS I WEAR THIS HOOD HE CANNOT CONCENTRATE
HA! HA! THAT'S GOOD!!
1-1

THIMBLE THEATER

NOW SHOWING—CAGED BIRDS
Tomorrow—Heavily Chaperoned.

AND NOW, MISTER - I'D BE VERY MUCH OBLIGED IF YOU'LL TELL ME WHY YOU BROUGHT ME AND MY WHIFFLE HEN HERE
WHAT IS YOUR GAME? SPEAK UP! I'LL STAND FOR NO MINCING OF WORDS, I WANT FACTS
FACTS?— WELL- I WANTED THIS BIRD AND I GENERALLY GET WHAT I WANT
LISTEN, BIG BOY- THAT WHIFFLE HEN WILL STAY WITH NOBODY BUT ME- WHERE I GO SHE WILL FOLLOW
I REALIZE THAT- BUT YOU FORGET— I NOT ONLY HAVE BERNICE-HA!-I HAVE YOU ALSO!
WHIFFLE
KIDNAPERY, EH? SO IT'S KIDNAPERY ?
1-2
E.C. SEGAR

THIMBLE THEATER

NOW SHOWING—HEAVILY CHAPERONED.
Tomorrow—A Slight Detail Overlooked.

OF COURSE YOU UNDERSTAND THAT KEEPING ME HERE IS NOTHING SHORT OF KIDNAPERY
CALL IT THAT IF YOU LIKE BUT IF THE BIRD WILL STAY WITH NOBODY BUT YOU THEN I'LL HAVE TO HOLD YOU ALSO
WHY IS THIS FUNNY LOOKIN' WHIFFLE HEN SO VALUABLE? WHAT DO YOU WANT WITH HER ?— OUTSIDE OF A STEW WHAT GOOD IS SHE ?
DO YOU THINK I'M FOOL ENOUGH TO TELL YOU THE SECRET OF THIS BIRD? NEVER-!! I AM THE KING OF DICE ISLAND, NOT A REAL KING BUT I OWN THE ISLAND AND THE LARGEST GAMBLING RESORT IN THE WORLD — THAT'S ABOUT ALL I'LL TELL YOU
HOW ARE YOU GOING TO KEEP ME HERE? I THINK I'LL LEAVE THIS APARTMENT RIGHT NOW
OH, NO YOU WON'T-
MR. SKUM HERE, WILL TAKE CARE OF THAT LITTLE DETAIL
Great Britain rights reserved
© 1929, King Features Syndicate, Inc.
1-3
SEGAR

THIMBLE THEATER

NOW SHOWING—A SLIGHT DETAIL OVERLOOKED.
Tomorrow—Castor Has His Fling.

SAY, WON'T YOU HELP ME ESCAPE? I WANT TO GO HOME
I'M WORKING FOR MR. FADEWELL, THE GAMBLER- ONE OF MY DUTIES IS TO HELP KEEP YOU HERE
MY EMPLOYER HAS RHEUMATISM AND IT IS HARD FOR HIM TO MOVE ABOUT
YEAH?!
SO YOU'VE GOT RHEUMATISM, HAVE YOU?
YES- I'M ALMOST HELPLESS
IN THAT CASE YOUR SIZE DON'T MEAN A THING- I'M NOT AFRAID OF ANY BIG CHEESE WITH RHEUMATISM- AND I'M GONNA KNOCK YA' ONE
I HAVE NO RHEUMATISM!
SEGAR
© 1929, King Features Syndicate, Inc., Great Britain rights reserved.
1-4

THIMBLE THEATER

NOW SHOWING—CASTOR HAS HIS FLING.
Monday—The Eavesdropper.

I'VE GOT TO ESCAPE I KNOW THEY'RE WORRYING ABOUT ME AT HOME - THAT BIG BRUTE WATCHES ME ALL THE TIME
LISTEN- I'M BEING PAID TO KEEP YOU HERE AND I'LL STAND NO MONKEY BUSINESS
TRY TO GET AWAY AND I'LL TEAR YOU UP AND THROW YOU INTO THE WASTE BASKET
AW, SHUT UP!
NOW REMEMBER THAT, YOU RUNT
NOBODY CAN CALL ME A RUNT AND LIVE
CRACK
DON'T NEVER DO THAT AGAIN. YOU MIGHT MISS ME AND BREAK SOMETHING
!
Great Britain rights reserved. © 1929, King Features Syndicate, Inc.
SEGAR

THIMBLE THEATER

NOW SHOWING—THE EAVESDROPPER.
Tomorrow—Dollars and Sense.

MR. SKUM, MAYBE YOU CAN TELL ME WHY BERNICE IS SO VALUABLE- AND WHAT ALL THIS MYSTERY IS ABOUT?
I AM MR. FADEWELL'S BODYGUARD- I KNOW NONE OF HIS SECRETS- HE OWNS A BIG GAMBLING RESORT ON A SMALL ISLAND OFF THE COAST OF AFRICA- THAT'S ALL I CAN TELL YOU
RENA- YOU HAVE SERVED ME WELL YOU ARE A SKILLED DETECTIVE AS WELL AS A PERFECT SECRETARY- I'M GOING TO TELL YOU ALL ABOUT THIS AFRICAN WHIFFLE HEN—
A VERY FEW PEOPLE KNOW OF THIS BIRD'S REMARKABLE AND STRANGE POWERS- IT IS ALMOST IMPOSSIBLE TO CAPTURE A WILD WHIFFLE HEN- BERNICE HERE, IS THE ONLY ONE IN CAPTIVITY. LISTEN—
ANY PERSON WHO RUBS THE THREE HAIRS ON HER HEAD WILL HAVE GOOD LUCK - MAYBE I'M A LITTLE BIT SUPERSTITIOUS BUT I BELIEVE IT'S TRUE - I LEARNED THIS IN INDIA— NOW - WITH GOOD LUCK ON MY SIDE I CAN TRIM EVERY MILLIONAIRE WHO VISITS MY GAMBLING RESORT — PLEASE REMEMBER - CASTOR OYL MUST KNOW NOTHING OF THIS
SEGAR
Great Britain rights reserved. © 1929, King Features Syndicate, Inc.
1-7

THIMBLE THEATER

NOW SHOWING—DOLLARS AND SENSE
Tomorrow—A. W. O. L

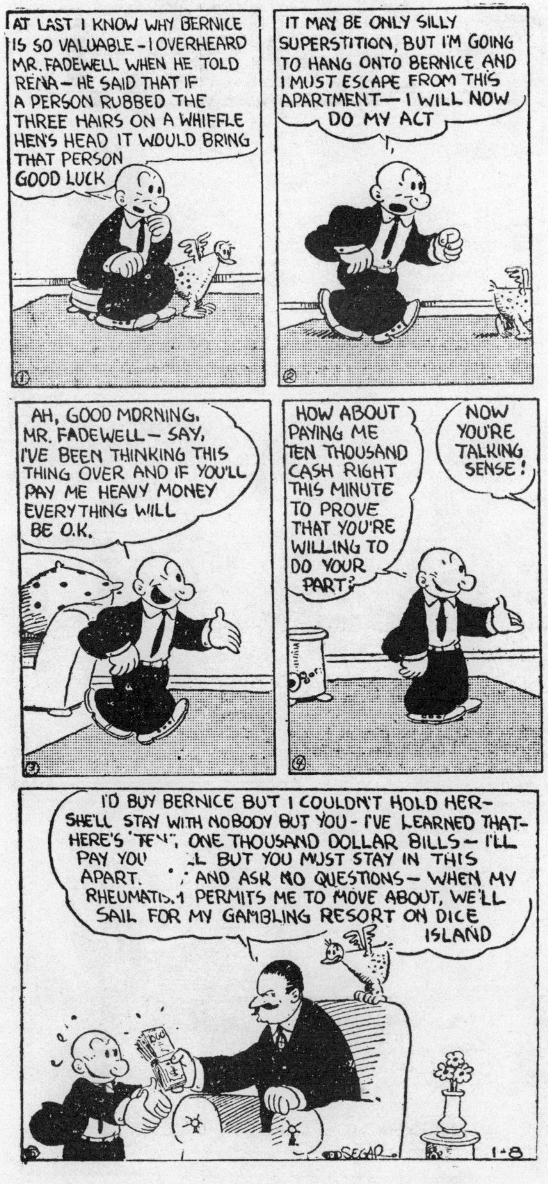

AT LAST I KNOW WHY BERNICE IS SO VALUABLE - I OVERHEARD MR. FADEWELL WHEN HE TOLD RENA - HE SAID THAT IF A PERSON RUBBED THE THREE HAIRS ON A WHIFFLE HEN'S HEAD IT WOULD BRING THAT PERSON GOOD LUCK
IT MAY BE ONLY SILLY SUPERSTITION, BUT I'M GOING TO HANG ONTO BERNICE AND I MUST ESCAPE FROM THIS APARTMENT— I WILL NOW DO MY ACT
AH, GOOD MORNING, MR. FADEWELL— SAY, I'VE BEEN THINKING THIS THING OVER AND IF YOU'LL PAY ME HEAVY MONEY EVERYTHING WILL BE O.K.
HOW ABOUT PAYING ME TEN THOUSAND CASH RIGHT THIS MINUTE TO PROVE THAT YOU'RE WILLING TO DO YOUR PART?
NOW YOU'RE TALKING SENSE!
I'D BUY BERNICE BUT I COULDN'T HOLD HER- SHE'LL STAY WITH NOBODY BUT YOU - I'VE LEARNED THAT- HERE'S ONE THOUSAND DOLLAR BILLS— I'LL PAY YOU BUT YOU MUST STAY IN THIS APART. AND ASK NO QUESTIONS— WHEN MY PERMITS ME TO MOVE ABOUT, WE'LL SAIL FOR MY GAMBLING RESORT ON DICE ISLAND
SEGAR
1-8

THIMBLE THEATER

NOW SHOWING—A. W. O. L.
Tomorrow—Ocean Waves.

MR. SKUM - YOU DON'T NEED TO GUARD THE DOOR ANY MORE. YOUR BOSS JUST GAVE ME $10,000 -. WE'RE PALS NOW - YOU COULDN'T THROW ME OUT OF THIS APARTMENT
I DON'T BELIEVE A WORD YOU SAY. I'LL GO ASK HIM
AH— MY CHANCE HAS ARRIVED!
MR. FADEWELL, HE SAID—
I DON'T CARE WHAT HE SAID! GET BACK TO THAT DOOR - I DON'T TRUST HIM EVEN NOW
COME ON, BERNICE!
WHIFFLE
1-9
SEGAR

THIMBLE THEATER

NOW SHOWING—OCEAN WAVES.
Tomorrow—A Sailor-Mad Maid.

YES, I'VE BEEN KIDNAPPED TWICE, AND I'VE FOUND OUT WHY BERNICE IS SO VALUABLE - IN INDIA SHE IS KNOWN AS A "LUCK HEN". YOU CAN WIN IN ANY GAME OF CHANCE BY RUBBING THE THREE HAIRS ON A WHIFFLE HEN'S HEAD - THINK OF IT!
BUNK!
!
WHIFFLE
THIS GAMBLER, MR. FADEWELL, WHO HELD ME A PRISONER IN HIS APARTMENT, HAS A GAMBLING RESORT ON DICE ISLAND - LET'S BUY A SMALL SHIP AND GO TO THIS RESORT AND WIN SOME BIG MONEY. ARE YOU WITH ME HAM?
YEAH- BUT HOW CAN WE BUY A SHIP?
MR. FADEWELL GAVE ME $10,000.00 TO SAIL WITH HIM TO HIS ISLAND AS SOON AS HIS RHEUMATISM GETS BETTER— I ESCAPED AND I'VE GOT THE MONEY. WE'LL GO BUY A BOAT RIGHT NOW
I'VE GOT AN OLD TUB I'LL SELL YOU FOR SIX THOUSAND. I USE HER FOR FISHIN' MOSTLY - SEAWORTHY TOO - IF YOU KNOW HOW TO HANDLE HER— DICE ISLAND? YOU'VE STUCK ME THERE. IT'S A SMALL SPECK OF DIRT SOMEWHERE OFF THE AFRICAN COAST— THAT'S ALL I KNOW - EXCEPTIN' I'VE HEARD SOME QUEER TALES ABOUT IT
WHIFFLE
1-10
SEGAR

THIMBLE THEATER

NOW SHOWING—A SAILOR-MAD MAID
Tomorrow—The "Jelly" Fish.

SHE'S A BARGAIN AT SIX THOUSAND, BOYS- NOT A HOLE IN HER EXCEPT A FEW IN THE BOTTOM WHERE THEY DON'T SHOW
WE'LL TAKE HER
HURRY, HAM, WE'VE GOT TO GET PROVISIONS. WE MAY BE MONTHS ON THE HIGH SEAS
LET'S SEE NOW— OH YES- ALSO ONE THOUSAND CANS OF BEANS— THREE DILL PICKLES AND A CAKE OF SOAP
SHIP SUPPLIES
I DON'T CARE WHAT YOU SAY- I'M GOING ALONG- SO THERE!
THE HECK YOU ARE, DICE ISLAND IS A LONG WAY OFF. DANGEROUS SEAS AND TROPICAL STORMS- YOU'RE NOT GOING WITH US, OLIVE
I MIGHT GET MY FEET WET SO I'D BETTER TAKE AN EXTRA PAIR OF SOCKS
OLIVE OYL
HAM GRAVY
SEGAR 1-11

THIMBLE THEATER

NOW SHOWING—THE "JELLY" FISH.
Monday—The Goose Chase

I'M A NATURAL BORN SHE SAILOR AND I'M GOING ALONG
ONLY MEN GO DOWN TO SEA IN SHIPS - NOT DAMES! WHOEVER HEARD OF A DAME SAILOR
OLIVE OYL
CASTOR OYL
LISTEN SWEETY- IT AIN'T NO PLACE FOR A LADY- OUR SHIP IS AN OLD "WIND JAMMER" MUSTY BUNKS AND IT SMELLS LIKE COD FISH
I'M GOING
MAW- YOU'VE GOT TO MAKE SIS STAY HOME. SHE'S ALL SET TO GO WITH US!
SEE HERE- BOY FRIEND- DO YOU THINK I'M GOING TO TRUST YOU AROUND THOSE TROPICAL DAMES- DOWN WHERE THE MOON IS AS BIG AS A HOUSE? WELL- I'M NOT!
BUT OLIVE
AW, COME ON, HAM- SOCK'ER ON THE NOSE AND LET'S BE OFF- WE GOTTA GET US A CREW-
OLIVE OYL
© 1920, King Features Syndicate, Inc., Great Britain rights reserved.
SEGAR 1-12

THIMBLE THEATER

NOW SHOWING—THE GOOSE CHASE.
Tomorrow—The "Green" Olive.

WE'VE GOT TO GET RID OF HER SOME WAY— IS SHE STILL FOLLOWING US?
YEAH, RIGHT BEHIND
CASTOR OYL
HAM GRAVY
LISTEN P-S-T P-S-T P-S-T
OK
ALL RIGHT SIS- YOU CAN GO WITH US- BUT I WANT YOU TO RUN AN ERRAND FIRST
ALL RIGHT
OLIVE OYL
HERE- GO BACK TO THAT STORE AND GET A DIME'S WORTH OF LONGITUDE
AND DON'T SPILL IT
OLIVE OYL
CASTOR OYL
1-14 SEGAR

THIMBLE THEATER

NOW SHOWING—THE "GREEN" OLIVE.
Tomorrow—The Water Lily.

HA, HA! WE'RE RID OF OLIVE, SENDING HER BACK TO THAT STORE WAS A GOOD IDEA
HAM GRAVY
CASTOR OYL
SHE'LL NEVER FIND US NOW—IMAGINE HER WANTING TO GO TO SEA WITH US! WELL—LET'S HUNT UP A CREW AND BE OFF
CASTOR OYL
GEE, IT'S SLIPPED MY MIND—WHAT WAS IT CASTOR TOLD ME TO GET
OLIVE OYL
WAS IT COFFEE? TEA? ROPE? NAILS? CANVAS? BUTTER? MATCHES?
OH—NOW I KNOW
A DIME'S WORTH OF LONGITUDE
TRY THE DRUG STORE. WE SOLD THE LAST POUND YESTERDAY
HEE! HEE!
OLIVE OYL
SEGAR
1-15

THIMBLE THEATER

NOW SHOWING—THE WATER LILY.
Tomorrow—"Gobs" of Work.

I WANT A DIME'S WORTH OF LONGITUDE
EH?
WHAT KIND OF A DRUG STORE IS THIS? WHY DON'T YOU WATCH YOUR STOCK? IT'S A WONDER YOU HAVE ANY TRADE AT ALL!
OLIVE OYL
PARDON ME MISTER, BUT IS THERE SUCH A THING AS LONGITUDE?
SURE THERE IS
WELL IT'S MIGHTY FUNNY, I'VE BEEN TRYING TO BUY A DIME'S WORTH ALL MORNING
DOGGONIT! WHERE'S CASTOR AND HAM? THEY SAID THEY'D WAIT FOR ME HERE
TOM COD
ALL WE'VE GOT TO DO IS FIND A CREW AND SAIL—GEE I'M GLAD WE GOT RID OF SIS
SENDING HER ON THAT ERRAND FIXED THAT
SEGAR
1-16

THIMBLE THEATER

NOW SHOWING—"GOBS" OF WORK.
Tomorrow—Money Talks.

YOU'LL FIND THE SCUM OF THE EARTH RIGHT HERE IN THIS PORT—SO WE'VE GOT TO BE CAREFUL IN PICKING OUR CREW
HEY THERE! ARE YOU A SAILOR?
CASTOR OYL
'JA THINK I'M A COWBOY?
O.K. YOU'RE HIRED
I'M GLAD WE GAVE OLIVE THE SLIP
YEAH—I'LL BET SHE'S STILL LOOKING FOR A DIME'S WORTH OF LONGITUDE
YOU MEAN ME?
YAS—YOU! YOU'RE THE WHOLE CREW—SNAP INTO IT—TIDY UP THE SHIP—BATTEN DOWN THE HATCHES—SCRUB THE DECKS—PULL UP THE ANCHOR—GET THREE SHEETS TO THE WIND AND THEN GO TO HELM
SMELLS LIKE CODFISH
SEGAR
1-17

THIMBLE THEATER

NOW SHOWING—MONEY TALKS.
Tomorrow—Trying to Get Their Man

YOU MEAN TO SAY I'M THE WHOLE CREW! ALL BY MYSELF? WHY THIS TUB OUGHTA HAVE TWELVE MEN
BUT LOOK AT THE HONOR! I'M LETTING YOU BE TWELVE MEN-THINK OF IT! YOU'RE TWELVE MEN- WHILE I'M JUST THE CAPTAIN- AND AM ONLY ONE MAN
SURE-YOU'RE THE WHOLE CREW- IT'S A PRIVILEGE- TWELVE MEN
ALL RIGHT- THEN I WANT THE PAY OF TWELVE MEN!
SAY-YOU'VE GOT THIS THING ALL WRONG! GEE WHIZ! DON'T BE LIKE THAT!
CASTOR OYL AND HIS WHIFFLE HEN HAVE VANISHED! ALL ATTEMPTS TO LOCATE THEM HAVE FAILED - I CARE NOTHING ABOUT HIM BUT I'D GIVE A FORTUNE FOR BERNICE - THE LUCK BIRD
1-18
SEGAR

THIMBLE THEATER

NOW SHOWING—TRYING TO GET THEIR MAN.
Monday—Stationary Voyagers

HOW DO YOU DO MRS. OYL! AH, ER-WILL YOU PLEASE TELL ME WHERE I CAN FIND YOUR SON, CASTOR?
I'LL TELL YOU NOTHIN' !!
SLAM
WHO WAS IT MAW? WHY DID YOU SLAM THE DOOR IN HER FACE?
BECAUSE SHE'S IN THE EMPLOY OF THAT BIG GAMBLER WHO HELD CASTOR A PRISONER IN HIS APARTMENT
HE WANTS THAT WHIFFLE HEN! THINKS THAT RUBBING THE THREE HAIRS ON HER HEAD WILL BRING GOOD LUCK- HE'D STOOP TO ANYTHING TO GET THAT BIRD SO DON'T TELL WHERE CASTOR IS GOING
IF I'DA KNOWED THIS- I'DA STAYED ASHORE- I'M ONLY HOOMAN
BUT I'M LETTING YOU BE THE WHOLE CREW! IT'S A PRIVILEGE!
CASTOR'S TRYING TO TALK POPEYE INTO DOING A TWELVE MAN JOB— I'LL GIVE HIM CREDIT IF HE SUCCEEDS
1-19
SEGAR

THIMBLE THEATER

NOW SHOWING—STATIONARY VOYAGERS.
Tomorrow—The Crew's at Sea.

HEY- GONNA SLEEP ALL DAY? IT'S FIVE O'CLOCK
OUR FIRST NIGHT AT SEA- WONDER HOW FAR WE'VE SAILED?
I'LL GO ON DECK AND SEE HOW POPEYE IS COMING ALONG
ASLEEP AT THE WHEEL- WELL FOR-!! WE HAVEN'T LEFT PORT! HAVEN'T EVEN LEFT PORT!
SLEEPIN? WHO ME?! WHY CAP'N I BEEN PUSHIN'ER IN AND OUT O'REEFS ALL NIGHT
WE HAVEN'T BUDGED AN INCH!
WELL, BLOW ME DOWN IF I DIDN'T FORGET TO HOIST ANCHOR!
AND YOU'VE BEEN DUCKIN REEFS ALL NIGHT?
A WHOLE NIGHT'S WIND WASTED
1-21
SEGAR

THIMBLE THEATER

NOW SHOWING—THE CREW'S AT SEA.
Tomorrow—Popeye's Success Spells Insomnia

EVERYTHING'S O.K. BUT THE CREW - I'M HAVING TROUBLE WITH HIM
OLD POPEYE - HA! HA! - HE'S SOMETHING TO LOOK AT
I STILL CLAIM THAT IF I'M TO DO THE WORK OF TWELVE MEN I OUGHTER GET THE PAY OF TWELVE MEN
WHATCHA HARPIN' ABOUT THAT ALLA TIME FOR!? GOOD NIGHT! YOU GIMME A FEVER
I'LL EXPLAIN IT ONCE MORE - I'M GIVING YOU THE PRIVILEGE OF BEING THE WHOLE CREW - TWELVE MEN - BUT ON PAY DAY YOU'RE ONLY ONE MAN - WHAT'S RIGHT IS RIGHT! YOU KNOW THAT
MY GOSH - WORDS FAIL ME. DON'T BE SO DUMB, POPEYE
WELL, YOU CAN SWEEP ME DOWN A SCUPPER IF I CAN DOPE THAT OUT
1-22
SEGAR

THIMBLE THEATER

NOW SHOWING—POPEYE'S SUCCESS SPELLS INSOMNIA.
Tomorrow—One "Belle" and All's Not Well.

WOT'S WRONG WITH CAP'N OYL, MATE?
SEARCH ME
'SMATTER CAP'N?
I'M WORRIED ABOUT YOU, POPEYE - YEAH, WORRIED SOMETHING AWFUL
WORRYIN' ABOUT OL' POPEYE - WELL BLOW ME DOWN CAP'N, YOU'VE TOUCHED ME SOFT SPOT - YOU GOT A HEART, CAP'N OYL, I CAN SEE THAT
I'M WORRIED ABOUT YOUR SLUMBER - YOU'VE GOT TO LOOK AFTER THINGS DURING THE DAY WHILE I REST UP
AND YOU'VE GOT TO TAKE THE WHEEL ALL NIGHT WHILE I GET SOME SLEEP
IF I WASN'T SO KIND HEARTED I WOULDN'T BE WORRYING LIKE THIS
1-23

THIMBLE THEATER

NOW SHOWING—ONE "BELLE" AND ALL'S NOT WELL.
Tomorrow—The Crockery Massager.

WELL, HOW'S SHE RUNNIN' THIS MORNIN' MATE?
EVERYTHING IS HOTSY TOOTSY
STOW'WAY IN THE SAIL LOCKER, CAP'N
BRING HIM AFT, POPEYE, BRING HIM TO ME
IT AIN'T A HIM CAP'N, IT'S A BLOOMIN' SHE
OLIVE!
BUN VOYAGE
WELL, BLOW ME DOWN!
SIS!
1-24
SEGAR

THIMBLE THEATER
NOW SHOWING—THE CROCKERY MASSAGER.
Tomorrow—As You Were

YEAH, CAP'N- STOWED AWAY IN THE FOR'D SAIL LOCKER
WELL, SHIVER MY TIMBERS - SHIVER MY TIMBERS!
TAKE YOUR HOOKS OFFA ME OR I'LL LAY YA IN A SCUPPER
SHE'S ON THIS SHIP AGAINST MY WISHES - MAKE 'ER WORK! PUT 'ER TO WASHIN' DISHES RIGHT NOW
THEY AIN'T NONE DIRTY, CAP'N
WELL- DIRTY SOME!! GOOD NIGHT! AIN'TCHA GOT NO INGENUITY?
AYE! AYE! SIR
STEP ALONG NOW! TO THE GALLEY WITCHA - CAP'N'S ORDERS
AW, SHUT UP, YOU BILGE RAT!
OLIVE OYL
SEGAR
1-25

THIMBLE THEATER
NOW SHOWING—AS YOU WERE.
Monday—The Clerk Took Olive for a "Sale."

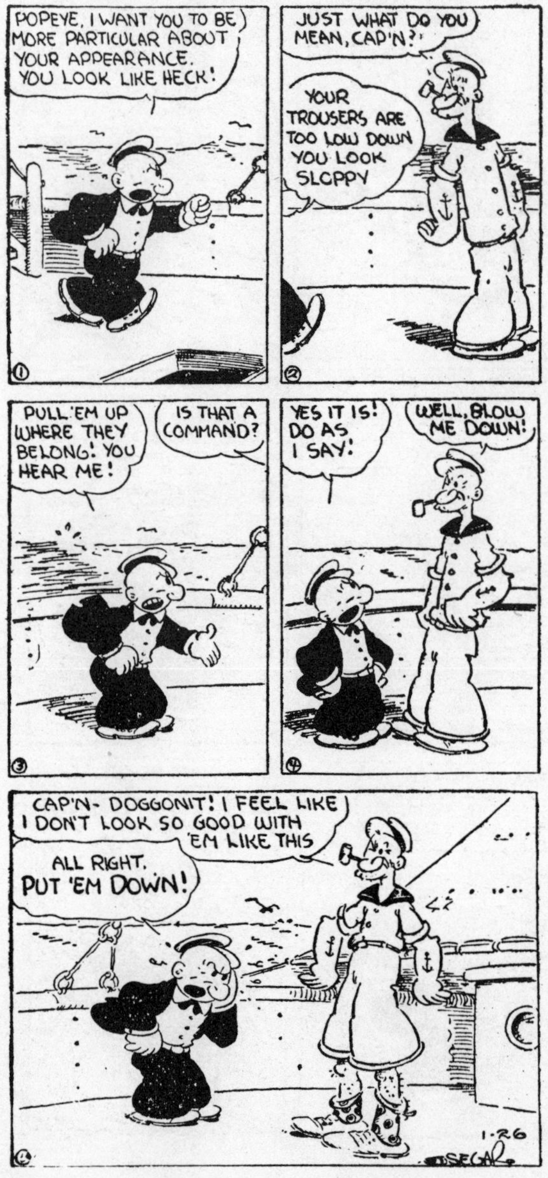

POPEYE, I WANT YOU TO BE MORE PARTICULAR ABOUT YOUR APPEARANCE. YOU LOOK LIKE HECK!
JUST WHAT DO YOU MEAN, CAP'N?
YOUR TROUSERS ARE TOO LOW DOWN YOU LOOK SLOPPY
PULL 'EM UP WHERE THEY BELONG! YOU HEAR ME!
IS THAT A COMMAND?
YES IT IS! DO AS I SAY!
WELL, BLOW ME DOWN!
CAP'N- DOGGONIT! I FEEL LIKE I DON'T LOOK SO GOOD WITH 'EM LIKE THIS
ALL RIGHT. PUT 'EM DOWN!
1-26
SEGAR

THIMBLE THEATER
NOW SHOWING—THE CLERK TOOK OLIVE FOR A "SALE."
Tomorrow—Measuring Her Distance.

SIS, HOW THE HECK DID YOU FIND OUR SHIP?
I HAPPENED TO FIND THE MAN YOU BOUGHT IT FROM
THE REST WAS EASY- I HIRED A FELLOW TO BRING ME OUT AND I STOWED AWAY TILL YOU WERE OUT TO SEA
TELL ME, CASTOR- DID YOU REALLY WANT A DIME'S WORTH OF LONGITUDE? OR DID YOU JUST SEND ME ON THAT ERRAND SO YOU COULD SLIP AWAY FROM ME?
FOR CRYIN' OUT LOUD SHE ISN'T WISE YET!
I WENT TO A DOZEN PLACES BUT I FINALLY GOT IT — THE CLERK LAUGHED WHEN HE HANDED IT TO ME — WHY HE DID THAT I DON'T KNOW
HA! HA! I'LL BET THE CLERK GAVE HER A BAG OF FLOUR OR SOMETHING
YES, MR. POPEYE - MY BROTHER DOESN'T WANT IT AND AFTER ME WASTING ALL THAT TIME GETTING THIS DIME'S WORTH OF LONGITUDE
DIME'S WORTH OF WHICH?
I SAID A DIME'S WORTH OF LONGITUDE.
WELL BLOW ME DOWN!! NUTS ON THE HIGH SEAS
1-28
SEGAR

THIMBLE THEATER
NOW SHOWING—MEASURING HER DISTANCE.

Tomorrow—Her Crowning Glory.

SO YOUR BROTHER SENT YOU TO A STORE TO BUY A DIME'S WORTH OF LONGITUDE ?
SURE HE DID
SAY- DON'T YOU KNOW WHAT LONGITUDE IS ?
NO I DON'T
LONGITUDE IS- DISTANCE EAST OR WEST ON THE EARTH'S SURFACE, MEASURED BY THE ANGLE WHICH THE MERIDIAN THROUGH A PLACE MAKES WITH SOME STANDARD MERIDIAN
!
AND HE SENT ME FOR A DIME'S WORTH OF THAT
SOCK
HEY- YOU CAN'T HIT THE CAPTAIN!! THAT'S MUTINY! GEE BUT YOU'RE DUMB!
SEGAR 1-29

THIMBLE THEATER
NOW SHOWING—HER CROWNING GLORY.

Tomorrow—Rolling the "Bones."

WHEN WE GET TO DICE ISLAND, I'LL TAKE BERNICE UP TO THE GAMBLING RESORT AND RUB THE THREE HAIRS ON HER HEAD
WHICH WILL BRING GOOD LUCK IN ANY GAME OF CHANCE—
THEN I'LL GAMBLE DAY AND NIGHT FOR A WEEK—
UNTIL I BREAK THE BANK AND CLEAN ALL OF THE MILLIONAIRE GAMBLERS—
THEN WE'LL BRING THE SHIP HOME WITH ITS HOLD FULLA GOLD
WELL, BLOW ME DOWN
1-30 SEGAR

THIMBLE THEATER
NOW SHOWING—ROLLING THE "BONES."

Tomorrow—The "Scalp" Massager.

I HEAR 'EM SAYIN' THAT BY RUBBIN' THE HAIRS ON THAT BIRD'S HEAD YOU GETS GOOD LUCK- NUTS ON THE HIGH SEAS I CALLS 'EM
H-M-M- TO-DAY IS PAY DAY FOR POPEYE- COME HERE, BERNICE
WHIFFLE
I WANT TO RUB THOSE THREE HAIRS ON YOUR HEAD AND TRY MY LUCK
YOU'VE GOT YOUR WEEK'S WAGES SO HOW ABOUT A LITTLE GAME OF CRAPS- JUST YOU AND ME?
CRAPS IS ME WEAKNESS— ROLL 'EM CAP'N YOU'RE FADED
COME ON YOU DICE — READ 'EM AND WEEP
SNAP
WELL, BLOW ME DOWN! I WORKED A WEEK FOR NOTHIN'
BETTER PRACTICE UP, POPEYE
WHIFFLE
1-31 SEGAR

THIMBLE THEATER

NOW SHOWING—THE "SCALP" MASSAGER.
Tomorrow—False Hair?

'MORNING, POPEYE - SAY HOW MUCH DO YOU MAKE A WEEK?
I'M WORKIN' FOR NOTHIN', MATE - BLOW ME DOWN IF I AIN'T!
WHAT! YOU MEAN CASTOR ISN'T PAYING YOU?
OH, SURE - HE HANDS OVER ME WAGES - THEN HE PULLS OUT A PAIR OF DICE AND TAKES IT AWAY FROM ME
AS MAN TO MAN - I'M ASKIN' YOU - IS THAT JUSTICE?
AND YOU REALLY THINK THAT RUBBING THE THREE HAIRS ON BERNICE'S HEAD BRINGS GOOD LUCK?
SURE - DIDN'T I RUB 'EM JUST BEFORE I WORKED ON POPEYE?
SEGAR

THIMBLE THEATER

NOW SHOWING—FALSE HAIR?
Monday—Deck "Cleaning."

POPEYE, IF YOU'LL WORK HARD AND TAKE GOOD CARE OF THE SHIP I'LL LET YOU IN ON SOME OF THE EASY MONEY
YOU SEE, WHEN WE GET TO DICE ISLAND I'LL RUB THE THREE HAIRS ON MY WHIFFLE HEN'S HEAD THEN I'LL GO UP TO THE GAMBLING RESORT AND WIN ALL THE JACK
STOW THAT - I WASN'T BORN YESTERDAY - YA THINK I'M IGNORANT?!
AS IF THE RUBBIN' OF THAT BIRD'S HEAD WOULD BRING GOOD LUCK -
BY RIGHTS I SHOULDN'T EVEN SPEAK TO YOU - YOU'RE ONLY SCUM'A THE BILGE - AND I'M THE CAPTAIN - YOU DON'T KNOW WHEN TO FEEL HONORED -
JUST WAIT'LL I THINK UP SOME MEAN CRACKS - I'LL TELL THAT SHRIMP SOMETHIN'
SEGAR

THIMBLE THEATER

NOW SHOWING—DECK "CLEANING."
Tomorrow—A "She-Sick" Gob.

YOU DON'T BELIEVE THAT I GET LUCK FROM RUBBING THE THREE HAIRS ON BERNICE'S HEAD DO YOU, POPEYE?
NO! - GET OUT YOUR DICE AND I'LL TAKE YOU FOR A CLEANIN'
THE OTHER DAY CASTOR GAVE HIM A WEEK'S WAGES AND THEN BROUGHT FORTH HIS DICE AND WENT THROUGH HIM FOR THE WORKS
CRAP GAME FOR'D, MATE
YEAH? GEE - THAT'LL BE JUST TOO BAD FOR POPEYE
SHOOT FOUR BITS
SHOOT!
TEN PASSES ISN'T SO BAD - AND THIS IS THE WAY I'LL CLEAN UP THAT GAMBLING RESORT WHEN WE GET TO DICE ISLAND
WELL, BLOW ME DOWN FOR A LUBBER, I QUITCHA!!
SEGAR

THIMBLE THEATER
NOW SHOWING—A "SHE-SICK" GOB

Tomorrow—The Fleet's In.

I'M TELLING YOU POPEYE- THIS IS A LUCK BIRD- I CAN WIN IN ANY GAME OF CHANCE BY RUBBING THE THREE HAIRS ON HER HEAD
I DON'T BELIEVE IT CAP'N - I WAS BRUNG UP DIFFERENT
SEE- I RUB HER HEAD-NOW I'LL PUT UP THE SHIP AGAINST YOUR SHIRT
YOU MEAN YOU'LL SHOOT THE SHIP AGAINST ME SHIRT?
THAT'S WHAT I SAID- THE SHIP'S YOURS IF I LOSE
IF I WIN THEN I'LL BE THE CAPTAIN AND YOU'LL BE THE CREW
YEAH THAT'S RIGHT
SHOOT
COME SEVEN
SNAP
CASTOR, LET HIM HAVE HIS SHIRT! IT AIN'T RIGHT
WELL I'LL PUMP OUT THE BILGE WITH AN EYE-DROPPER IF YOU CAN BEAT THIS
2-5
SEGAR

THIMBLE THEATER
NOW SHOWING—THE FLEET'S IN

Tomorrow—Fickle Lady Luck.

I NEVER TOOK A GOOD LOOK AT YOUR FACE BEFORE - GEE-WHAT HAPPENED TO IT, POPEYE?
WHAT'S THE MATTER WITH IT?
WHY IT LOOKS LIKE A SHIP WRECK
I GET A BIG KICK OUTTA KIDDIN' OL' POPEYE
HA! HA! I'D HATE TO GO THROUGH LIFE WITH A THING LIKE THAT ON MY NECK
BLOW ME DOWN! CANAL BOATS FOR FEET ON A LADY!
THROW 'IM TO THE ANCHOVIES! YOU HEAR ME!
SEGAR
2-6

THIMBLE THEATER
NOW SHOWING—FICKLE LADY LUCK.

Tomorrow—A. W. O. L.

IT'S PAY DAY AGAIN, HERE'S YOUR WAGES, WELL-HOW ABOUT IT? SHALL I GET OUT THE DICE?
YEAH I'LL ROLL 'EM AWHILE
I'LL RUB THE THREE HAIRS FOR LUCK SO I CAN'T LOSE, POPEYE'S WORKING FOR NOTHING AND DON'T KNOW IT!
COME ON, LET'S HOP TO IT
JUST A SECOND, CAP'N-I'LL BE RIGHT BACK
HURRY UP, POPEYE, I'M READY TO TAKE YOUR CASH
SHOOT- YOU'RE FADED
SAY, YOU'VE GOT ME FOR FIFTY BUCKS
SURE- SHOOT THE WORKS
NO YOU WON'T- I QUIT
WHAT'S THE MATTER WITH YOU? I RUB YOUR HEAD FOR GOOD LUCK AND THEN I LOSE FIFTY BERRIES
WHIFFLE
2-7
SEGAR

THIMBLE THEATER

NOW SHOWING—A. W. O. L.

Tomorrow—Bernice, the Sailor's Sweetheart.

I ALWAYS HAD GOOD LUCK BEFORE AFTER RUBBING BERNICE'S HEAD. BUT YESTERDAY POPEYE TOOK ME FOR FIFTY BUCKS. I CAN'T UNDERSTAND THAT!
HEY, SKIPPER- WANT TO SHOOT A FEW CRAPS?
ALL RIGHT, I'LL TAKE YOU ON IN A MINUTE
DON'T FAIL ME THIS TIME- REMEMBER-YOU'RE SUPPOSED TO BE A LUCK BIRD
COME ON, POPEYE- ALL SET
I'LL BE RIGHT BACK CAP'N
WHERE'D HE GO ANYWAY? HE LEFT LIKE THAT BEFORE WE STARTED THE GAME LAST TIME TOO
2-8
SEGAR

THIMBLE THEATER

NOW SHOWING—BERNICE, THE SAILOR'S SWEETHEART.

Monday—His Secret Love.

WELL, I LOST AT CRAPS FOR THE SECOND TIME! POPEYE WENT THROUGH ME AGAIN
DID YOU RUB THE THREE HAIRS ON BERNICE'S HEAD?
SURE I DID- THAT'S WHAT STUMPS ME. I SHOULD HAVE HAD GOOD LUCK AFTER THAT
MAYBE POPEYE RUBBED HER DOME AFTER YOU DID- THAT WOULD KILL YOUR LUCK
NO- POPEYE DOESN'T BELIEVE IN THE LUCK STUFF. HE GAVE ME THE "HORSE LAUGH" WHEN I TOLD HIM BERNICE WAS A LUCK BIRD
WELL, IF WE DON'T GET ANY LUCK OUT OF THAT BIRD WE'RE JUST SIMPLY UP AGAINST IT
YEAH, THAT'S RIGHT
YEAH, I GUESS THAT'S RIGHT WE'RE SUNK
RUB! RUB RUB
2-9
SEGAR

THIMBLE THEATER

NOW SHOWING—HIS SECRET LOVE.

Tomorrow—A Sailor-Made Gal.

WHY DON'T YOU SEE WHAT HE SAYS- THERE'S NO HARM IN ASKING HIM
YOU'RE RIGHT ABOUT THAT- YEAH, I GUESS I WILL
HEY, POPEYE, YOU HAVEN'T BEEN RUBBING THAT WHIFFLE HEN'S HEAD TO GET LUCK, HAVE YOU?
WHO ME? NO-NO- NOT ME!
CROSS ME HEART! I NEVER DID AND NEVER WILL DO SUCHA FOOLISH THING
NO-NO- NO! OH MY NO!
YOU'RE ALL WRONG HAM- HE'S INNOCENT. I KNOW INNOCENCE WHEN I SEE IT
RUB RUB
2-11
SEGAR

THIMBLE THEATER
NOW SHOWING—A SAILOR-MADE GAL

Tomorrow—The Soreheads.

SHE'S LOST HER LUCK, THAT'S ALL THERE IS TO IT– I'VE LOST AT CRAPS TWICE IN A ROW, AND AFTER RUBBING HER HEAD TOO
NOW LISTEN, SUPPOSE POPEYE RUBBED THE THREE HAIRS ON THE WHIFFLE HEN'S HEAD AFTER YOU. THEN HE'D GET ALL THE LUCK
NAW– IT ISN'T THAT! I TOLD HIM ABOUT BERNICE BEING A LUCK BIRD, BUT HE WOULDN'T EVEN LISTEN TO ME
HAM- I THINK CASTOR IS RIGHT- POPEYE DOESN'T BELIEVE IN THAT BIRD, THINKS THE LUCK STUFF IS A LOT OF HOOEY
WELL IT'S MIGHTY FUNNY
I'LL SAY IT IS
WHAT THEY DON'T KNOW WON'T HURT 'EM
THERE WONT BE NO LUCK LEFT IN THIS BIRD – I'LL RUB IT ALL INTO ME OWN BODY- BLOW ME DOWN IF I DON'T
2-12
SEGAR

THIMBLE THEATER
NOW SHOWING—THE SOREHEADS

Tomorrow—A Wolf in Sheik's Clothes.

WHAT'S UP, HAM?
I'VE MADE A DISCOVERY, OLIVE!
CASTOR, I'M TELLING YOU SOMEBODY'S BEEN RUBBING BERNICE'S HEAD FOR LUCK, AND A HECK OF A LOT TOO
HOW DO YOU KNOW, HAM?
JUST LOOK- HEAD'S ALL SORE AND EVERYTHING
GOOD NIGHT!
SEGAR 2-13

THIMBLE THEATER
NOW SHOWING—A WOLF IN SHEIK'S CLOTHES.

Tomorrow—Salt Water Never Freezes.

HAM'S RIGHT- SOMEBODY'S BEEN RUBBING HER HEAD! AND I'M GOING TO FIND OUT WHO! I SURE WILL!
POPEYE – I WANT THE TRUTH! HAVE YOU BEEN RUBBING BERNICE'S HEAD FOR LUCK?
HOW DO YOU LIKE ME NEW SHIRT, CAP'N? AIN'T SHE HOT, CAP'N?
DON'T TRY TO CHANGE THE SUBJECT- ANSWER MY QUESTION
AND ONLY TWO BUCKS- BARGAIN WHAT?
I'LL BET IT WAS HIM ALL RIGHT
ANSWER ME- DID, OR DIDN'T YOU?
HE'S THE LIMIT
ALL WOOL TOO- BLOW ME DOWN IF IT AIN'T
2-14
SEGAR

THIMBLE THEATER

NOW SHOWING—SALT WATER NEVER FREEZES.

Tomorrow—The Height of Hostility.

WE CAN'T GET ANYTHING OUT OF POPEYE- HE'S THE BIGGEST LIAR ON THE HIGH SEAS
WHO'S A LIAR?
YOU ARE, THAT'S WHO! GET FOR'D, YOU SHIPWRECK IN THE FACE!!
LISTEN HERE, POPEYE! YOU CAN QUIT ANY TIME! SURE- GET THE HECK OUTTA HERE! BEAT IT!
YOU JUST WATCH YOUR STEP AND DO AS I SAY OR YOU CAN WALK HOME!
WHADDAYA THINK THIS IS, A BUGGY RIDE?!
2-15
SEGAR

THIMBLE THEATER

NOW SHOWING—THE HEIGHT OF HOSTILITY.

Monday—That Sailor's No Gentleman.

DID YOU RUB BERNICE'S HEAD FOR LUCK TILL IT GOT ALL SORE?
OF COURSE NOT
DID YOU, HAM?
NO!
IT WASN'T ME, IT WASN'T HER, AND IT WASN'T HIM SO IT WAS YOU!
!
COME ON, MATE — LET'S TEACH THAT BUM SAILOR SOMETHING
WE'LL PUT HIM IN IRONS!
WELL BLOW ME DOWN THE WAY THEY TREATS ME IS SOMETHING SCANDILUM!!
COME DOWN! YOU HEAR ME!!
2-16
SEGAR

THIMBLE THEATER

NOW SHOWING—THAT SAILOR'S NO GENTLEMAN.

Tomorrow—'Tis Better to Give Than Receive.

I'M THE CAPTAIN OF THIS VESSEL AND I'LL STAND FOR NO TRIFLING FROM THE CREW- POPEYE LIED TO ME
SAY THE WORD AND I'LL GO BEAT HIM UP!
YEAH- GO AHEAD, SOCK HIM- IT'LL DO HIM GOOD!
G-R-R-R
I'LL BET HE RUNS WHEN HE SEES ME COMING-G-R-R-
I'M GONNA WIPE UP THE DECK WITH YOU AND STEP IN YOUR FACE — I'M LIKE THAT!
CRACK
YOU'RE JUST WHAT I THOUGHT YOU WAS- A LOW DOWN ROUGHNECK- I WONT FIGHT WITH YOU!
!
2-18
SEGAR

THIMBLE THEATER
NOW SHOWING—'TIS BETTER TO GIVE THAN RECEIVE.

Tomorrow—Freedom of Speech.

NO ORDINARY SEAMAN CAN BOP MY MATE AND GET AWAY WITH IT! I'M LIKE THAT!
HEY— TURN AROUND- !!
AND REMEMBER, POPEYE—YOU'RE NOT ALLOWED TO HIT THE CAPTAIN
I TELL YOU- YOU'RE NOT ALLOWED TO HIT THE CAPTAIN! YOU HEAR ME! I'M THE CAPTAIN!
STOP!
NOW CUT IT OUT!
SOCKIN' ME UNAWARES-HE DID, BLOW ME DOWN HE DID!
TRYIN' TO HIT THE CAPTAIN- GEE- HE DON'T KNOW NOTHIN'
2-19 SEGAR

THIMBLE THEATER
NOW SHOWING—FREEDOM OF SPEECH.

Tomorrow—A Good Gamble.

LET'S GANG 'IM
YES - LET'S ALL GRAB HIM HE'S TOO FRESH!
YEAH- WE'LL PUT HIM IN IRONS
G-R-R-R
IF YOU PUT ME IN IRONS, WHO'S GONNA DO THE HARD WORK?
GEE— THAT'S SO!
WELL- WE'LL LET YOU OFF THIS TIME
YEAH- WE'LL LET YOU OFF THIS TIME, BUT YOU BETTER WATCH OUT
2-20 SEGAR

THIMBLE THEATER
NOW SHOWING—A GOOD GAMBLE.

Tomorrow—Isle of Their Dream.

LAND AHOY- CAP'N! BLOW ME DOWN! LAND TO STA'BOARD!
WELL- LOWER A BOAT, YOU SHIPWRECK IN THE FACE! DON'T STAND THERE LIKE COLUMBUS DISCOVERING AMERICA
DON'T BE SO POLITE CAP'N DON'T BE SO
POLITE!
STAR BOARD, POPEYE
THAT'LL DO POPEYE- NO BACK TALK!
LEMME BE! YA THINK I DON'T KNOW HOW TO ROW A BOAT
GEE- I WONDER IF THIS COULD BE DICE ISLAND! SOME LUCK IF IT IS
SHOOT TWO BITS
!
2-21

THIMBLE THEATER
NOW SHOWING—ISLE OF THEIR DREAM.

Tomorrow—Lady Luck's Jilted Suitor.

YEP- I'VE GOT A HUNCH THAT THIS IS DICE ISLAND
GEE-WOULDN'T THAT BE LUCK?!
LUCK! YOU SAID IT- CAP'N OYL'S NO NAVIGATOR- HE THINKS THE COMPASS IS AN EIGHT DAY CLOCK- SAW HIM SET HIS WATCH BY IT
CASTOR, DO YOU REALLY THINK THIS IS DICE ISLAND?
SURE IT IS. COME LOOK AT THE NATIVES
G'WAN- LUCK BOX, I AIN'T SHOOTIN' NO CRAPE WITH YOU
SHOOT A BUCK
SIX BITS
FO' BITS I EIGHTS
SHOOT! I AIN'T SIDE BETTIN' ON NO EIGHT
SEGAR

THIMBLE THEATER
NOW SHOWING—LADY LUCK'S JILTED SUITOR.

Monday—The Empty Pocket Club.

HEY THERE, MISTER, IS THIS "DICE ISLAND"?
YES, THIS IS DICE ISLAND
WHO ARE YOU, MISTER? YOU DON'T LOOK AS THOUGH YOU'VE ALWAYS BEEN LIKE THAT
ME? I WAS A MILLIONAIRE WHEN I CAME HERE- THE GAMBLING PALACE CLEANED ME AT ONE SITTING- I'M JUST A BUM NOW- IF YOU'VE GOT ANY MONEY KEEP AWAY FROM FADEWELL'S BUNCH
SEGAR

THIMBLE THEATER
NOW SHOWING—THE EMPTY POCKET CLUB.

Tomorrow—An Ace in the Hole.

OUW ~~ !! I'VE BEEN UP TO THE GAMBLING PALACE AND THEY TOOK ME FOR FIVE HUNDRED THOUSAND! ALL I HAD!
I'M BROKE! HOW'LL I GET HOME?! WHAT'LL I DO?
GO ASK THOSE FELLOWS- I'M A STRANGER HERE ON DICE ISLAND
CAN ANY OF YOU GENTLEMAN TELL ME HOW I'M GOING TO GET HOME?
!
YOU WON'T GET HOME- YOU'LL STAY HERE AND LIVE ON COCOANUTS LIKE THE REST OF US HAS-BEEN MILLIONAIRES
AND DON'T HIGH HAT ME- I LOST TWO MILLION
ANOTHER SUCKER
SEGAR

THIMBLE THEATER

NOW SHOWING—AN ACE IN THE HOLE.
Tomorrow—The "Doughboy's" Parade.

HAW! HAW! SO YOU'RE GOING UP TO THE GAMBLING PALACE AND BREAK THE BANK WITH TWO THOUSAND DOLLARS-HA! HA!
SURE I AM!
I GUESS HE THINKS I'M GOOFY- BUT HE DOESN'T KNOW ABOUT MY LUCK BIRD
HA! HA!
YEAH WITH TWO THOUSAND BUCKS HE'S GOING TO BREAK THE BANK
DID YOU TELL HIM ABOUT US GOING IN MILLIONAIRES AND COMING OUT BUMS?
THOSE OLD HAS-BEEN MILLIONAIRES ARE UP AGAINST IT- IF THEY WENT HOME BROKE THEIR WIVES WOULD KILL 'EM SO THEY JUST MOPE AROUND THE ISLAND BEEFING ABOUT THEIR TOUGH LUCK
IT'S DANGEROUS FOR RICH MEN TO GAMBLE-THEY SHOULD HAVE BEEN SATISFIED WITH THEIR MILLIONS- NOW WITH ME THERE'S EVERYTHING TO WIN AND NOTHING TO LOSE BUT MY SHIRT—
2-26 SEGAR

THIMBLE THEATER

NOW SHOWING—THE "DOUGHBOY'S" PARADE.
Tomorrow—An Irritable Customer.

LET'S GET THIS BUSINESS OVER- NOW HERE'S MY PLAN- I'LL RUB BERNICE'S HEAD FOR LUCK - THEN WE'LL GO UP TO THE GAMBLING PALACE ⟶
AND YOU THREE STAY OUTSIDE — AS I WIN THE MONEY I'LL THROW IT OUT OF A WINDOW — YOU GRAB IT AND TAKE IT DOWN TO THE ROW BOAT-
WHEN YOU GET THE BOAT FULL LET ME KNOW AND I'LL QUIT —
LET'S GO!
BLOW ME DOWN!
$ $ $
$ $
$ $ $ $ $
RUB RUB
2-27 SEGAR

THIMBLE THEATER

NOW SHOWING—AN IRRITABLE CUSTOMER.
Tomorrow—Chicken Feed.

I'LL THROW THE MONEY OUT THE WINDOW TO YOU AS FAST AS I WIN IT- TAKE IT TO THE ROW BOAT- WHEN THE BOAT'S FULL LET ME KNOW AND I'LL QUIT
SOME DUMP! IT WOULD MAKE A MILLIONAIRE FEEL LIKE A PAUPER
AH, STRANGER, WELCOME. AND WOULD YOU LIKE TO WIN SOME MONEY?
SURE- YA FATHEAD!! THINK I COME HERE TO LOSE?
!
THERE'S A LOVELY CRAP GAME ON YOUR LEFT SIR
DON'T WORRY ABOUT ME- I'LL PICK MY OWN GAME AND I'LL FURNISH MY OWN DICE TOO
2-28 SEGAR

THIMBLE THEATER
NOW SHOWING—CHICKEN FEED.
Tomorrow—Don't Insult the Help.

WELL- I DON'T SEE NO MONEY COMIN' OUT THE WINDER YET
GIVE HIM TIME, POPEYE
SURE
THE TIME HAS COME, BERNICE OLD GIRL. IF THERE'S ANY LUCK IN YOU - GIVE IT TO ME NOW!!
RUB RUB
I'VE ONLY GOT TWO THOUSAND, SO I'LL TEST MY LUCK IN A SMALL WAY BEFORE I CUT LOOSE
SHOOT TEN THOUSAND DOLLARS
SHOOT FIFTY THOUSAND BUCKS
SHOOT TWO BITS
!
SEGAR 3-1

THIMBLE THEATER
NOW SHOWING—DON'T INSULT THE HELP.
Monday—Pardon the Error.

HEY MANAGER, WHY CAN'T I GET INTO ONE OF THESE GAMES? ISN'T THIS A PUBLIC GAMBLING HOUSE?
YOU CAN GET INTO ANY GAME BUT YOU CAN'T INSULT OUR CUSTOMERS BY SHOOTING TWO BITS
TABLE No. 21
I ONLY WANTED TO TRY OUT MY LUCK - YA' THINK I'M GONNA SHOOT THE WORKS RIGHT OFF THE BAT?!
WELL, COME ON I'LL GET A GAME FOR YOU
NOW YOU'RE TALKING
PORTER, THIS GENTLEMAN WISHES TO LOSE TWO BITS - SHOW HIM SOME ACTION
AH SHOOTS NOTHIN' LESS'N A BUCK
© 1929, King Features Syndicate, Inc., Great Britain rights reserved.
SEGAR 3-2

THIMBLE THEATER
NOW SHOWING—PARDON THE ERROR.
Tomorrow—That "Grand" and Glorious Feeling.

I CAN'T TAKE ANY CHANCES WITH MY $2000. I WANT TO TEST MY LUCK IN A SMALL WAY AT FIRST
AH, THERE'S A SMALL GAME
SHOOT A QUARTER
SHOOT A HALF! COME ON - SAY WILL NOBODY COVER MY HALF?
HERE - I'LL FADE YOU FOR A HALF
! ? !
NOT A HALF A DOLLAR, YOU SAP! - A HALF A MILLION
OH!
WELL YOU DON'T HAVE TO BE LIKE THAT, DO YOU? GEE - YOU MAKE ME FEEL TERRIBLE! WHERE'S YOUR HOSPITALITY?!
WHY DON'T YOO TAKE UP MARBLES?
BEAT IT!
3-4 SEGAR

THIMBLE THEATER
NOW SHOWING—THAT "GRAND" AND GLORIOUS FEELING.
Tomorrow—The Gold Strike.

HEY YOU - I'VE GOT TWO THOUSAND DOLLARS AND I WANT TO GAMBLE AGAINST THE HOUSE
YOU'RE A PEST
LISTEN, TAKE HIS TWO "GRAND" AND THEN KICK HIM OUT— HE'S ONE OF THOSE THINGS
OKE!
COME ON. I'VE GOT A GAME FOR YOU WITH ONE OF OUR "HOUSEMEN"
NOW'S MY CHANCE - GIMME LUCK, BERNICE
RUB
RUB
ALL RIGHT, SON - GET OUT YOUR CHICKEN FEED - IT WON'T BE LONG NOW
YOU'RE IN THE HOUSE FOR TEN THOUSAND AND WE'VE ONLY BEEN SHOOTIN' THREE MINUTES
YOU AIN'T SEEN NOTHIN' YET WAIT'LL I BEGIN!! - TURN UP YOU "LITTLE JOE" PAPA NEEDS A COUNTRY HOME!
WHAM
SNAP
5-5

THIMBLE THEATER
NOW SHOWING—THE GOLD STRIKE.
Tomorrow—The Gold Rush.

COME ON, OL' BONES - GET HOT! AND STAY HOT! DON'T FOOL ME, DICE! FEVER IN THE SOUTH! COME ON, FIVE! FIVE ME, DICE!
'S GOING RIGHT THROUGH YOU - SAY I THOUGHT YOU WAS A CRAP SHOOTER
WHAM
SNAP
SO DID I!
SHOOT THE WORKS
HE SAID TO STAND UNDER THE WINDOW AND HE'D THROW THE MONEY OUT TO US WHEN HE "WIND" IT - IF YA' ASKIN' ME I SAY HE'S A FLOP
NOBODY'S ASKING YOU, POPEYE
WELL YA' DON'T SEE NONE COMIN' OUT - BLOW ME DOWN YA' DON'T
CUT THAT OUT. HEY!! CUT THAT OUT!
20,000

THIMBLE THEATER
NOW SHOWING—THE GOLD RUSH.
Tomorrow—Castor's Winning Way.

HELP!
GET ME SOME MORE SACKS TO PUT MY MONEY IN —— COME, YOU SEVEN! THERE SHE IS MISTER — SHOOT THE WORKS — READ 'EM AND WEEP
I'D GIVE MY WEALTH FOR HIS LUCK ANYTIME
ME TOO
HE TALKS TO THE DICE, AND THEY OBEY
IT'S UNCANNY !!
LOOK AT THE MANAGER HE'S HALF CRAZY
SHOOT A MILLION!
HE'S GOT A REASON
!
!
5-7

THIMBLE THEATER

NOW SHOWING—CASTOR'S WINNING WAY.

Tomorrow—Suffering from Exhaustion.

WHEN YOU GET THAT DOWN TO THE BOAT I'LL GET BUSY AND WIN SOME MORE
BLOW ME DOWN! THIS IS HARD WORK!
WHEW!
HEY, CAP'N OYL WE'RE ALL IN FROM CARRYIN' MONEY. AIN'TCHER NEVER SATCHISFIED?
3-8
SEGAR

THIMBLE THEATER

NOW SHOWING—SUFFERING FROM EXHAUSTION.

Monday—The Golden Goose.

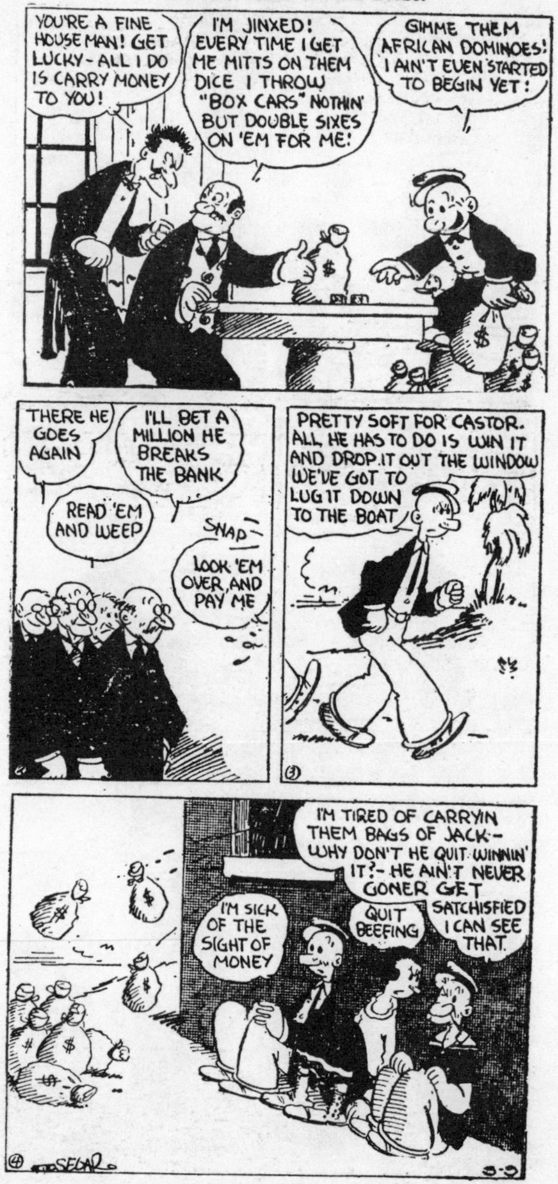
YOU'RE A FINE HOUSEMAN! GET LUCKY - ALL I DO IS CARRY MONEY TO YOU!
I'M JINXED! EVERY TIME I GET ME MITTS ON THEM DICE I THROW "BOX CARS" NOTHIN' BUT DOUBLE SIXES ON 'EM FOR ME!
GIMME THEM AFRICAN DOMINOES! I AIN'T EVEN STARTED TO BEGIN YET!
THERE HE GOES AGAIN
I'LL BET A MILLION HE BREAKS THE BANK
READ 'EM AND WEEP
SNAP
LOOK 'EM OVER, AND PAY ME
PRETTY SOFT FOR CASTOR. ALL HE HAS TO DO IS WIN IT AND DROP IT OUT THE WINDOW
WE'VE GOT TO LUG IT DOWN TO THE BOAT
I'M TIRED OF CARRYIN THEM BAGS OF JACK - WHY DON'T HE QUIT WINNIN' IT? - HE AIN'T NEVER GONER GET
SATCHISFIED I CAN SEE THAT.
I'M SICK OF THE SIGHT OF MONEY
QUIT BEEFING
SEGAR
3-9

THIMBLE THEATER

NOW SHOWING—THE GOLDEN GOOSE

Tomorrow—No Sale

LOOK - HE THROWS THE MONEY OUT OF THE WINDOW TO HIS FRIENDS AS FAST AS HE WINS IT! THERE NEVER WAS A CLEAN-UP LIKE THIS ON DICE ISLAND
WHERE DOES HE GET THAT LUCK?
AND, HE'S SHOOTIN' AGAINST THE HOUSE TOO
IF OLD FADEWELL, THE OWNER OF THIS GAMBLING RESORT KNEW THIS - OH, BOY!
I HEAR HE STARTED WITH ONLY TWO THOUSAND
LISTEN TO HIM TALK TO THOSE DICE
STAY HOT, DICE STAY HOT! COME ON YOU, "LITTLE JOE"
SNAP!
THE BOAT'S FULL WHY DOESN'T HE QUIT?
I'M TIRED OF CARRYING THIS FILTHY LUCRE
AIN'T 'E EVER GO'NER GET SATCHISFIED? BLOW ME DOWN!
SEGAR
3-11

THIMBLE THEATER
NOW SHOWING—NO SALE

Tomorrow—A Dose of His Own Medicine

THIMBLE THEATER
NOW SHOWING—A DOSE OF HIS OWN MEDICINE

Tomorrow—The Pauper

THIMBLE THEATER
NOW SHOWING—THE PAUPER

Tomorrow—The Dough Goes to Popeye's Head

THIMBLE THEATER

NOW SHOWING—
THE DOUGH GOES TO POPEYE'S HEAD
Tomorrow—Money On the Brain

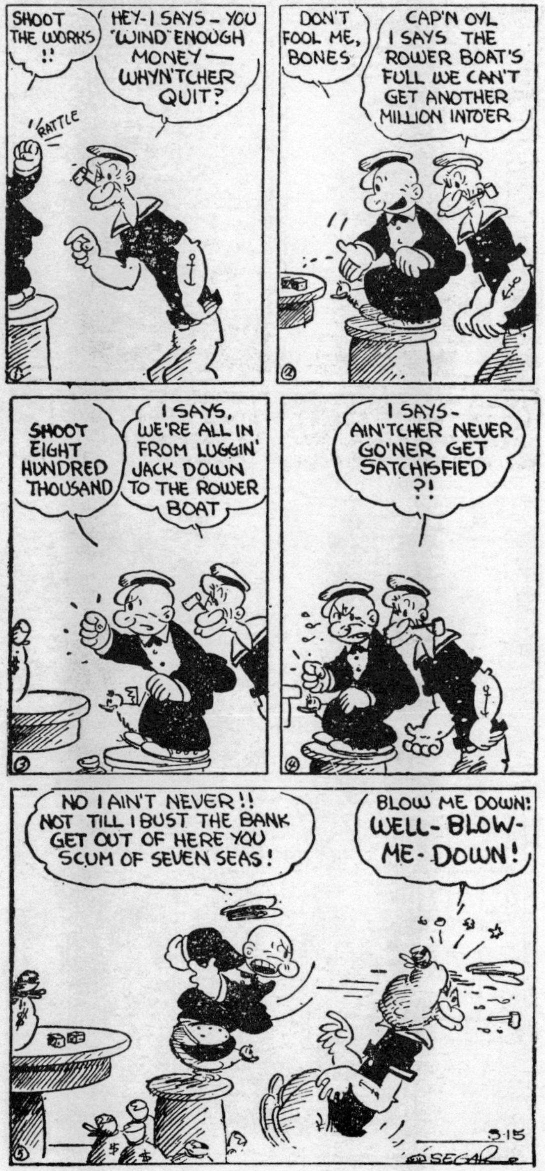

SHOOT THE WORKS !!
HEY- I SAYS - YOU "WIND" ENOUGH MONEY — WHYN'TCHER QUIT?
RATTLE
DON'T FOOL ME, BONES
CAP'N OYL I SAYS THE ROWER BOAT'S FULL WE CAN'T GET ANOTHER MILLION INTO'ER
SHOOT EIGHT HUNDRED THOUSAND
I SAYS, WE'RE ALL IN FROM LUGGIN' JACK DOWN TO THE ROWER BOAT
I SAYS- AIN'TCHER NEVER GO'NER GET SATCHISFIED ?!
NO I AIN'T NEVER !! NOT TILL I BUST THE BANK GET OUT OF HERE YOU SCUM OF SEVEN SEAS!
BLOW ME DOWN! WELL- BLOW- ME- DOWN!
3-15
SEGAR

THIMBLE THEATER

NOW SHOWING—MONEY ON THE BRAIN
Monday—"Bone Dry"

POPEYE WENT IN TO TRY AND MAKE CASTOR STOP GAMBLING - DO YOU THINK HE'LL SUCCEED?
SNAP
I HOPE HE DOES—WE'VE GOT MORE MONEY THAN WE CAN GET TO THE SHIP NOW.
WHAT DID HE SAY, POPEYE? IS HE GOING TO QUIT?
NO- BLOW ME DOWN, NO!
HE CALLS ME NAMES AND SAYS HE'S GO'NER KEEP RIGHT ON "WINDING" MONEY
AND THEN 'E SOCKS ME WITH A MILLION DOLLARS
IF THERE'S ANYTHING I CAN'T STAND IT'S GETTIN' SOCKED WITH A MILLION DOLLARS
BLOW ME DOWN!
3-16
SEGAR

THIMBLE THEATER

NOW SHOWING—"BONE" DRY.
Tomorrow—A Calm and "Collected" Orator.

IT'S ALL OVER! IT'S ALL OVER NOW!
THE GREAT PALACE OF CHANCE IS NO MORE - HE HAS BROKEN THE BANK
DID YOU HEAR THAT? HE'S BUSTED THE BANK!
AND HE STARTED WITH ONLY TWO THOUSAND DOLLARS
THERE'S ONLY FIFTEEN CENTS LEFT
!
ALL RIGHT- SHOOT FIFTEEN CENTS.
!
3-18
SEGAR

THIMBLE THEATER

NOW SHOWING—A CALM AND "COLLECTED" ORATOR.

Tomorrow—The Good Samaritan.

I'VE BUSTED THE BANK-SO THIS WILL BE ALL-TAKE IT DOWN TO THE BEACH AND WAIT FOR ME
SOME OF YOUR GAMES ARE STRAIGHT AND I HAPPEN TO KNOW THAT SOME ARE CROOKED-YOU'VE WRECKED MANY A MILLIONAIRE-YOUR VICTIMS LINE THE BEACHES WITH NOT EVEN ENOUGH MONEY TO GET HOME
AND NOW, MR. MANAGER OF THE GREAT DICE ISLAND HOUSE OF CHANCE, LET ME GIVE YOU SOME GOOD ADVICE —
GAMBLING DOES NOT PAY—ASK ANYBODY-ADIOS!
WHIFFLE
I THINK I'LL TAKE UP MARBLES.
3-19
SEGAR

THIMBLE THEATER

NOW SHOWING—THE GOOD SAMARITAN.

Tomorrow—Excess Baggage.

WHAT ARE WE GOING TO DO WITH THAT PILE OF MONEY? WE CAN'T GET IT INTO THE BOAT
AND SOMETHING TELLS ME THAT IF WE DON'T LEAVE THIS ISLAND AT ONCE THOSE GAMBLERS WILL MAKE TROUBLE
YOU "WINDED" TOO MUCH!
DON'T WORRY! I'VE GOT A PLACE FOR IT!
COME HERE ALL YOU HAS-BEEN MILLIONAIRES WHO LOST YOUR SHIRTS IN THE HOUSE OF CHANCE. COME GET YOUR FORTUNES BACK!
DIVIDE IT UP-GO HOME TO YOUR FAMILIES AND NEVER LAY YOUR MITTS ON A PAIR OF DICE AGAIN.
GOOD HEAVENS! THANKS!!
SEGAR 3-20

THIMBLE THEATER

NOW SHOWING—EXCESS BAGGAGE.

Tomorrow—Four Little Pigs.

WELL SNORK, HOW'S THINGS? WHAT'S THE MATTER WITH YOU SNORK? SPEAK UP!
GOOD NIGHT! IT'S THE BOSS — HOW ARE YOU, MR. FADEWELL?-ER-AH-AHEM— —.
HAVE A HEART, MR. FADEWELL, I COULDN'T HELP IT- HE KEPT WINNING AND WINNING TILL HE BROKE THE BANK! NOT A CENT LEFT
WHAT'S THAT ?!!
SNORK- YOU'RE NOT GOING TO DIE OF OLD AGE.
SOCK
THE SHIP'S ANCHORED A MILE OUT-AND WE'VE GOT A ROUGH SEA!
WHIFFLE
YOU SHOULDN'TA WIND SO MUCH-I AIN'T EVEN GOT ROOM TO ROWER THE BOAT
REMEMBER, POPEYE, IF YOU LOSE ONE BAG-OFF GOES YOUR HEAD!
SEGAR 3-21

THIMBLE THEATER
NOW SHOWING—FOUR LITTLE PIGS.
Tomorrow—Thumbs Down.

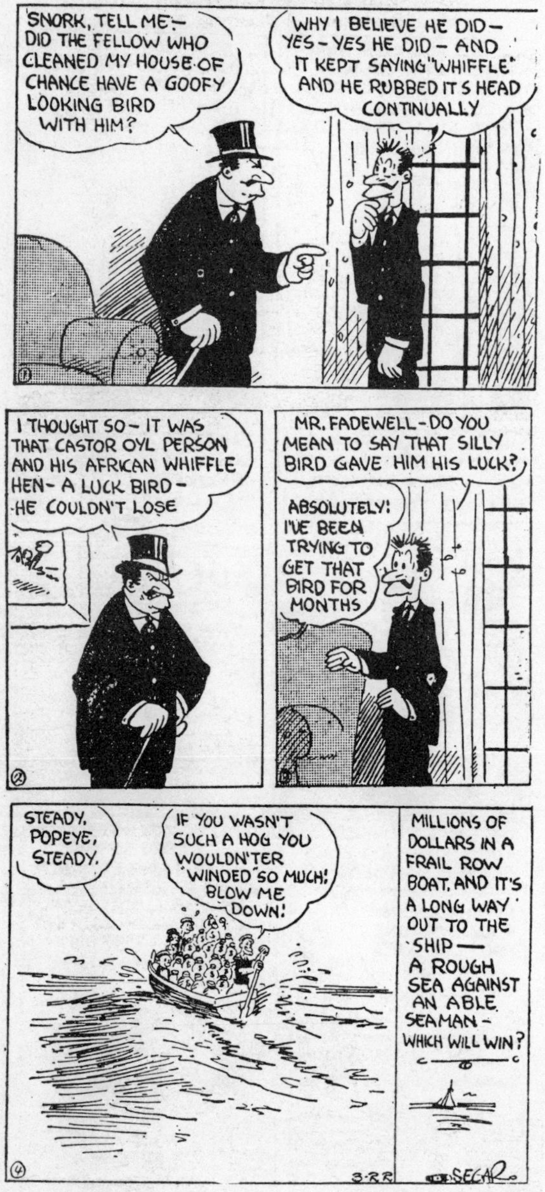

SNORK, TELL ME— DID THE FELLOW WHO CLEANED MY HOUSE OF CHANCE HAVE A GOOFY LOOKING BIRD WITH HIM?
WHY I BELIEVE HE DID— YES - YES HE DID - AND IT KEPT SAYING "WHIFFLE" AND HE RUBBED IT'S HEAD CONTINUALLY
I THOUGHT SO - IT WAS THAT CASTOR OYL PERSON AND HIS AFRICAN WHIFFLE HEN - A LUCK BIRD - HE COULDN'T LOSE
MR. FADEWELL - DO YOU MEAN TO SAY THAT SILLY BIRD GAVE HIM HIS LUCK?
ABSOLUTELY! I'VE BEEN TRYING TO GET THAT BIRD FOR MONTHS
STEADY, POPEYE, STEADY.
IF YOU WASN'T SUCH A HOG YOU WOULDN'TER "WINDED" SO MUCH! BLOW ME DOWN!
MILLIONS OF DOLLARS IN A FRAIL ROW BOAT, AND IT'S A LONG WAY OUT TO THE SHIP— A ROUGH SEA AGAINST AN ABLE SEAMAN - WHICH WILL WIN?
3-22
SEGAR

THIMBLE THEATER
NOW SHOWING—THUMBS DOWN.
Monday—Sea "Shelling."

QUICK, SNORK! FIND OUT IF CASTOR OYL AND HIS BUNCH ARE STILL ON THE ISLAND
STEADY, POPEYE
SAY WHO'S ROWSRIN' THIS BOAT?
A ROUGH SEA AND A FRAIL ROW-BOAT LOADED DOWN!
THEY'RE ON THEIR WAY TO THEIR SHIP - THE SEA IS ROUGH AND IT'S A SMALL TUB LOADED HEAVILY THEY'LL SINK SURE
I WOULDN'T GIVE TWO CENTS FOR THEIR CHANCES AGAINST THOSE WAVES
IF THEY SINK - THE MONEY'S LOST - IF THEY MAKE THE SHIP BY SOME MIRACLE WE'LL GO TAKE IT AWAY FROM THEM! THEY LOSE EITHER WAY
3-23
SEGAR
Great Britain rights reserved.
© 1929, King Features Syndicate, Inc.

THIMBLE THEATER
NOW SHOWING—SEA "SHELLING."
Tomorrow—Feeding the Fish.

THE WAVES ARE BREAKING ALL OVER THEM - THE MONEY WILL BE ON THE FLOOR OF THE OCEAN SOON - THEY'LL NEVER MAKE THEIR SHIP. THEY'RE LOST!
AND IF THEY DO MAKE THEIR SHIP THEY'RE LOST - I'LL GO KNOCK 'EM ALL OVER AND TAKE THE MONEY
HOLD EVERYTHING!
CAP'N OYL — BY THROWING THE MONEY OVER BOARD WE GOT A CHANCE FOR OUR LIVES -
ALL RIGHT, POPEYE - DUMP IT IN
BLOW ME DOWN! I'M GLAD IT AIN'T MY MONEY !!
3-25
SEGAR

THIMBLE THEATER
NOW SHOWING—FEEDING THE FISH.
Tomorrow—Calm Because It Collected.

WELL I'LL BE —— ! THEY'RE GETTING READY TO THROW THE MONEY OVER-BOARD!
IF THEY DO THAT OUR CHANCES ARE SHOT
WHY DIDN'T I MURDER THAT RUNT WHEN I HAD HIM IN MY APARTMENT A FEW MONTHS AGO'
THE BOAT CAN'T LIVE MUCH LONGER IN THESE BREAKERS WITH A LOAD LIKE THIS! ALL RIGHT, POPEYE, DUMP IT OUT
OUW I'M SICK !!
ME TOO
ME TOO
THERE'S - ONE - TWO — THREE MILLION THAT'LL NEVER BE SPENT! BLOW ME DOWN. AND ME WAGES IS ONLY TWENTY FIVE A WEEK
SPLASH
SEGAR 3-26

THIMBLE THEATER
NOW SHOWING—CALM BECAUSE IT COLLECTED.
Tomorrow—A Sensitive Soul.

STOP, POPEYE - DON'T THROW ANY MORE OVER - I THINK THE WIND'S LAYING!
IT'S QUIETING DOWN, MR. FADEWELL, AND THEY'VE STOPPED THROWING THE MONEY OVER BOARD
FINE!! NOW ALL WE HAVE TO DO IS, TAKE IT AWAY FROM THEM
THANK HEAVEN WE ONLY THREW AWAY FIVE MILLION
WHIFFLE
STILL AS A LAKE! BLOW ME DOWN!
SEGAR 3-27

THIMBLE THEATER
NOW SHOWING—A SENSITIVE SOUL.
Tomorrow—A Business Trip.

LISTEN SNORK, I HAVE A WELL THOUGHT-OUT PLAN - YOU ARE TO TAKE THE LEADING PART - ROW OUT TO THEIR SHIP AND TELL THEM I DROVE YOU FROM THE ISLAND - GAIN THEIR CONFIDENCE AND THEN DROP SOMETHING INTO THEIR SOUP
THAT'LL BE FUN
MILLIONS OF DOLLARS! AND ALL SAFE ON BOARD THE GOOD SHIP 'TOMCOD' — SAFE??
SHALL I HOIST ANCHOR, CAP'N OYL?
DID YOU THINK WE SHOULD DRAG IT?
TALKIN' TO ME LIKE THAT! AND HIM NOT KNOWIN' NORTH FROM SOUTH - THINKS THE COMPASS IS A CLOCK! I'M ONLY A COMMON SAILOR BUT I GOT A SOUL, I GOT SENSITIVITY. BLOW ME DOWN!
3-28
SEGAR

THIMBLE THEATER
NOW SHOWING—A BUSINESS TRIP.
Tomorrow—A Shark On Board.

WE'LL GO UP TO MY YACHT AND LOWER A ROW BOAT - NOW WHEN YOU BOARD THEIR SHIP YOU WANT TO BE CAREFUL - MAKE THEM THINK YOU HATE ME AND THAT I KICKED YOU OFF THE ISLAND - THEY'LL FALL FOR IT
THEY WONT LAST LONG WITH ME ON BOARD
WELL - SO FAR EVERYTHING HAS TURNED OUT GREAT! WHAT'LL WE DO WITH ALL THAT CASH
I'LL GO SLUMMING EVERY DAY WHEN I GET HOME
JUST LOOK! MONEY ALL OVER THE DECK! GET BUSY, TIDY UP THE SHIP AND YOU'D BETTER NOT LET ANY CASH STICK TO YOUR FINGERS! SNAP INTO IT, YOU NITWIT!
WHY DO YOU GOTTER BE LIKE THAT ?!
DON'T WORRY CHIEF - I'LL MAKE SHORT WORK OF THAT BUNCH
THERE'S A MILLION IN IT FOR YOU, SNORK
AND I'LL FOLLOW AT A SAFE DISTANCE
SEGAR

THIMBLE THEATER
NOW SHOWING—A SHARK ON BOARD.
Monday—Unappreciated Hospitality.

THAT LITTLE SHRIMP RUBBED IT INTO ME AFTER BREAKING THE BANK UP AT THE GAMBLING PALACE - BUT NOW WE SHALL SEE
I'LL KNOCK 'EM ALL OVER AND FEED 'EM TO THE ANCHOVIES
WHAT DO YOU THINK OF ME NOW? I KNOW MY ONIONS, EH? WE'LL LIVE IN LUXURY THE REST OF OUR LIVES
YEAH, HE'S GOOD! HE AIN'T GOT BRAINS ENOUGH TO CLOG ME PIPE — ONCE HE ASKS ME TO REEF THE ANCHOR. HE'S IGGORANT BLOW ME DOWN!
SEGAR

THIMBLE THEATER
NOW SHOWING—UNAPPRECIATED HOSPITALITY.
Now Showing—Popeye's "Blow" Is No Treat.

EVERYTHING'S O.K. AND WE'LL BE HOME WITH THE MONEY IN ABOUT A MONTH
FOR HEAVEN'S SAKE HELP ME!!! OLD FADEWELL RAN ME OFF THE ISLAND BECAUSE I LET YOU WIN ALL THAT MONEY
WHY'S HE SORE AT YOU? YOU DIDN'T LET ME BREAK HIS GAMBLING PALACE - MY LUCK DID THAT -
YES, BUT YOU DON'T KNOW OLD FADEWELL, HE'S THE MEANEST MAN ON EARTH! I CAME OUT HERE IN A ROW BOAT HOPING THAT YOU'D TAKE ME TO AMERICA WITH YOU
H-M-M
ALL RIGHT - I BELIEVE YOUR STORY - MAKE YOURSELF AT HOME, YOU'RE ONE OF US
THANKS
HA! HA! WHAT A SAP!
4-1
SEGAR

THIMBLE THEATER

NOW SHOWING—POPEYE'S "BLOW" IS NO TREAT.

Tomorrow—The Skin He Loves to Touch.

WHAT A CUTE MUSTACHE!
OLD FADEWELL RAN MR. SNORK OFF THE ISLAND SO WE'RE TAKING HIM TO AMERICA WITH US
YES— AND LET'S ALL BE FRIENDS
BLOW ME DOWN
!
HEY!
HEY
HEY!
SEGAR 4-2

THIMBLE THEATER

NOW SHOWING—THE SKIN HE LOVES TO TOUCH.

Tomorrow—The Sandman's Coming.

POPEYE, I WANT TO KNOW WHY YOU SOCKED MR. SNORK ON THE BUTTON!? HE'S MY GUEST AND IS GOING BACK TO AMERICA WITH US
WHAT DID YOU SOCK HIM FOR? ANSWER ME!!
I DON'T LIKE HIS' LOOKS
YOU BIG PARSNIP, DO YOU GO AROUND SOCKIN' PEOPLE JUST BECAUSE YOU DON'T LIKE THEIR LOOKS?
CRACK
HEY!
HEY
HEY
HEY
HEY!
WHAT'S THE MATTER WITH THAT CRAZY IDIOT? HE BOPPED ME AGAIN!
POPEYE! HEY, POPEYE!
4-3
SEGAR

THIMBLE THEATER

NOW SHOWING—THE SANDMAN'S COMING.

Tomorrow—A Sightseeing Tour.

HOW MANY TIMES HAVE I GOT TO TELL YOU TO QUIT SOCKIN' MR. SNORK?- YOU MUST BE CRAZY!
NOW REMEMBER THAT!! I'M THE CAPTAIN AND YOU'VE GOT TO OBEY ME, YOU UNCIVILIZED BEAST
I GUESS HE'LL LET YOU ALONE AFTER THE BAWLING OUT I GAVE HIM - HE DOESN'T KNOW HOW TO TREAT GENTLEMEN
I'LL SHOOT HIM IF HE EVER TRIES THAT AGAIN
I APPRECIATE YOUR TAKING ME TO AMERICA WITH YOU - AND I'D LIKE TO HELP - YOU'RE SHORTHANDED SO WHY NOT LET ME COOK?
SURE- THAT'LL BE GREAT! GO TO IT
IN CHARGE OF THE GALLEY- WHAT LUCK! I CARRY THEIR LIVES IN MY HAND
SOME DAY WE'LL HAVE SOUP AND SEASONED WELL FROM THIS LITTLE BLACK BOTTLE- ONE DROP WILL PUT THEM TO SLEEP FOR A WEEK AND MAYBE FOREVER
4-4
SEGAR

THIMBLE THEATER
NOW SHOWING—A SIGHTSEEING TOUR.
Tomorrow—A Seaman's Monocle.

CAP'N OYL, I DONT TRUST THAT GUY SNORK, YOU SHOULDN'T OUGHTER GIVED HIM A JOB AS COOK
I KNOW WHAT I'M DOING—YOU'RE WASTING YOUR BREATH TALKING TO ME-GO BLOW THE SAILS
THAT CHEAP SAILOR IS GOING TO CAUSE ME SOME TROUBLE-HE SEEMS TO SEE THROUGH MY PLANS AND THEREFORE HE'LL BE MY FIRST VICTIM
WE'LL START A BANK WHEN WE GET OUR MONEY HOME - WONT THAT BE HOT?
YOU AIN'T HOME YET, CAP'N OYL AND YOU MAY NEVER GET THERE ALIVE - OR DEAD NEITHER
G'WAN, YOU SHIP-WRECK!
THERE'S A YACHT FOLLOWIN' US - THINGS DON'T SMELL GOOD TO ME - I GOT INSTINCT - I KNOWS WHAT I KNOWS
SEGAR
4-5

THIMBLE THEATER
NOW SHOWING—A SEAMAN'S MONOCLE.
Monday—The Thing's Contagious.

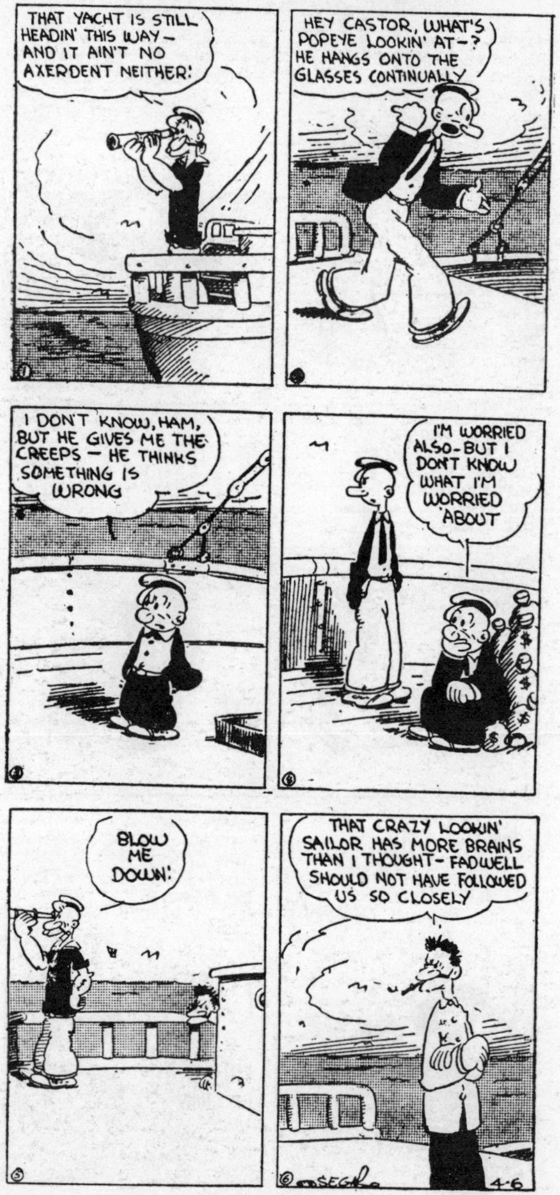
THAT YACHT IS STILL HEADIN' THIS WAY—AND IT AIN'T NO AXERDENT NEITHER!
HEY CASTOR, WHAT'S POPEYE LOOKIN' AT—? HE HANGS ONTO THE GLASSES CONTINUALLY
I DON'T KNOW, HAM, BUT HE GIVES ME THE CREEPS — HE THINKS SOMETHING IS WRONG
I'M WORRIED ALSO-BUT I DON'T KNOW WHAT I'M WORRIED ABOUT
BLOW ME DOWN!
THAT CRAZY LOOKIN' SAILOR HAS MORE BRAINS THAN I THOUGHT-FADWELL SHOULD NOT HAVE FOLLOWED US SO CLOSELY
SEGAR
4-6

THIMBLE THEATER
NOW SHOWING—THE THING'S CONTAGIOUS
Tomorrow—An Epidemic On Board.

I DIDN'T SLEEP A WINK LAST NIGHT-SOMETHING SEEMS TO BE HANGING OVER MY HEAD—GEE WHAT A FEELING!
I'M WORRIED AND I DON'T KNOW WHAT'S WORRYING ME! MAYBE I'M GOING TO DIE
I THINK POPEYE IS THE CAUSE OF ME FEELING THIS WAY-HE HANGS ONTO THAT TELESCOPE AS IF HE EXPECTED TROUBLE TO COME UPON US FROM BEHIND!
IT WOULD BE EASY IF THAT SAILOR WAS OUT OF THE WAY-HE'S GOT A SHARP EYE, AND IS WISE TO FADEWELL'S YACHT FOLLOWING US — I'LL HAVE TO BUMP HIM OFF FIRST
CASTOR, I'VE GOT A TERRIBLE FEELING-JUST LIKE SOMETHING IS GOING TO HAPPEN
WHAT! YOU GOT IT TOO ?!!
SEGAR
4-8

THIMBLE THEATER
NOW SHOWING—AN EPIDEMIC ON BOARD.
Tomorrow—Three of a Kind.

WHY DOESN'T SNORK GET BUSY? I COULD HAVE KNOCKED 'EM ALL OFF BY NOW — H'M'M. THERE'S A SAILOR WITH A TELESCOPE LOOKING THIS WAY
I SUPPOSE OLD FADEWELL IS GETTING IMPATIENT WAITING FOR THE SIGNAL — I'LL HOIST THIS BLACK FLAG BEFORE MANY DAYS
SOMETHING'S GOING TO HAPPEN. I KNOW IT - I FEEL JUST LIKE THAT
I'VE GOT SORT OF A WOMAN'S INTUITION MYSELF
BOYS! OH BOYS! MERCY! IT'S AWFUL - I'VE GOT SUCH A STRANGE FEELING
JUST LIKE SOMETHING TERRIBLE WAS GOING TO HAPPEN
4-9
SEGAR

THIMBLE THEATER
NOW SHOWING—THREE OF A KIND.
Tomorrow—Injured Innocence.

I JUST KNOW SOMETHING IS WRONG - I CAN'T STAND THIS STRAIN MUCH LONGER
CONTROL YOURSELF OLIVE! DON'T BE LIKE THAT!! P-P-PULL YOURSELF T-T-TO-G-GETHER-RR
HOW ABOUT YOU? YOU'RE SH-SH-SHAKIN' LIKE A LEAF
WHO ME? YOU MEAN ME?
WITH ME IT'S DIFFERENT, I GOT A TROPICAL CHILL I AIN'T SCARED ——— MUCH
MAYBE IT'S OUR IMAGINATION AND HAVING ALL THIS MONEY THAT IS CAUSING US TO FEEL THIS WAY
GUN-KNIFE OR THE LITTLE BLACK BOTTLE? WHICH WILL BE THE EASIEST — FOR ME?
4.10
SEGAR

THIMBLE THEATER
NOW SHOWING—INJURED INNOCENCE.
Tomorrow—Thumbs Down.

YOU BETTER WATCH SNORK, THINGS AIN'T RIGHT - THERE'S A YACHT FOLLOWIN' US
YEAH ?!
POPEYE, YOU'VE GOT ME SO WORKED UP I DON'T KNOW WHETHER I'M COMING OR GOING
HEY, SNORK!
SNORK!
I WANT TO SPEAK TO YOU, SNORK
S-S-SAY - ARE YOU PERFECTLY SURE YOU'RE ON THE SQUARE? YOU AIN'T GOT NOTHIN' UP YOUR SLEEVE HAVE YOU, SNORK
HOW YOU TALK!
WHY THE IDEA WHY THE VERY IDEA! YOU SHOULD BE ASHAMED!! YOU WRONG ME!!
OH SURE! ALL RIGHT 'SALL RIGHT
GOOD NIGHT! ARE THEY ALL GETTING WISE TO ME?
I'LL HAVE TO WORK FAST
4-11
SEGAR

THIMBLE THEATER
NOW SHOWING—THUMBS DOWN.
Tomorrow—Unanchored.

I KNOW SOMETHING'S WRONG
SOMETHING'S GOING TO HAPPEN TO US—
POPEYE -IT'S YOUR FAULT- YOU'VE GOT US BELIEVING THAT THINGS ARE NOT AS THEY SHOULD BE— WE'RE ALL JUMPY!
I KNOWS WHAT I KNOWS- I SMELLS SOMETHING AND I'M WARNIN' YOU
SOMETHING TERRIBLE IS GONER HAPPEN!
LISTEN, YOU SHIPWRECK- YOU'RE THE CAUSE OF US SUFFERING LIKE THIS - NOW IF SOMETHING TERRIBLE DOESN'T HAPPEN WE'LL FEED YOU TO THE FISH
WELL BLOW ME DOWN— I LOSE EITHER WAY!
SEGAR
4-12

THIMBLE THEATER
NOW SHOWING—UNANCHORED.
Monday—The Chin He Loves To Touch.

HOW MANY TIMES HAVE I GOTTER TELL YOU TO KEEP OUTTER MY SIGHT?
CRACK
ARE YOU GOING TO LET HIM GET AWAY WITH THIS?— PUT HIM IN IRONS
I'M SORRY, MR. SNORK, BUT I CAN'T HANDLE HIM- HE'S BEYOND ME
SEGAR
4-13

THIMBLE THEATER
NOW SHOWING—THE CHIN HE LOVES TO TOUCH.
Tomorrow—A Wealth of Discomfort.

YOO HOO!
YOO HOO!
WELL-WHAT DO YOU WANT?
A CRACK AT YOUR BUTTON
YOU SHOULDN'T DO THAT POPEYE - SNORK MAY BE INNOCENT- WE CAN'T PROVE THAT THERE'S A PLOT UNDERWAY TO GET OUR MONEY
THAT SETTLES IT- JUST AS SOON AS I GET MY BREATH I'LL GO OUT AND BLOW HIM INTO NINETY BILLION PIECES AND FLIT HIM TO THE FISH
SEGAR
4-15

THIMBLE THEATER
NOW SHOWING—A WEALTH OF DISCOMFORT.
Tomorrow—A Back-iring Villain.

AT FIRST I INTENDED TO MERELY PUT THEM TO SLEEP FOR A FEW WEEKS WITH A DRUG- BUT THINGS ARE DIFFERENT NOW, THAT POPEYED SAILOR IS GETTING WISE
HE'S BEEN SOCKING ME AROUND JUST A LITTLE TOO FREELY- NO MAN ON EARTH CAN BUST ME ON THE CHIN MORE THAN THREE TIMES AND LIVE
I'VE GOT THAT TERRIBLE STRANGE FEELING AGAIN
SOMETHING TELLS ME WE'LL NEVER GET HOME WITH THIS MONEY
ME TOO - I FEEL JUST LIKE I DID BEFORE. ONLY WORSE
SEGAR

THIMBLE THEATER
NOW SHOWING—A BACK-FIRING VILLAIN.
Tomorrow—Yellow Streaks.

SOMETHING MUST BE WRONG! I SUPPOSE SNORK ISN'T HAVING IT SO EASY- THE WAY HE TALKED, I THOUGHT HE'D BUMP 'EM ALL OVER THE FIRST DAY
THAT FUNNY LOOKING SAILOR SELDOM TAKES HIS GLASS OFF THIS YACHT IF I DON'T GET A SIGNAL SOON I'LL RAM THEIR TUB AND TAKE A CHANCE ON SAVING THE MONEY
AFTER ALL, MONEY ISN'T EVERYTHING- IF WE DIDN'T HAVE THIS CASH ON BOARD WE WOULDN'T FEEL AS THOUGH SOMEONE WAS PLOTTING TO GET IT
COME ON- LET'S DUMP IT OVER
NO—— MAYBE ALL THIS IS JUST OUR IMAGINATIONS
SEGAR 4-17

THIMBLE THEATER
NOW SHOWING—YELLOW STREAKS.
Tomorrow—Barking "Dogs."

THAT YACHT IS STILL TRAILIN' ALONG — BLOW ME DOWN IT'S A PLOT!
I KNOWS PLOTS WHEN I SMELLS 'EM - AND I KNOWS MUTINY AND THE SEVEN SEAS AND THE WAYS OF THE EGGS WHAT SAILS 'EM
HEY- LET'S KEEP TOGETHER! I GET JUMPY WHEN I'M ALONE
WHAT MAKES US ALL FEEL LIKE THIS?!
MAYBE IT'S HAVING ALL THAT MONEY ON BOARD
YEAH- AND MAYBE IT'S SOMETHING ELSE
SEGAR 4-18

THIMBLE THEATER

NOW SHOWING—BARKING "DOGS."

Tomorrow—The Quiet Before a Storm.

IF THERE'S A PLOT UNDERWAY WE COULD STOP IT BY THROWING THE MONEY INTO THE SEA— LET'S DUMP IT OVER AND HAVE SOME PIECE OF MIND
NOT THAT HAM—THROW AWAY THEM MILLIONS?? OH MY, NO! THINK UP SOMETHING ELSE
BUT IT MIGHT SAVE OUR LIVES
NO! NO! NO! NO! NO! NO! NO! NO! NO! NO!
!
SQUEEK
SQUEEK
I'LL HAVE TO GO BACK TO MY CABIN AND OIL MY SHOES
SQUEEK
SQUEEK
CURSES!! NOBODY HAS ANY LUCK AROUND HERE BUT MY VICTIMS!!
4-19
SEGAR

THIMBLE THEATER

NOW SHOWING—THE QUIET BEFORE A STORM.

Monday—About Face.

NOT A BREATH OF AIR! THE SAILS HANG LIKE DISH RAGS— THE STILLNESS IS MADDENING!
I'VE HEARD THAT STILLNESS AT SEA LIKE THIS WAS AN ILL OMEN
EVERYTHING IS JUST RIGHT FOR A TERRIBLE TRAGEDY!!
DON'T TALK LIKE THAT! I'M JUST ABOUT READY TO JUMP OUT OF MY SKIN! STOP IT! STOP IT!
BLOW ME DOWN I DON'T LIKE THIS STILLNESS—IT WERE A DAY LIKE THIS THAT THE CREW OF THE OLD BLUE BELL MUTINIED
SEGAR
4-20

THIMBLE THEATER

NOW SHOWING—ABOUT FACE.

Tomorrow—Mulish But No Donkey.

I DON'T LIKE THIS TERRIBLE STILLNESS
THERE'S TRAGEDY IN THE AIR
YEAH— I CAN FEEL IT
TURN AROUND— I WOULDN'T SHOOT A DOG IN THE BACK— POPEYE, YOUR TIME HAS COME—YOU SEE NOW THAT IT DOESN'T PAY TO INTERFERE WITH MY PLANS— OR SOCK ME AROUND THE WAY YOU'VE BEEN DOING
!
4-22
SEGAR

THIMBLE THEATER
NOW SHOWING—MULISH BUT NO DONKEY.
Tomorrow—A Hair-Breadth Escape.

I SAID "TURN AROUND" I WOULDN'T SHOOT ANYBODY IN THE BACK-
WELL BLOW ME DOWN! IN THAT CASE I WONT MOVE
DOGGONIT IF SOMETHING'S GOING TO HAPPEN I WISH IT WOULD HURRY UP ABOUT IT—THIS UNEASY FEELING IS TERRIBLE
WHIFFLE
SNORK-I KNOW WHY YOU WON'T SHOOT ME IN THE BACK- YOU WANT IT TO LOOK LIKE SELF DEFENSE
YES— I WANT THIS TO LOOK LIKE SELF DEFENSE - WILL YOU PLEASE TURN AROUND?
NO! BLOW ME DOWN! NO!
4-23
SEGAR

THIMBLE THEATER
NOW SHOWING—A HAIR-BREADTH ESCAPE.
Tomorrow—The Obliging Popeye.

IF YOU WONT TURN AROUND I SUPPOSE I'LL HAVE TO SHOOT YOU IN THE BACK- YOU HAVE ABOUT TEN SECONDS TO LIVE, YOU SCUM OF CREATION!
WHAT A PREDICKERMINT !!!
WHIFFLE!
WHAT IN THE
4-24
SEGAR

THIMBLE THEATER
NOW SHOWING—THE OBLIGING POPEYE.
Tomorrow—Auto-Intoxication.

WHIFFLE
CURSES- WHAT IN THE ~?
!
STOP! HANDS UP!
YESSIR
SOUNDS LIKE A SCUFFLE BACK AFT, HAM- GO SEE.
NO! YOU GO SEE
NO- YOU. GO SEE
4-25
SEGAR

THIMBLE THEATER

NOW SHOWING—AUTO-INTOXICATION.
Tomorrow—The Retiring Officer.

HANDS UP? SURE - WITH PLEASURE
WHIFFLE
BANG
CASTOR - I HEARD A SHOT! A SHOT!
NAW - IT WAS JUST A TIRE A BLOW OUT - SURE!
4-26
SEGAR

THIMBLE THEATER

NOW SHOWING—THE RETIRING OFFICER.
Monday—A Punctured Alibi.

CASTOR I'M CERTAIN I HEARD A SHOT! SH-SH-SURE!
A SHOT BACK AFT!
N-N-N N-NO!
DON'T BE LIKE THAT 'SA PUNCTURE, TIRE BLEW OUT!
I TELL YOU IT WAS A SHOT - WHY DON'T YOU GO SEE-E-E? YOU'RE THE CAPTAIN!
YOU CAN BE CAPTAIN!
BANG
4-27
SEGAR

THIMBLE THEATER

NOW SHOWING—A PUNCTURED ALIBI.
Tomorrow—Castor Hates a Guy Without Courage.

SHOTS CASTOR - TWO SHOTS - FROM BACK AFT - I KNOW SHOTS!!
N-N-N-NO! N-N-N-NOT SHOTS! DON'T SAY THAT!
BLOW OUTS - 'SALL IT WAS! SOME FELLOW HAD PUNCTURES!
HA! HA! HAD PUNCTURES! SURE - JUST BLOWOUTS
SINCE WHEN HAVE AUTOMOBILES BEEN RUNNING AROUND HERE ON THE HIGH SEAS?
OF COURSE YOU HAD TO THINK OF THAT!!
4-29
SEGAR

THIMBLE THEATER

NOW SHOWING—CASTOR HATES A GUY WITHOUT COURAGE.

Tomorrow—"Sense of Direction."

CASTOR - I TELL YOU IT'S YOUR DUTY TO GO SEE WHAT'S HAPPENING BACK AFT! YOU'RE THE CAPTAIN
HAM, OLD BOY. YOU'RE MY FRIEND AND I'M GONNA LET YOU BE CAPTAIN OF THIS BIG FINE SHIP -
YOU'RE CAPTAIN NOW - SO IT'S YOUR DUTY TO GO SEE WHAT'S HAPPENING BACK AFT
NO - I'M NOT CAPTAIN - I'M NOT EVEN MATE ANYMORE - I QUITS!
I'M ONLY A ORDINARY SAILOR NOW - AND AIN'T GOT NOTHIN' TO DO WITH NOTHIN'
COWARD!
4.30
SEGAR

THIMBLE THEATER

NOW SHOWING—SENSE" OF DIRECTION.

Tomorrow—The Master's "Shiverlry."

CASTOR, YOU SHOULD GO AFT AND SEE WHAT'S WRONG!
NO, HAM, YOU GO!
SOCK
BANG
WH-WHY DON'T YOU BOTH GO?
THAT'S IT! WE'LL BOTH GO!
HAM, YOU GO SEE WHAT'S HAPPENING BACK AFT —
AND I'LL GO SEE IF EVERYTHING'S ALL RIGHT UP FOR'D
WE'LL BOTH GO FOR'D AND HAVE A GOOD LOOK AROUND -
5.1
SEGAR

THIMBLE THEATER

NOW SHOWING—THE MASTER'S "SHIVERLRY."

Tomorrow—Long Range Courage.

SOCK
CRASH
SOMEBODY DO SOMETHING!
WHY DON'T YOU DO SOMETHING?
YEOW - I'M A NERVOUS WRECK!
BANG
ALL HANDS TURN TO — MAN THE LIFE BOATS!
AND REMEMBER I GO FIRST BECAUSE I'M THE CAPTAIN!
I-YI-YI-TH-THINK HE'S AFRAID?
Y-YEAH I B-B'LIEVE HE IS TOO!
5.2
SEGAR

THIMBLE THEATER

NOW SHOWING—LONG RANGE COURAGE.
Tomorrow—"Piping" Down.

BANG
CRASH
SOCK
OH! WHAT CAN BE GOING ON BACK AFT ?!
CASTOR - YOU'RE THE CAPTAIN - WHY DON'T YOU DO SOMETHING?
WHO ME?
ALL RIGHT - ALL RIGHT - IF IT'S UP TO ME - WHY ALL RIGHT
BY GOLLY HE'S BRAVER THAN I THOUGHT
YEAH, I'LL SAY!
HEY - STOP THAT BACK THERE!
SEGAR 5·3

THIMBLE THEATER

NOW SHOWING—"PIPING" DOWN.
Monday—The Diving "Plumbers."

CRASH
OUW - SOMETHING TERRIBLE MUST BE GOING ON BACK AFT
BANG
BANG
BANG
GOOD NIGHT!
HEY, CASTOR! WHERE YOU GOING?
WHATCHA GONNA DO, CASTOR ??
BANG
AS CAPTAIN OF THIS SHIP IT'S MY DUTY TO GO BELOW AND LOOK FOR LEAKS RIGHT NOW.
? ?
5.4
SEGAR

THIMBLE THEATER

NOW SHOWING—THE DIVING "PLUMBERS."
Tomorrow—Sherman Was Right.

THE BATTLE IS STILL RAGING - POPEYE SEEMS TO BE HOLDING HIS OWN AGAINST SNORK AND HIS GUN - HOW AN UNARMED MAN CAN STAND UP AGAINST A GAT IS HARD TO UNDERSTAND - STILL OLD POPEYE IS AN UNUSUAL FELLOW - A ROUGH MAN EVEN AMONG SEAMEN
CASTOR - HAM AND OLIVE - ARE NERVOUS WRECKS - SCARED STIFF - THEY DON'T KNOW WHAT'S HAPPENING BACK AFT AND THEY'RE AFRAID TO GO SEE
BANG
CRASH
WHAT'D YOU SAY YOU WERE GOING TO DO CASTOR ?
YEAH, WHAT?
I SAID "AS CAPTAIN OF THIS SHIP IT'S MY DUTY TO GO BELOW AND LOOK FOR LEAKS RIGHT NOW."
YOU'RE GOING TO STAY RIGHT UP HERE WITH US
LAY OFF! IT'S MUTINY TO TOUCH THE CAPTAIN
BANG
BANG
BANG
CRASH
BANG
LET'S ALL GO BELOW AND LOOK FOR LEAKS!
5·6
SEGAR

THIMBLE THEATER
NOW SHOWING—SHERMAN WAS RIGHT.
Tomorrow—Let's Be Feminine.

WHY DON'T YOU DROP? I'VE SHOT YOU A DOZEN TIMES—ARE YOU A DEMON?!! I THOUGHT IT WOULD BE EASY BUT I CAN'T EVEN STOP YOU WITH A GUN!
WHY YOU
BANG BANG BANG BANG BANG
WONDER WHAT WAR THIS IS?!
LET'S GET BACK DOWN AND LOOK FOR LEAKS
SURE
SEGAR 5-7

THIMBLE THEATER
NOW SHOWING—LET'S BE FEMININE.
Tomorrow—A Lady "Rooster."

IT'S QUIETED DOWN SOME BACK AFT - DO YOU THINK IT'S ALL OVER?
I-YI-YI- CAN'T THINK- WHA'YOU THINK?
S-SEEMS TO BE O.K. DON'T HEAR NOTHIN'
BANG CRASH BANG BANG
CRASH
YEOW! I CAN'T STAND ANYMORE OF THIS!
SAY LISTEN- L-LET'S ALL FAINT!
5-8 SEGAR

THIMBLE THEATER
NOW SHOWING—A LADY "ROOSTER."
Tomorrow—Bernice Is Shooting the Shoots.

COME ON- LET'S ALL FAINT
BANG
SAY- I'VE BEEN TRYING TO FAINT FOR AN HOUR
ME TOO!
I'LL TAKE DEAD AIM—
WHIFFLE!
BLOW ME DOWN! THAT BIRD HAS SAVED ME LIFE TWICE!
WHIFFLE
SEGAR 5-9

THIMBLE THEATER

NOW SHOWING—BERNICE IS SHOOTING THE SHOOTS.

Tomorrow—A Lady's Privilege.

GET OFF MY GUN. YOU CRAZY BIRD!! I'LL BLOW YOU TO —
WHIFFLE
WELL I'LL BE ~
G-R-R- IF I COULD ONLY GET MY HANDS ON YOU
WHIFFLE
I'LL PLUG YOU THIS TIME EVEN WITH THIS GOOFY BIRD HELPING YOU
WHIFFLE
JUST LISTEN TO THE LANGUAGE! AIN'T IT AWFUL?
WISH I COULD FAINT!
5-10
SEGAR

THIMBLE THEATER

NOW SHOWING—A LADY'S PRIVILEGE.

Monday—The Latest Report.

BANG
CRASH
BANG
OH, MY GOSH!
PLOP
OLIVE FAINTED!
OLIVE FAINTED!!
YEP- SHE'S FAINTED!
SOME PEOPLE HAVE ALL THE LUCK!
SURE- SHE DOESN'T KNOW SOMETHING'S WRONG BACK AFT NOW
5-11
SEGAR

THIMBLE THEATER

NOW SHOWING—THE LATEST REPORT.

Tomorrow—A True Confession.

BANG
WELL- THAT'S THAT!
EVERYTHING'S QUIET BACK AFT- WHAT DO YOU SUPPOSE IT WAS?
SAY- I'LL BET IT WAS POPEYE AND SNORK
5-13
SEGAR

THIMBLE THEATER
NOW SHOWING—A TRUE CONFESSION.
Tomorrow—Quivering Targets.

HEY, CASTOR-HERE COMES SNORK AND HE'S GOT A GUN!
HEAVENS! MAYBE IT'S MUTINY!
MR. SNORK, WHAT DOES THIS MEAN ?
WHERE IS-POP-POP-POP-POP-POP-POP-POP POP-POPEYE?!
I SHOT HIM
!
!
!
5-14
SEGAR

THIMBLE THEATER
NOW SHOWING—QUIVERING TARGETS.
Tomorrow—The Petter.

SO YOU SH-SHOT POPEYE?
YAS!
I'LL BET HE'S GOING TO SHOOT US TOO!
!!
'SMUTINY, THAT'S WHAT, 'SMUTINY !!
I'M SHAKING LIKE A LEAF!
KEEP TREMBLING, HE CAN'T HIT US
SEGAR
5-15

THIMBLE THEATER
NOW SHOWING—THE PETTER.
Tomorrow—A Dead Weight.

STOP TREMBLING LIKE THAT-I'M NOT GOING TO SHOOT YOU-
OH, YOU'RE NOT GOING TO SHOOT US?! WELL, THAT'S FINE! THANKS EVER SO MUCH!
BUT IF YOU INTERFERE WITH MY PLANS, I'LL KNOCK YOU OVER LIKE RATS- YOU'LL GET WHAT POPEYE GOT!
MR. SNORK- WHERE IS BERNICE, MY WHIFFLE HEN?
I DON'T KNOW- BUT I DO KNOW WHERE I WISH SHE WAS
COME HERE, BERNICE, OLD GAL- LEMME RUB THEM THREE HAIRS FOR LUCK
HEAVEN KNOWS I NEED SOME LUCK RIGHT ABOUT NOW! BLOW ME DOWN!
5-16
SEGAR

THIMBLE THEATER

NOW SHOWING—A DEAD WEIGHT.
Tomorrow—The Departed and the Departing.

HEY, SNORK - I THOUGHT YOU SAID YOU SHOT POPEYE - WHERE IS HE?
HE'S AFT - RIGHT WHERE HE FELL
HE IS NOT!! HE IS NOT BACK AFT! I'VE LOOKED EVERYWHERE
WHAT HAVE YOU DONE WITH POOR POPEYE? YOU MONSTER!
SEE - HE ISN'T HERE
I SUPPOSE HE ROLLED INTO THE OCEAN - IF SO YOU'LL NEVER FIND HIM - HE'S SO FULL OF LEAD HE'D SINK LIKE AN ANCHOR
5-17
SEGAR

THIMBLE THEATER

DEPARTING.
Monday—Moans in the Night

SNORK - LOWEST MONSTER THAT EVER LIVED — THE PURE OCEAN BREEZES BECOME FOUL WITH EVILNESS AFTER PASSING WITHIN ELEVEN FEET OF HIS WICKED BODY —
HE'S JUST A LITTLE WORRIED BECAUSE HE CAN'T FIND POPEYE'S REMAINS —
'SMIGHTY FUNNY! HE FELL RIGHT HERE - BUT HE ISN'T HERE
DO YOU REALIZE THAT THIS FELLOW SNORK IS PLANNING TO TAKE ALL OUR MONEY? THERE'S A YACHT FOLLOWING US - DID YOU KNOW THAT?
YES, I KNOW - IT WAS A PLOT FROM THE VERY BEGINNING - BUT IT DOESN'T PAY TO GET ROUGH - YOU KNOW WHAT POPEYE GOT
POPEYE WAS RIGHT! HE WARNED US! POOR POPEYE!
WHY DIDN'T WE LISTEN TO HIM?
I'D BETTER GET THROUGH WITH THIS JOB - I'LL SIGNAL FADEWELL'S YACHT, GRAB THE CASH AND BE OFF FOR PARTS UNKNOWN
SEGAR
5-18

THIMBLE THEATER

NOW SHOWING—MOANS IN THE NIGHT.
Tomorrow—Three Wise Birds.

WHAT THE HECK'S THAT ??!
WHAT THE HECK'S THAT ?!
WHAT THE HECK IS THAT ?!
OOOOOO
THERE IT IS AGAIN! GOOD HEAVENS! WHAT CAN IT BE?
OUW
DON'T MENTION SUCH THINGS! DON'T TALK LIKE THAT!
SNORK, DO YOU BELIEVE IN GHOSTS? I THOUGHT I HEARD POPEYE MOANING
HE'S A BAD GUY WHEN THE SUN SHINES, BUT HE AIN'T SO MUCH AT NIGHT
WHIFFLE!
OUUW
© 1929, King Features Syndicate, Inc. Great Britain rights reserved.
5-20
E. C. SEGAR

THIMBLE THEATER
NOW SHOWING—THREE WISE BIRDS.
Tomorrow—The Ghost Talks.

YOU THINK IT'S A GHOST? YOU THINK IT MAYBE MIGHT POSSIBLY COULD BE A GHOST?
A GHOST ON A SHIP! MY GOSH! NO PLACE TO RUN! GHOSTS ASHORE IS BAD ENOUGH
THERE AIN'T NO SUCH THINGS AS GHOSTS! YA' THINK IT COULD BE A GHOST HAM?
OUUUUW
GHOSTS CAN'T MAKE A NOISE!! THEY AIN'T GOT NO LARYNXES! YA' GOTTA HAVE A LARYNX!
IT'S COMING OUT OF THE HOLD—AND IT SOUNDS LIKE POPEYE'S VOICE. SOMEBODY SHOULD GO DOWN AND SEE
OOOOUW
YEAH—SOMEBODY, MOST ANYBODY BUT NOT ME—I'M THE CAPTAIN AND I'VE GOT TO STAY ON DECK AND WATCH FOR STORMS—
I'M ONLY A PASSENGER, BESIDES LADIES DON'T GO DOWN INTO SHIPS' HOLDS
JUST THINK OF ME AS BEING SOMEPLACE ELSE. I AIN'T EVEN WITH YOU—
Great Britain rights reserved
© 1929, King Features Syndicate, Inc.
SEGAR
5-21

THIMBLE THEATER
NOW SHOWING—THE GHOST TALKS.
Tomorrow—Rubbing to Erase Lead Marks.

IT'S A GHOST! A GHOST SUFFERING THE TORMENTS OF TEN BILLION DEMONS! A SOUL IN AGONY FROM THE TORTURES OF——
SHUT UP!!
OOOOOUW
LISTEN—YOU STOP BEING LIKE THAT OR THERE'S GOING TO BE ANOTHER GHOST ON THIS SHIP—A RUNT GHOST
IT DOES SOUND LIKE POPEYE'S VOICE—HE'S COME BACK TO HAUNT ME
OOUW
OH—HOW I WISH IT WAS DAYLIGHT I'LL GO NUTS IN ABOUT A MINUTE
OOUW
QUICK, BERNICE! I NEED LUCK—LET ME RUB THEM THREE HAIRS—LEMME RUB THE WHIFFLE
OUW
Great Britain rights reserved.
© 1929, King Features Syndicate, Inc.
5-22
SEGAR

THIMBLE THEATER
NOW SHOWING—RUBBING TO ERASE LEAD MARKS.
Tomorrow—A Crime Wave.

THERE IT IS AGAIN! WHAT A NIGHT!
OOOUUW
SAY, SNORK—MAYBE POPEYE ISN'T DEAD—MAYBE THAT'S HIM GROANING. YOU SHOULDN'T HAVE SHOT POOR OLD POPEYE
I PLUGGED HIM FIFTEEN TIMES—SELF DEFENSE YOU KNOW—ALWAYS REMEMBER THAT—SELF DEFENSE—HE'S DEAD ALL RIGHT
WELL—GHOSTS DON'T GROAN—BECAUSE THEY AIN'T GOT NO LARYNXES
AW, IT'S ONLY THE OLD TIMBERS OF THE SHIP MAKING THAT NOISE
COME HERE, BERNICE, I NEED MORE LUCK
WHIFFLE.
BY RUBBING THE WHIFFLE, I MAY GET ENOUGH LUCK TO PULL ME THROUGH
SEGAR

THIMBLE THEATER
NOW SHOWING—A CRIME WAVE.
Tomorrow—Metal for the Meddlesome.

I DON'T KNOW WHAT ALL THAT GROANING WAS BUT I'LL NOT STAY ON THIS SHIP ANOTHER NIGHT
I'LL SIGNAL TO FADEWELL AND BE DONE WITH THIS JOB- POPEYE S OUT OF THE WAY AND I CAN HANDLE THE REST
WHAT'S SNORK DOING WITH THAT BLACK FLAG ?
WHAT'S HE WAVING IT LIKE THAT FOR? SIGNALING!!
AH- THERE'S SNORK'S SIGNAL- EVERYTHING IS READY- I'LL PULL ALONGSIDE IMMEDIATELY
5-24
SEGAR

THIMBLE THEATER
NOW SHOWING—METAL FOR THE MEDDLESOME.
Monday—The "Heel" and a Healer.

HEY, CASTOR-SNORK'S BACK AFT WAVING A BLACK FLAG!
WHAT'S HE DOING THAT FOR? - WHAT THU-? WHAT THU — ?!
HE'S SIGNALING SOMEBODY - 'SMUTINY!
'SMUTINY!
HEY THERE, SNORK- WHAT'S GOING ON HERE? WHAT'S COMING OFF?
YOU'LL FIND OUT- YOU SAPS! AND WATCH YOUR STEPS OR I'LL FILL YOU FULL OF LEAD LIKE I DID POPEYE - I'M A HARD MAN!
'SMUTINY JUST LIKE I SAID
5-25
SEGAR

THIMBLE THEATER
NOW SHOWING—THE "HEEL" AND A HEALER.
Tomorrow—He Who Gets Slapped.

SO IT'S MUTINY IS IT? MUTINY, EH?
YAS- IT'S MUTINY-AND IT MAY BE WORSE- ONE FALSE MOVE AND YOU'LL EAT LEAD
I HAVE SIGNALED TO FADEWELL'S YACHT-HE WILL PULL ALONGSIDE, AND RELIEVE YOU OF THOSE BAGS OF CASH- THEN WE'LL SINK YOUR SHIP —
AND YOU CAN ALL SINK WITH IT OR SWIM THREE THOUSAND MILES TO THE NEAREST LAND
YOU RAT!
YOU DOG!
YOU SNAKE !!
BEFORE I DIE, I'M GOING TO TAKE ONE MORE CRACK AT THAT GUY'S CHIN. COME HERE, BERNICE!
WHIFFLE
I'VE GOTTER RUB THE WHIFFLE! I SURE NEED LUCK
5-27
SEGAR

THIMBLE THEATER

NOW SHOWING—HE WHO GETS SLAPPED.
Tomorrow—The Shimmy Queen.

YOU BIG BRUTE! I'VE GOT A GOOD NOTION TO SMACK YOUR FACE
JUST TRY THAT
HEY! CUT THAT OUT! HEY! CUT THAT OUT!
HEY! STOP DOING IT!
HEY! CUT THAT OUT!
BANG
BANG
BANG
HALP
5-28
SEGAR

THIMBLE THEATER

NOW SHOWING—THE SHIMMY QUEEN.
Tomorrow—Do a "Hole" Job.

WILL YOU KEEP OUT OF MY WAY!?
BANG
BANG
BANG
BANG!
AS I WAS SAYING-NO DUMB DAME LIKE YOU CAN SMACK MY FACE AND NOT PAY!!
HALP!
SAY, HAM, I'VE GOT A GUN IN MY CABIN-I THINK I'LL BLOW THAT GUY UP!
O.K. WITH ME
I HEARD SHOTS-SOMETHING'S WRONG UP THERE-I GOTTER CRAWL ON DECK AND SOCK SNORK ON THE CHIN JUST ONCT MORE BEFORE I DIE
5-29
SEGAR

THIMBLE THEATER

NOW SHOWING—DO A "HOLE" JOB.
Tomorrow—Shell-Shocked Castor.

IT'S HARD SAILING AND ME WIND AIN'T RIGHT BUT I MUST GET ON DECK! SOMETHING'S GOING ON
WHIFFLE
I'LL HAVE TO RUB THE WHIFFLE AGAIN-BERNICE, I NEED ALL THE LUCK YOU'VE GOT
SO YOU THOUGHT YOU COULD SLAP MY FACE AND MAKE ME LIKE IT, EH?!
HALP!
SAY, IF YOU'VE GOT A GUN IN YOUR BUNK YOU'D BETTER GET IT AND SHOOT SNORK. WE CAN'T LET HIM HANDLE OLIVE THAT WAY
YEAH, I GUESS I'D BETTER
YA' THINK I OUGHTA SHOOT HIM DEAD, OR JUST CRIPPLE HIM FOR LIFE?
SHOOT HIM DEAD! DON'T NEVER DO THINGS BY HALVES
5-30
SEGAR

THIMBLE THEATER

NOW SHOWING—SHELL-SHOCKED CASTOR.
Tomorrow—The Exterminator.

THIS IS GOOD FUN! HEH! HEH! I LOVE TO CHOKE DUMB DAMES! I LIKE IT!!
SLAP MY FACE. WILL YOU?!
HALP!
HEY, HAM-YA THINK I OUGHTA SHOOT 'IM IN FRONT OR IN BACK?
EITHER WAY'S O.K., CASTOR, GO ON, DO YOUR STUFF
TAKE GOOD AIM AND DON'T HIT YOUR SISTER!
DON'T GET COLD FEET
SAY, MAYBE I'D BETTER POISON HIM
HALP!
5-31
SEGAR

THIMBLE THEATER

NOW SHOWING—THE EXTERMINATOR.
Monday—Protecting a Lady's Molars.

H-A-L-P!
COME ON, CASTOR-DON'T STALL AROUND LIKE THAT-GIVE HIM THE WORKS
SAY, HAM! MAYBE YOU'D BETTER SHOOT HIM
HALP!
NO-IT'S YOUR GUN I NEVER USE OTHER PEOPLE'S GUNS!
O.K. HERE GOES
HURRY UP, CASTOR, BEFORE HE SHAKES HER TEETH OUT
I THINK I'D BETTER SNEAK UP ON HIM-I WANT TO MAKE A "GOOD CLEAN JOB" OF THIS
HALP!
6-1
SEGAR

THIMBLE THEATER

NOW SHOWING—PROTECTING A LADY'S MOLARS.
Tomorrow—The Empty Barrel.

YEAH-I WANT TO MAKE A GOOD CLEAN JOB OF THIS SO I'D BETTER SNEAK UP ON HIM
SLIP UP BEHIND HIM, CASTOR-TAKE GOOD AIM AND DON'T HIT OLIVE
HE CAN'T CHOKE MY SISTER-NOT WHILE I'M CAPTAIN OF THIS SHIP!
GOOD NIGHT! LOOK AT CASTOR!! I'D BETTER GET THE BROOM AND DUST PAN
I'M A BAD GUY-AND AS A RULE I DON'T STAND FOR DUMB DAMES SLAPPING MY FACE-IN JUST ABOUT A MINUTE I'M GOING TO SHAKE YOUR TEETH OUT
HALP!
SEGAR
6-3

THIMBLE THEATER
NOW SHOWING—THE EMPTY BARREL.
Tomorrow—Blank Cartridges.

I'D BE WILLING TO CROAK IF I COULD GET ONE MORE "SOCK" AT SNORK
THE WORLD WILL SOON BE RID OF THE WORST SNAKE THAT EVER BREATHED- CASTOR'S GETTING READY TO PULL THE TRIGGER
?
CLICK
WHAT THU-?!
SEGAR 6-4

THIMBLE THEATER
NOW SHOWING—BLANK CARTRIDGES.
Tomorrow—Blows and Shots.

WELL- WHAT IN THE ~~~ !?! WELL I'LL BE -!!
CLICK CLICK CLICK
GOOD NIGHT! I FORGOT TO LOAD IT!!
WAIT'LL I GET SOME BULLETS! JUST WAIT'LL I GET SOME BULLETS
6-5 SEGAR

THIMBLE THEATER
NOW SHOWING—BLOWS AND SHOTS.
Tomorrow—The Smoke Screen.

JUST WAIT TILL I GET SOME BULLETS
SOCK
BANG BANG BANG BANG
SEGAR 6-6

THIMBLE THEATER
NOW SHOWING—THE SMOKE SCREEN.
Tomorrow—Out of Range.

BANG BANG BANG
BANG
WELL-THAT'S THAT-WHEN THE SMOKE CLEARS AWAY-YOU CAN GET A BROOM AND SWEEP 'IM UP
HOPE YOU DIDN'T MISS HIM
?
STICK 'EM UP
6-7

THIMBLE THEATER
NOW SHOWING—OUT OF RANGE.
Monday—Bullet-Proof.

I GUESS OUR GOOSES ARE COOKED!
GEESE, YOU IGNORANT SAP, NOT GOOSES
YES-I'M THROUGH TRIFLING WITH YOU. I'LL TAKE NO MORE CHANCES
I DON'T KNOW WHAT FADEWELL WILL DO WITH YOU - HIS YACHT WILL BE ALONG SIDE ANY MINUTE NOW
MOVE EVEN ONE SIXTEENTH OF AN INCH AND I'LL CUT LOOSE
6-8

THIMBLE THEATER
NOW SHOWING—BULLET-PROOF.
Tomorrow—Popeye Gives Till It Hurts.

ALL OUR TROUBLE FOR NOTHING
OLD FADEWELL WILL TAKE EVERY CENT OF OUR MILLIONS
YOU'LL BE LUCKY IF YOU GET HOME WITH YOUR LIVES- FADEWELL'S YACHT WILL BE HERE IN A MINUTE AND HE'S A HARD MAN
WHY POPEYE! I THOUGHT YOU WERE SHOT!!
WELL— WHATCHER THINK THESE IS, BUTTON HOLES?
GOOD HEAVENS! HE'S ALIVE
AND NOW SNORKY, JUST AS SOON AS I RUB THE WHIFFLE FOR LUCK- I'LL TAKE YOU ON!
I MUST BE DREAMING! POPEYE YOU'RE DEAD I SHOT YOU FIFTEEN TIMES
6-10

THIMBLE THEATER

NOW SHOWING—POPEYE GIVES TILL IT HURTS.

Tomorrow—A Disabled Accomplice.

LOOK POPEYE'S RUBBING THE WHIFFLE FOR LUCK
YOU CAN'T BE ALIVE! I SHOT YOU FIFTEEN TIMES!
SIXTEEN
BANG
A COUPLA BULLETS MORE OR LESS AIN'T GONNER STOP ME NOW, SNORK. I'M AFTER YOUR NECK!
YOU DEMON!
WHIFFLE!
6-11
SEGAR

THIMBLE THEATER

NOW SHOWING—A DISABLED ACCOMPLICE.

Tomorrow—Snork, the Ship Wreck.

ATTA BOY. POPEYE. SOCK IT TO 'IM!
BOP
BIFF
WHIFFLE!
SOCK
SOCK
GOOD WORK. YOU CRACKED HIM UP GOOD
I GUESS SNORK WON'T BOTHER US ANY MORE
WHIFFLE
LOOK, POPEYE, FADEWELL'S YACHT IS PULLING ALONGSIDE
CURSES!
SEGAR
© 1929, King Features Syndicate, Inc., Great Britain rights reserved.
6-12

THIMBLE THEATER

NOW SHOWING—SNORK, THE SHIPWRECK.

Tomorrow—The Bigger They Come, the Harder They Fall.

FADEWELL'S YACHT IS ALONGSIDE!
AND FADEWELL IS COMING ON BOARD
HEY, YOU BIG CHEESE! WHAT DO YOU MEAN BY BOARDING MY SHIP WITHOUT MY PERMISSION?! I'M THE CAPTAIN
I CAME TO RELIEVE YOU OF THOSE BAGS OF CASH. WHERE'S MY MAN SNORK?
I THOUGHT HE HAD IT ALL FIXED!! WHERE IS SNORK?
HERE'S SNORK- HE AIN'T FEELIN' SO GOOD TO-DAY- HAD A LITTLE 'GO' WITH A TOUGH SAILOR- EVERY TIME HE COMES TO, I KNOCK 'IM OUT AGAIN SO YOU'D BETTER TAKE 'IM ALONG BEFORE I LOSE MY TEMPER
6-13
SEGAR

THIMBLE THEATER

NOW SHOWING—THE BIGGER THEY COME, THE HARDER THEY FALL.

Tomorrow—A Glutton for Punishment.

FADEWELL- GET OFF OF MY SHIP- GET ABOARD YOUR YACHT AND BE GONE, YOU PIRATE
THE FACT THAT SNORK HAS FAILED MEANS NOTHING TO ME - I CAME FOR THAT MONEY AND I'M GOING TO GET IT!
YOU AIN'T GO'NER !
STEP ASIDE, YOU GNAT!
LOOK OUT, POPEYE, HE'S A BIG HEAVY BRUTE - HE'LL TEAR YOU TO PIECES!
SOCK
CLICK
JUST A COUPLA POPS AND HE WENT OUT- I LIKES 'EM BIG
6·14
SEGAR

THIMBLE THEATER

NOW SHOWING—A GLUTTON FOR PUNISHMENT.

Monday—Swiss Cheese Isn't Strong.

POPEYE, YOU'RE A BRAVE MAN, AND YOU SURE CAN FIGHT!
I KNOCK 'EM GOOD. I'LL SAY THAT
HE'S A MAN ALL RIGHT! IF HE WASN'T SUCH A FUNNY LOOKIN' THING, I'D GIVE HIM A KISS
SAY, HASN'T SNORK AND FADEWELL COME TO YET?
THEY'VE BEEN OUT TWO HOURS-! HA! HA! WHEN POPEYE SOCKS 'EM, THEY'RE 'SOCKED'
HOW ABOUT BRINGIN' 'EM TO SO I CAN KNOCK 'EM OUT AGAIN? I AIN'T QUITE SATCHISFIED YET
SEGAR
6·15

THIMBLE THEATER

NOW SHOWING—SWISS CHEESE ISN'T STRONG.

Tomorrow—The Fallen Hero.

WOT'LL I DO WITH 'EM, SKIPPER? THEY'RE COMIN' OUT OF IT
WHERE AM I?
LET 'EM LOOK AT THIS MONEY TILL THEY GET SICK AND THEN THROW 'EM OVER THE SIDE INTO THEIR YACHT
YOU'RE NEXT, SNORK - OVER YOU GO
AND THANKS TO POPEYE, OUR MONEY IS STILL ON BOARD THE GOOD SHIP "TOM COD"
WHIFFLE!
I AIN'T FEELIN' SO GOOD WITH THESE SIXTEEN BULLET HOLES IN ME - I CAN'T STAND WHAT I US'TER
SEGAR
6·17

THIMBLE THEATER

NOW SHOWING—THE FALLEN HERO.
Tomorrow—Silence Would Be Golden.

HEY EVERYBODY— LET'S GIVE THREE CHEERS FOR POPEYE!
THREE CHEERS ME EYE - THAT WON'T HELP A GUY WITH SIXTEEN BULLET HOLES IN HIM
WHAT I NEEDS IS THREE DOCTORS, NOT THREE CHEERS
POPEYE!
PLOP
HERE, POPEYE - RUB THE WHIFFLE FOR LUCK - QUICK. RUB THE WHIFFLE!
TOO LATE! TOO LATE NOTHIN' WILL HELP ME NOW - I'VE LOST TOO MUCH "RED INK" - BLOW ME DOWN, I'M COOKED!
6-18
SEGAR

THIMBLE THEATER

NOW SHOWING—SILENCE WOULD BE GOLDEN.
Tomorrow—There's Still a Kick in the Old Mule.

COME ON, POPEYE — DON'T PASS OUT ON US! RUB THE WHIFFLE, IT MAY PULL YOU THROUGH, MAY GIVE YOU ENOUGH LUCK
JUST LEMME BE- LEMME BE!
LOOK, POPEYE, YOU MUST LIVE - WE'RE GOING TO CUT YOU IN ON ALL THIS MONEY YOU'LL GET YOUR SHARE
I'M TIRED OF THIS WORLD, BLOW ME DOWN CAN'TCHER LEMME BE!!?
THIS CERTAINLY HAS BEEN A TRAGIC TRIP
I'M AFRAID HE CAN'T PULL THROUGH SIXTEEN BULLET WOUNDS IS SOMETHING!
WHIFFLE!
DON'T LAY SO STILL LIKE THAT, SPEAK TO ME!
AW, SHUT UP!
6-19
SEGAR

THIMBLE THEATER

NOW SHOWING—THERE'S STILL A KICK IN THE Old Mule.
Tomorrow—Both in the Same Boat.

IT'S A MYSTERY TO ME HOW HE EVER LASTED THIS LONG - POOR POPEYE.
EVEN A COUPLA BULLETS WOULD HAVE KILLED MOST MEN
COME ON, HAM - WE CAN'T LET HIM LAY THERE AND DIE LIKE THAT - NOT ON THE HARD COLD DECK
WE'LL TAKE HIM INTO MY ROOM AND MAKE HIM COMFORTABLE
WE CAN'T MAKE HIM COMFORTABLE WITH SIXTEEN BULLETS IN HIS SYSTEM
LISTEN - KEEP YOUR HOOKS OFFA ME - I'M GO'NER DIE RIGHT HERE - SEE?
WELL, CAN YOU BEAT THAT!!
GEE! WHAT A STUBBORN GUY!
WHIFFLE
IF YOU DON'T LEMME BE, I'M GO'NER SMACK YA' ONE!
6-20
SEGAR

THIMBLE THEATER

NOW SHOWING—BOTH IN THE SAME BOAT.
Tomorrow—A Cured Patient.

HAM, PICK HIM UP AND CARRY HIM IN TO MY BED - I DON'T WANT IT SAID THAT I LET POOR OLD POPEYE LAY OUT HERE ON THE HARD COLD DECK AND DIE
YES, I'D BETTER DO THAT, JUST THINK, SIXTEEN BULLET HOLES IN HIM - HE'S SLIPPING AWAY FAST
I'LL HAVE TO HANDLE HIM GENTLY - EVEN NOW HE MAY BE BREATHING HIS LAST
WHAT THU-!
SAY- HOW MANY TIMES DO I GOTTER TELL YA' TO LAY OFF - I'M GO'NER DIE RIGHT HERE
I'VE LIVED ON DECK AND I'M GO'NER DIE ON DECK
OUW! SOMEBODY PUT ME TO BED!
I'M GETTIN' TIRED OF ARGUING WITH YOU GUYS! NOW LEMME BE!
6-21
SEGAR

THIMBLE THEATER

NOW SHOWING—A CURED PATIENT.
Monday—Excess Baggage.

NOBODY CAN LIVE WITH SIXTEEN BULLETS IN HIS BODY
CASTOR, WHAT ON EARTH ARE YOU GOING TO DO?
CLINK
CLANK
OPERATE
CLINK
DOGGONE IT! I REALLY OUGHTA HAVE MORE TOOLS
?
HEY, OLIVE— BRING THE CAN-OPENER THAT OUGHT TO BE GOOD
!
HELP! SOMEBODY DO SOMETHING!
SEGAR
6-22

THIMBLE THEATER

NOW SHOWING—EXCESS BAGGAGE.
Tomorrow—Children of Fortune.

HE CAN'T LAST MUCH LONGER- HE'LL PROBABLY TOPPLE OVER TO-DAY
HOW DO YOU FEEL THIS A.M. POPEYE?
I NEVER FELT BETTER IN ME LIFE— IT TAKES MORE'N SIXTEEN BULLETS TO SINK OLD POPEYE - BLOW ME DOWN. IT DO!
I'LL THROW A FEW MORE SHEETS TO THE WIND AND WE'RE ALL GO'NER BE HOME IN THREE WEEKS
HE ISN'T GOING TO CROAK. CAN YOU BEAT THAT!
THREE WEEKS LATER—
HOME!
MONEY AND THE OLD WHIFFLE TOO ALL SAFE HOME
GO HIRE A TRUCK, POPEYE, WE'VE GOT TO GET THIS MONEY HOME BEFORE DARK
WHIFFLE
AYE. AYE, CAP'N
6-24
SEGAR

THIMBLE THEATER
NOW SHOWING—CHILDREN OF FORTUNE.
Tomorrow—Dear Ol' Dad.

OUGHTA BE HEARIN' FROM OUR KIDS SOON, EH, PA?
OH, THEY'LL BE POPPIN' IN ON US FOR FREE BOARD BEFORE MANY DAYS BROKE AS USUAL. I'LL BET ON THAT
RIGHT THIS WAY, MEN, DUMP IT OVER HERE
?
?
'LO FOLKS
SEGAR 6-25

THIMBLE THEATER
NOW SHOWING—DEAR OL' DAD.
Tomorrow—The "Height" of Fashion.

JUST LOOK AT THE BAGS OF LIBERTY OUR BOY BROUGHT HOME!
H-M-M-M - I ALWAYS SAID MY BOY WOULD AMOUNT TO SOMETHING! YEP - I ALWAYS SAID THAT
WHY, PAW, YOU'VE SAID A HUNDRED TIMES THAT HE'D NEVER BE WORTH THE GRAVY ON HIS VEST
WELL, SON, NOW THAT YOU'VE GOT MILLIONS AND MILLIONS OF DOLLARS, WHAT ARE YOU GOING TO DO?
ABSOLUTELY NOTHING
AND TO PROVE THAT I'M A REAL FATHER - I'LL QUIT MY JOB AND HELP YOU
SEGAR 6-26

THIMBLE THEATER
NOW SHOWING—THE "HEIGHT" OF FASHION.
Tomorrow—Yes, Sir, That's His Baby.

YOU MEAN THAT, CAP'N? YOU MEAN THAT?
SURE I MEAN IT, POPEYE, HERE'S A MILLION BUCKS FOR YOU
CAP'N OYL YOU'RE A FINE MAN - AND IF YOU EVER WANT OLD POPEYE, YOU'LL FIND HIM DOWN AT THE DOCKS SHOOTIN CRAPS - LEMME KNOW WHEN YOU NEEDS A FREN'
O-K
WELL WHAT IN THE—?! OH, I SEE - OLIVE'S BEEN SHOPPING FOR HERSELF - BOY! AIN'T SHE WARM!
WHIFFLE !?!
WELL, FER CRYIN' OUT LOUD!
!
SAYS WHICH?
6-27
SEGAR

THIMBLE THEATER

NOW SHOWWING—YES, SIR, THAT'S HIS BABY.

Tomorrow—The Gal's Gonna Have Her Fling.

WHOISHEE, CASTOR? I DIDN'T KNOW WE HAD COMPANY
CANTCHA TELL ME WHO THE DAME IS? WHY DON'T YOU INTERDUCE ME?
NO KIDDIN, DON'T YOU KNOW?
DON'T BE A SAP, FATHER, I'M YOUR DAUGHTER, OLIVE
EVERYBODY BRING WATER!!
THE IDEA! WHY THE VERY IDEA!
SEGAR
6-28

THIMBLE THEATER

NOW SHOWING—THE GAL'S GONNA HAVE HER FLING.

Monday—A Dutiful Daughter.

WHAT'S GOING ON HERE, CASTOR? WHAT'S COMING OFF?
IT'S ONLY DAD - HE'S GIVING OLIVE THE OLD THUNDER ABOUT DECENCY
BLA BLA
HE LIKES SHORT SKIRTS OUTSIDE THE FAMILY
AIN'T IT SO
BOY! THE OLD MAN'S HOT!
ALL WOOLED UP
NEXT THING YOU'LL BE PAINTIN' YOUR FACE AND SMOKIN' CIGARETTES
AND CHEWING TOBACCO, IF I TAKE A NOTION - I'M RICH - AND FROM NOW ON I'M GONNA LIVE!
6-29
SEGAR

THIMBLE THEATER

NOW SHOWING—A DUTIFUL DAUGHTER.

Tomorrow—The Ruler.

LISTEN AT HIM!
YEAH HE LIKES SHORT SKIRTS OUTSIDE THE FAMILY
NOW AIN'T YOU A HOT SKETCH? THAT DRESS WOULDN'T EVEN MAKE A DECENT BATHING SUIT
IT AIN'T FIT! AND THAT'S ALL THERE IS TO IT AIN'T FIT.
I LIKE IT!
NO DAUGHTER OF MINE CAN WEAR A DRESS LIKE THAT - TAKE IT OFF - YOU HEAR ME? TAKE IT OFF
HONEST TO PETE! YOU'RE THE LIMIT
7-1
SEGAR

THIMBLE THEATER

NOW SHOWING—THE RULER.

Tomorrow—Pa Doesn't Cover Much Space.

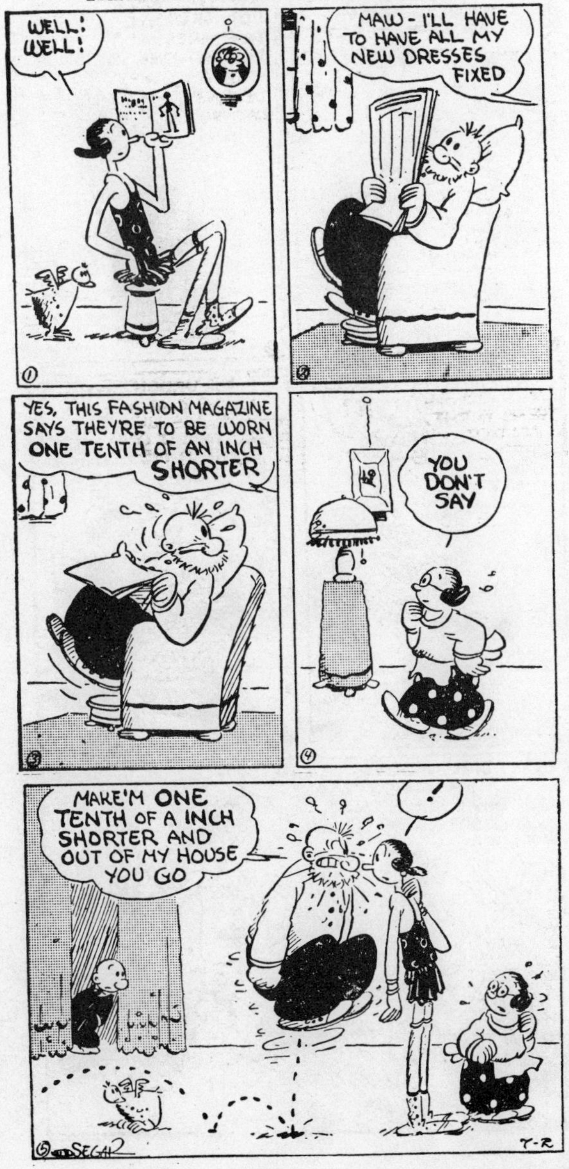

WELL! WELL!
MAW - I'LL HAVE TO HAVE ALL MY NEW DRESSES FIXED
YES, THIS FASHION MAGAZINE SAYS THEY'RE TO BE WORN ONE TENTH OF AN INCH SHORTER
YOU DON'T SAY
MAKE'M ONE TENTH OF A INCH SHORTER AND OUT OF MY HOUSE YOU GO
!

THIMBLE THEATER

NOW SHOWING—PA DOESN'T COVER MUCH SPACE.

Tomorrow—Covering a Multitude of Shins.

YOU'RE SURE DRESSING IN STYLE SINCE WE GOT A PILE OF CASH, AIN'T YOU, SIS?
CLOTHES MAKE THE WOMAN - THERE'S NO DENYING THAT
WHY SHOULDN'T I BE "PERTY" LIKE OTHER GIRLS?
SURE
AIN'T I A PIP? AIN'T I, CASTOR?
YOU'RE A PIP—
FROM THE EYEBROWS UP

THIMBLE THEATER

NOW SHOWING—COVERING A MULTITUDE OF SHINS.

Tomorrow—The Unwelcome Suitor.

YOU'RE NOT GOING OUT IN THAT - YOU WANT TO DISGRACE A NICE YOUNG MAN LIKE HAM? GO PUT ON A DIFFERENT DRESS
GOOD NIGHT!
WHERE'D YOU GET THAT?
WELL - NOW THAT'S BETTER - S'MUCH BETTER!
WAIT A MINUTE, HAM
LE'S GO

THIMBLE THEATER

NOW SHOWING—THE UNWELCOME SUITOR.
Tomorrow—Cut That Out, Olive.

HAM'S A NICE YOUNG MAN AND YOU CAN'T GO OUT WITH HIM IN THAT OUTFIT
YOU HEARD ME, GAL
GEE, I OUGHT TO SAY SOMETHING TO HELP OLIVE, POOR KID
THE IDEA! GOIN' OUT IN A DRESS LIKE THAT WITH A NICE BOY LIKE HAM! YOU'D DISGRACE HIM
S'ALL RIGHT MR. OYL, S'ALL RIGHT— I AIN'T SO NICE
OH, YA AIN'T HUH!!
WHAT THA—?!
SEGAR 7-5

THIMBLE THEATER

NOW SHOWING—CUT THAT OUT, OLIVE.
Monday—Lamp the Impersonation.

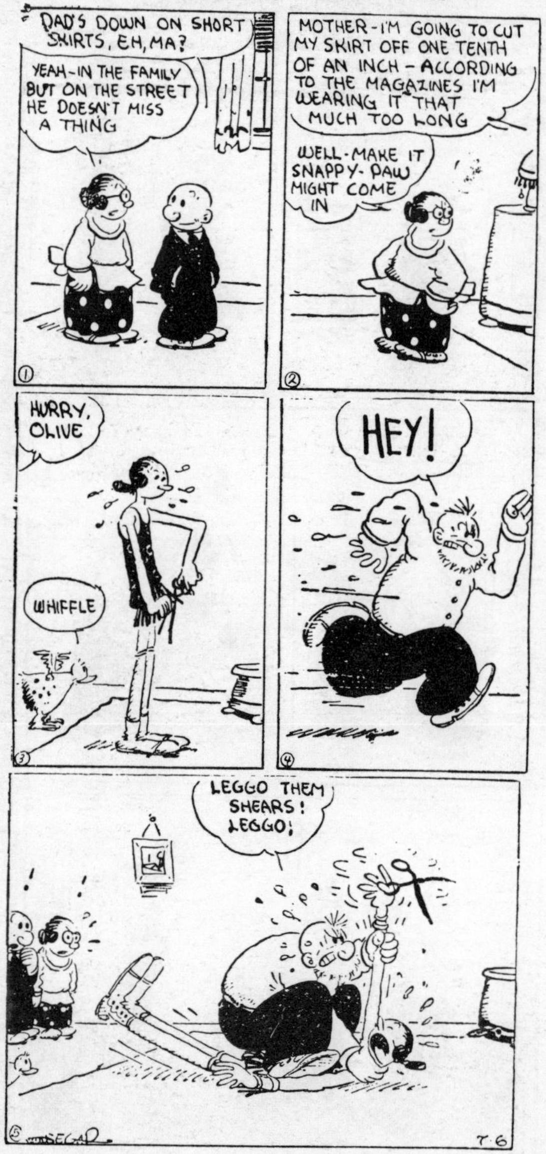

DAD'S DOWN ON SHORT SKIRTS, EH, MA?
YEAH—IN THE FAMILY BUT ON THE STREET HE DOESN'T MISS A THING
MOTHER—I'M GOING TO CUT MY SKIRT OFF ONE TENTH OF AN INCH—ACCORDING TO THE MAGAZINES I'M WEARING IT THAT MUCH TOO LONG
WELL—MAKE IT SNAPPY—PAW MIGHT COME IN
HURRY, OLIVE
WHIFFLE
HEY!
LEGGO THEM SHEARS! LEGGO!
SEGAR
7-6

THIMBLE THEATER

NOW SHOWING—LAMP THE IMPERSONATION.
Tomorrow—Socks.

HOW DO YOU LIKE MY NEW DRESS, MOTHER? AIN'T IT HOT?
YEAH, IT'S SO HOT IT BURNS ME UP! YOU SHOULD SEE YOURSELF!! I'LL BET YOU NEVER USE A MIRROR
PAW, YOU KEEP YOUR MOUTH SHUT AND LET OLIVE ALONE
DON'T LISTEN TO HIM, HONEY, HE'S OUT OF HIS HEAD—ALL WET FROM THE EARS UP
THIS IS JUST THE WAY YOU LOOK—NO—YOU DON'T LOOK THIS GOOD BECAUSE YOU AIN'T GOT MY FIGURE
NAW—DON'T DO THAT MA, NOT THAT!
YOU HEARD ME—GO GET THE SHOT GUN!
SEGAR 7-8

THIMBLE THEATER
NOW SHOWING—SOCKS.
Tomorrow—Fashion Hints.

SIX INCHES SHORTER WOULD BE O.K. WOULDN'T IT, MOTHER?
HALF A FOOT SHORTER WOULD BE ALL RIGHT - I HEAR THEY'RE GOING TO WEAR 'EM MUCH SHORTER
I'LL DO MURDER! SO HELP ME, I'LL DO MURDER!
GET OUTTA HERE YOU OLD PRUNE - WE WAS TALKING ABOUT STOCKINGS
GIVE IT TO HIM - MA!
SEGAR

THIMBLE THEATER
NOW SHOWING—FASHION HINTS.
Tomorrow—The Fortune Hunter.

MONEY WILL BE THE RUINATION OF MY DAUGHTER. THERE SHOULD BE A LAW AGAINST WEARIN' THEM DRESSES
THIS IS THE VERY LATEST PAW - YOU SHOULD BE PROUD OF ME
WHIFFLE
PAW - YOU LET OLIVE ALONE - QUIT HARPIN' AT'ER ALL THE TIME - YOU AIN'T GOT NO SENSE ANYWAY!
ALL RIGHT - I QUIT - I'M DONE! I'M THROUGH!
NEVER MIND, HONEY, DON'T PAY ANY ATTENTION TO HIM
YOU CAN GO DOWN MAIN STREET YELLIN' FIRE IN YOUR DEE-VEE-BEES FOR ALL I GIVE A WHOOP!
SEGAR
Great Britain rights reserved.
© 1929, King Features Syndicate, Inc.

THIMBLE THEATER
NOW SHOWING—THE FORTUNE HUNTER.
Tomorrow—A Fisherman Looking for Fish.

I DO WISH SOME HANDSOME MAN WOULD FALL IN LOVE WITH ME - HAM'S ALL RIGHT BUT HE HAS NO IMAGINATION
HE DON'T NEED ANY
NEVER MIND, HONEY, SOME DAY A SWELL PRINCE WILL SEE YOU AND THEN ——
BROKE—! JULIUS J. HERRINGBONE - BROKE!
I SUPPOSE I'LL HAVE TO GO TO WORK - IMAGINE A HERRINGBONE WORKING! THE LAST OF THE HERRINGBONES WORKING!
CASTOR OYL, HIS SISTER OLIVE OYL AND HAM GRAVY RETURNED FROM PARTS UNKNOWN WITH A SHIP LOAD OF MONEY IT IS RUMORED THAT — ETC —
OLIVE OYL! WHAT A BEAUTIFUL NAME - AND RICH!

THIMBLE THEATER

NOW SHOWING—A FISHERMAN LOOKING FOR FISH.
Tomorrow—Fisherman's Bait.

THIS ARTICLE STATES THAT SHE IS RICH AND SINGLE-OLIVE OYL WHAT A BEAUTIFUL NAME! IT MAY NOT BE NECESSARY FOR ME TO SEEK EMPLOYMENT AFTER ALL
IMAGINE A HERRINGBONE WORKING - ESPECIALLY JULIUS J. HERRINGBONE
SOMEBODY'S AT THE DOOR, MOTHER
MY NAME IS JULIUS J. HERRINGBONE - THE LAST OF THE HERRINGBONES. YOU HAVE HEARD OF THE HERRINGBONE FAMILY, OF COURSE
HEY, OLIVE, MR. HERRINGFIN IS HERE TO SEE YOU! COME ON IN. HE BRUNG FLOWERS!
!
?!
!
SEGAR
7-12

THIMBLE THEATER

NOW SHOWING—FISHERMAN'S BAIT."
Monday—A Rose Between Two Thorns.

WHO IS THAT BIRD WAITING IN THERE TO SEE, OLIVE!? I WANT TO KNOW!
HE SAYS HIS NAME IS JULIUS J. HERRINGBONE. IT'S A HIGH SOUNDING NAME - I'LL SAY THAT
MAYBE HE'S A SOMEBODY
YA THINK I'M GONNA STAND FOR THAT?! AIN'T ME AND HER BEEN SWEETIES FOR "16" YEARS?!
DON'T BE LIKE THAT, HAM — LAY OFF
HOLD HIM, CASTOR, HE'S GOT RED INK IN HIS EYE!
I'LL MURDER HIM GOOD THAT'S WHAT I'LL DO
7-13

THIMBLE THEATER

NOW SHOWING—A ROSE BETWEEN TWO THORNS.
Tomorrow—A Call to Arms.

THINK I'M GOING TO STAND FOR THIS?! AIN'T ME AND OLIVE BEEN SWEETIES FOR SIXTEEN YEARS OFF AN ON?
BETTER BE CAREFUL, HAM
YES, MISS OLIVE, YOU ARE REALLY MORE BEAUTIFUL THAN I IMAGINED
OH, MY GOSH! YEAH?!
I FELL IN LOVE WITH YOUR NAME WHEN I SAW IT IN THE PAPER-"OLIVE OYL" HOW HEAVENLY!

THIMBLE THEATER

NOW SHOWING—A CALL TO ARMS.

Tomorrow—An Ex-Suitor With No Pull.

LOOK, MA, HAM'S STICKING RIGHT THERE ON THE SOFA WITH THEM- HE WON'T LET THAT NEW FELLOW CUT HIM OUT
THE POOR SAP!
YOU MAY PUT YOUR ARMS AROUND ME, MR. HERRINGBONE
!
SEGAR
7-16

THIMBLE THEATER

NOW SHOWING—AN EX-SUITOR WITH NO PULL.

Tomorrow—The Sugar-Cured Ham.

IT'S TRUE HAM'S BEEN HANGING AROUND FOR SIXTEEN YEARS- BUT HE NEVER GOT SERIOUS TILL OLIVE GOT ANOTHER SWEETY- AND NOW HE'S WILD!
SHE OUGHT TO MARRY JULIUS J. HERRINGBONE. HE COMES FROM A GOOD FAMILY. SO HE SAYS
SURE- THERE'S MILLIONS OF SAPS LIKE HAM GRAVY IN THIS WORLD BUT THERE AIN'T MANY HERRINGBONES
P-S-T- COME HERE IF YOU WANT TO SEE SOME DRAMA! REAL HEAVY DRAMA
SHE'S MINE!!
I'M HIS! I LOVE HIM ONLY!
I'M ALL HIS!
YOU AIN'T- YOU'RE MINE! DOGGONE YOU HERRINGBONE, GIMME MY GAL!
SEGAR
7-17

THIMBLE THEATER

NOW SHOWING—THE SUGAR-CURED HAM.

Tomorrow—Foot Salve.

SHE'S BEEN MY SWEETY- MY SWEETY- FOR SIXTEEN YEARS - BUT NOW - NOW - I DON'T WANT HER!
WHIFFLE
IF YOU DON'T WANT HER, I WANT HER
AW RIGHT- G'WAN TAKE'R!
AND I WISH YOU CAR LOADS OF LUCK- ALL ROTTEN
7-18
SEGAR

THIMBLE THEATER

NOW SHOWING—FOOT SALVE.
Tomorrow—One Too Many.

- AND YOUR EYES ARE BLACK PEARLS
YOUR HAIR IS THREADS OF SILK FROM THE FINEST WORMS OF JAPAN AND SPUN BY FAIRIES
YOUR SLENDER FIGURE HAS THE GRACE OF A SWAN
AND YOUR FEET- YOUR FEEEET-
YES! YES! MY FEET
HE'S STUCK NOW
YOU'RE WORTH MILLIONS OF DOLLARS AREN'T YOU?
I CERTAINLY AM!
-AND YOUR FEET ARE O.K. TOO
SEGAR
7-19

THIMBLE THEATER

NOW SHOWING—ONE TOO MANY.
Monday—It's a "Matrimony."

FATHER, GO TALK TO MR. HERRINGBONE WHILE I SLIP ON ANOTHER DRESS
YES-I SUPPOSE THE HERRINGBONES WERE SOMEBODIES AND ALL THAT- BUT THE OYL FAMILY- WELL- THE OYLS HAVE BEEN RUNNING ALONG SMOOTHLY FOR CENTURIES
PLEASE UNDERSTAND ME - I AM NOT BLOWING - BUT I AM A DIRECT DESCENDANT OF JAMES J. HERRINGBONE JAMES J. FINANCED THE MAYFLOWER AND SAILED WITH HER
WHIFFLE
YES - A GREAT OLD FAMILY- BUT THEY ARE GONE I AM THE LAST
BUNK!
I AM THE LAST OF THE HERRINGBONES
THANK HEAVEN!
SEGAR
7-20

THIMBLE THEATER

NOW SHOWING—IT'S A "MATRIMONY."
Tomorrow——Telling the World.

YOU'RE JEALOUS, HAM, THAT'S WHAT'S EATIN' YOU! HERRINGBONE'S O.K.
OH, I AM NOT!
SURE HE'S O.K. YOU'RE JUST JEALOUS
I'M NOT EITHER! DON'T BE FOOLISH
HERE IS OUR DICE ISLAND MONEY, A THIRD IS YOURS - ONE THIRD IS MINE - OLIVE'S THIRD WILL SOON BE IN THE HANDS OF JULIUS J. HERRINGBONE - I'M SURE OF IT!
YOU THINK HE ISN'T ON THE LEVEL ?
MR. HERRINGBONE. YOU ARE SIX MONTHS BEHIND WITH YOUR ROOM RENT AND BOARD
A MERE NOTHING, MISS SPINICH
I EXPECT TO MARRY THE RICH OLIVE OYL WHO RETURNED FROM PARTS UNKNOWN WITH A SHIP LOAD OF MONEY
YOU DON'T SAY!!
DON'T EVER MENTION RENT TO ME AGAIN, MISS SPINICH. I AM A HERRINGBONE AND VERY SENSITIVE IN MATTERS OF THAT SORT
I GUESS YOUR CREDIT'S GOOD
SEGAR
7-22

THIMBLE THEATER
NOW SHOWING—TELLING THE WORLD.
Tomorrow—A Sign of True Love.

THERE'S THIRTY MILLION DOLLARS IN THIS BAG - I HAD OUR MONEY CHANGED INTO $10,000. BILLS SO IT WOULDN'T TAKE UP SO MUCH ROOM
GOOD IDEA
SAY, HAM, DO YOU WANT YOUR SHARE OF THE CASH? I HAD IT CHANGED INTO BIG BILLS - IT'S ALL IN ONE BAG NOW
IN ONE BAG!? SOMEONE MIGHT CARRY IT OFF
I'M NOT READY TO INVEST IT YET SO JUST LEAVE IT WITH YOURS
ARE YOU SURE IT'S SAFE?
SURE IT'S SAFE
SEE - AFTER READING THAT SIGN NOBODY'LL BOTHER ABOUT LOOKING IN THERE
!
THERE ISN'T ANY MONEY IN THIS ROOM
SEGAR

THIMBLE THEATER
NOW SHOWING—A SIGN OF TRUE LOVE.
Tomorrow——A Boy in Love.

I DON'T THINK YOUR SIGN HELPS A THING, CASTOR - I REALLY DON'T
I THINK IT'S CLEVER
THERE ISN'T ANY MONEY IN THIS ROOM
YOU IDIOT - THAT WOULD BE THE FIRST PLACE A THIEF WOULD LOOK! WHY ADVERTISE THE HIDING PLACE?
ME? IDIOT! WHO ME? YOU MEAN ME ?
JULIUS J. HERRINGBONE, WHAT IS IT TO YOU WHETHER THAT MONEY IS SAFE OR NOT?!
WHY - WHY - ER - NOTHING! IT'S NOTHING TO ME
YOU SEE, CASTOR, IT'S JUST AS I SAID - THAT MAN IS A FORTUNE HUNTER - WITHOUT MONEY SHE'D BE DIRT IN HIS EYE
IT ISN'T MY MONEY YOU LOVE, IS IT, JULIUS? IS IT, JULIUS?
IT IS YOU, OLIVE! YOUR BEAUTY, YOU ALONE - NOTHING BUT YOU!

THIMBLE THEATER
NOW SHOWING—A BOY IN LOVE.
Tomorrow—Can't Keep a Secret.

SURE - IF YOU DIDN'T HAVE A FORTUNE YOU'D JUST BE DIRT IN HIS EYE
HAM'S RIGHT! HE DOESN'T CARE A WHOOP FOR YOU, SIS - IT'S YOUR MONEY
DON'T TELL ME THAT!!! I LOVE HIM!
OH I'M SO GLAD YOU CALLED - I MUST SPEAK TO YOU, JULIUS - ALONE -
?
WHAT'S UP?
IT'S ABOUT MY MONEY - YOU'D LOVE ME EVEN IF I DIDN'T HAVE A PENNY - WOULDN'T YOU, JULIUS?
YOU STILL HAVE YOUR MONEY? IT HASN'T BEEN STOLEN OR ANYTHING?
CERTAINLY I STILL HAVE IT
I CARE NOT FOR CASH. IT IS YOU - IT IS LOVE! YOU ARE THE ROSE OF MY HEART!
SEGAR

THIMBLE THEATER
NOW SHOWING—CAN'T KEEP A SECRET.
Tomorrow——A Woman's Intuition.

THERE ISN'T ANY MONEY IN THIS ROOM
KEEP OUT
WHIFFLE!
THERE ISN'T ANY MONEY IN THIS ROOM
WHIFFLE
WHIFFLE
KEEP OUT
WHIFFLE
BERNICE - WHAT ARE YOU "WHIFFLING" LIKE THAT FOR?
WHIFFLE
WHIFFLE
MAYBE SOMEBODY WENT INTO THAT ROOM
HUH? YOU THINK THAT'S IT?!
WHIFFLE
7-26
SEGAR

THIMBLE THEATER
NOW SHOWING—A WOMAN'S INTUITION.
Monday——The Perfect Alibi.

SHE'S A STRANGE BIRD - I'LL SAY THAT!
BERNICE - ARE YOU TRYING TO TELL US THAT SOMEBODY WENT INTO THAT ROOM?
THERE ISN'T ANY MONEY IN THIS ROOM
KEEP OUT
WHIFFLE!
AW, I GUESS IT'S NOTHING - THE DOOR'S LOCKED - NOBODY'S IN THERE
BERNICE IS WHIFFLING AGAIN - SHE SEEMS TO BE TRYING TO TELL US SOMETHING
WHIFFLE
WHIFFLE
WHIFFLE
THAT BIRD!!
I THINK WE OUGHT TO GO IN AND SEE
WELL, MAYBE WE SHOULD
THERE ISN'T ANY MONEY IN THIS ROOM
KEEP OUT
WHIFFLE
7-27
SEGAR

THIMBLE THEATER
NOW SHOWING—THE PERFECT ALIBI
Tomorrow—A Self-Made Hero

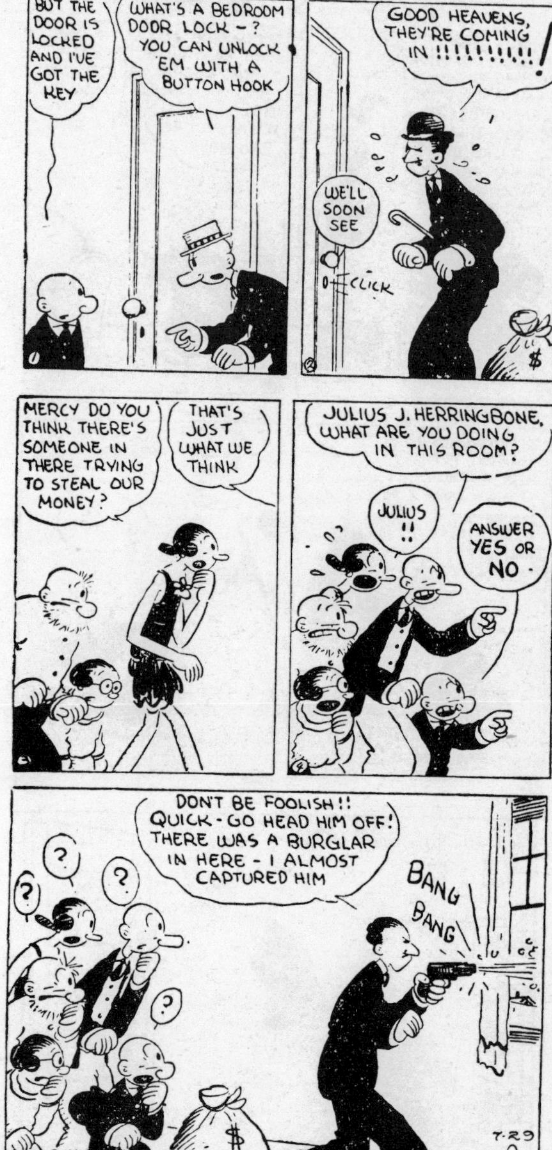
BUT THE DOOR IS LOCKED AND I'VE GOT THE KEY
WHAT'S A BEDROOM DOOR LOCK - ? YOU CAN UNLOCK 'EM WITH A BUTTON HOOK
GOOD HEAVENS, THEY'RE COMING IN!!!!!!!!!!
WE'LL SOON SEE
CLICK
MERCY DO YOU THINK THERE'S SOMEONE IN THERE TRYING TO STEAL OUR MONEY?
THAT'S JUST WHAT WE THINK
JULIUS J. HERRINGBONE, WHAT ARE YOU DOING IN THIS ROOM?
JULIUS!!
ANSWER YES OR NO.
DON'T BE FOOLISH!! QUICK - GO HEAD HIM OFF! THERE WAS A BURGLAR IN HERE - I ALMOST CAPTURED HIM
BANG
BANG
7-29
SEGAR

THIMBLE THEATER
NOW SHOWING—A SELF-MADE HERO
Tomorrow—Barking Dogs

?
?
!
DARN! MISSED HIM EVERY SHOT— I ALMOST CAPTURED THAT BURGLAR SINGLE HANDED— BUT ANYWAY I CHASED HIM OFF—
BANG
BANG
?
$
AND SAVED YOUR MONEY FOR YOU
$
MY HERO!
P.S.T. DO YOU BELIEVE THAT HAM? SOUNDED PRETTY THIN TO ME
LOOKED REAL. IF HE FAKED IT HE'S A GOOD ACTOR. I'LL SAY THAT
YOU ARE BRAVE, JULIUS, I AM PROUD OF YOU.
I ONLY DID WHAT ANY RED-BLOODED "HE" MAN WOULD HAVE DONE
Great Britain rights reserved.
© 1929, King Features Syndicate, Inc.
SEGAR
7-30

THIMBLE THEATER
NOW SHOWING—BARKING DOGS
Tomorrow—A Chinese Lullaby

YOU ARE GLIM, THE DETECTIVE?
I AM GLIM, THE GREAT DETECTIVE
MR. GLIM SLUTHERY
WE WANT YOU TO GET A LINE ON ONE JULIUS J. HERRINGBONE, NO ARREST. UNDERSTAND. WE JUST WANT THE DOPE
REWARD
THE RAT
ETC.— AND ABOVE ALL DO NOT LET HIM KNOW YOU ARE ON HIS TRAIL
O.K. I'LL SLIP UP ON HIM
SQUEEK
SQUEEK
SQUEEK
SQUEEK
SQUEEK
SQUEEK
SEGAR
7-31

THIMBLE THEATER
NOW SHOWING—A CHINESE LULLABY
Tomorrow—Who's Your Girl Friend, Julius?

I NEED MONEY AND I'LL GET IT ONE WAY OR ANOTHER— THE SAFEST WAY WOULD BE TO MARRY HER— STILL—
BEFORE I HIRE YOU, MR. GLIM, I MUST HAVE SOME PROOF OF YOUR SKILL AS A DETECTIVE
COVER YOUR EYES FOR THREE SECONDS
CLICK
CLICK
PLOP
KETCHEM WASHEE?
Great Britain rights reserved.
© 1929, King Features Syndicate, Inc.
SEGAR
8-1

THIMBLE THEATER
NOW SHOWING—WHO'S YOUR GIRL FRIEND, JULIUS?

Tomorrow—Where's There's Smoke, There's Fire

!
GLIM IS TRAILING HERRINGBONE, WONDER WHAT HE'LL FIND OUT?
SQUEEK
SQUEEK
SQUEEK
!
!
SQUEEK
SQUEEK
SQUEEK
SEGAR 8-2

THIMBLE THEATER
NOW SHOWING—WHERE THERE'S SMOKE, THERE'S FIRE.

Monday—Popeye's Man and Olive's

CASTOR, DID YOU HIRE A DETECTIVE TO FIND OUT THINGS ABOUT MR HERRINGBONE ?
I AIN'T SAYIN' YES. AND I AINT SAYIN' NO! BESIDES WHAT'S IT TO YOU?
SURE WHAT'S IT TO YOU? YOU'RE BLIND WITH LOVE YOU CAN'T SEE THINGS LIKE US
AW, SHUT UP
SOMEBODY AROUND THIS HOUSE THINKS I'M A CROOK, AND I DON'T LIKE IT! I DON'T LIKE IT!
I'VE A HUNCH THAT YOUR BROTHER HAS PUT A "DICK" ON MY TRAIL - WHAT HAVE I DONE - I AM AN HONEST CITIZEN
NEVER MIND- JULIUS I BELIEVE IN YOU
WHIFFLE
8-5
© 1929, King Features Syndicate, Inc., Great Britain rights reserved.

THIMBLE THEATER
NOW SHOWING—POPEYE'S THE MAN

Tomorrow—The Perfect Lover

I BELIEVE YOU'RE RIGHT- OUR DETECTIVE IS A FLOP-
SURE- WHAT WE NEED IS ACTION— LIGHTNING DISGUISES WILL GET US NOWHERE
I'LL GO FIND POPEYE. WE CAN DEPEND ON OLD POPEYE- HE'LL HELP US
SHOOT TWO BITS
SHOOT
HELLO, POPEYE
WELL, BLOW ME DOWN!
SURE, I'LL HELP YOU- AND I HOPE I GETS A CRACK AT SOMEBODY- I AIN'T HAD NO FIGHTS FOR TWO DAYS
I'LL LET YOU HANDLE IT IN YOUR OWN WAY
THERE HE IS- SIS IS MADLY IN LOVE WITH HIM- HAM AND I THINK HE'S AFTER OUR MONEY
SHALL I DO IT IN HERE OR TAKE 'IM OUTSIDE?
SEGAR 8-5

THIMBLE THEATER
NOW SHOWING—THE PERFECT LOVER

Tomorrow—By Special Request

HELLO, POPEYE SAY HOW DO YOU LIKE MY NEW CLOTHES?
BLOW ME DOWN - THEY'RE SWELL - WHAT THERE IS OF 'EM
© 1929, King Features Syndicate, Inc., Great Britain rights reserved.
OLIVE YOU'RE THE PERTIEST GAL I EVER SAW - I'D QUIT THE SEA FOR YOU ANY DAY - HOW ABOUT US BEIN' SWEETIES ?
MR. HERRINGBONE IS MY SWEETY, POPEYE. YOU'RE TOO LATE
HERRINGFISH! H-M-M- HIS NAME'S AS GOOFY AS HIS FACE
WELL, I GUESS I GOT A RIGHT TO GIVE MY OLD FRIEN' A HUG, AIN'T I OLIVE?
MERCY NO. POPEYE NO! NO!
WHEN I HUGS 'EM, HERRINGFISH - THEY KNOWS THEY BEEN HUGGED
8-6
SEGAR

THIMBLE THEATER
NOW SHOWING—BY SPECIAL REQUEST

Tomorrow—Popeye's Error

I CAN'T GO BUST 'IM FOR NOTHIN' - I GOTTA HAVE A REASON - I FIGHTS BETTER WHEN I GOT A REASON
GO ON- BOP HIM ANYWAY
SURE!
YOU'RE JUST KIDDING ME, POPEYE
NO I AIN'T - YOU'RE SWEETER'N A PEACH
I OBJECT TO YOU OR ANYONE ELSE TALKING LIKE THAT TO MISS OYL
HUH?- YOU DON'T LIKE IT ?
NO! I DON'T LIKE IT !!
!
WELL- HERE'S ME BUTTON - LE'SSEE YOU TAKE A CRACK AT IT - COME ON, SOCK IT!
8-7
© 1929, King Features Syndicate, Inc., Great Britain rights reserved.
SEGAR

THIMBLE THEATER
NOW SHOWING—POPEYE'S ERROR

Tomorrow—A Crook Revealed

COME ON, LET'S GO OUTSIDE AND GIVE 'EM ROOM TO FIGHT
YEAH - I DARES YOU TO SOCK ME -
THIS IS TERRIBLE !
IS THAT ALL YOU GOT? NOW I'M GONNA UNCORK ONE -
CRACK
BLOW ME DOWN, I DIDN'T HAVE NO FUN AT ALL - HE WENT OUT THE FIRST POP - I'LL THROW 'IM SOMEPLACE AND LET 'IM SLEEP IT OFF -
SURE - I THROWED 'IM INTO THAT ROOM - HE NEEDS SLEEP
Great Britain rights reserved
© 1929, King Features Syndicate, Inc.
GOOD NIGHT, POPEYE. OUR MONEY IS IN THERE - GET HIM OUT QUICK! CASTOR AND I THINK HE'S A CROOK
8-8
SEGAR

THIMBLE THEATER
NOW SHOWING—A CROOK REVEALED
Tomorrow—A Lady Deceived

SURE - I KNOCKED 'IM OUT AND THROWED 'IM INTO THAT ROOM TO SLEEP
GET HIM OUT QUICK! OUR MONEY IS IN THERE. MILLIONS IN BIG BILLS IN ONE BAG
BLOW ME DOWN, I DIDN'T KNOW THAT - BUT HE WON'T STEAL NOTHIN' HE'S OUT COLD
WHY HE'S GONE - GONE! HE'S NOT IN HERE - AND - AND THE MONEY ——
IT'S GONE TOO! OUR MONEY IS GONE!
NOW! YOU SEE, SIS, DIDN'T HAM AND ME TELL YOU HE WAS A CROOK
OH MY! OH. MY LOVER - HE'S A CROOK! HOW I LOVED HIM - A CROOK! OH! OH! OH! OH! OH! OH! OH!
8-9
SEGAR

THIMBLE THEATER
NOW SHOWING—A LADY DECEIVED
Monday—The Optimist

CASTOR - TELL ME THE TRUTH - DO YOU REALLY THINK THAT MY JULIUS TOOK OUR MONEY?
ABSOLUTELY! NO DOUBT ABOUT IT. SURE HE DID
YEAH - AND WE TOLD YOU HE WAS A CROOK ALL ALONG!
BAW!
THE ONLY MAN I EVER CARED FOR WITH ALL MY HEART! BAW!
POOR SIS!
SHE GOT A TOUGH BREAK!
WELL, SHE MADE HER BED. NOW LET'ER LAY IN IT. WE TOLD HER
OH FATE! WHY THIS KICK IN THE FACE? WHY? WHY? WHY?
Great Britain rights reserved.
© 1929, King Features Syndicate, Inc.
8-10
SEGAR

THIMBLE THEATER
NOW SHOWING—THE OPTIMIST
Tomorrow—A Big Little Guy

MY LOVER A CROOK! OH, I WISH I'D NEVER EVEN BEEN BORN!
BAW!
STOP CRYING, OLIVE - YOU'RE GETTING YOUR FEET ALL WET AND THERE AIN'T NO MAN WORTH A BAD COLD
I WONDER IF I LOOK THE WAY I FEEL - LOSING TEN MILLION HAS UNJOINTED MY BACKBONE I'M A HUMAN RAG -
TRA-LA LA-LE-LA - TRA-LA-LE LA-LA-LEE - DUM-LA-LA TE-TA DI-DE-DUM-TUM-TUM-LA - DUM-TUM-TUM-TEE - TEE-TUM-TEE - LA-LA -
SAY, YOUNG MAN YOU'RE ACTING MIGHTY HAPPY FOR A GUY WHO'S JUST LOST TEN MILLION!
WHO ME? OH SURE
!
TRA-LE-LA-LA LA-LA-LA-DUM-DUM DUM-TE TUM
8-12
SEGAR

THIMBLE THEATER
NOW SHOWING—A BIG LITTLE GUY
Tomorrow—The Laughing Hyena

I FEEL LIKE A RAG SINCE HERRINGBONE ROBBED US- NOTHING TO LIVE FOR- I THINK I'LL TAKE A TRIP TO THE GREAT UNKNOWN
I FEEL LIKE THAT
SINGING AGAIN HE BEATS ME
TRA-LA LA-LA
TE-TUM TEE TUM TE-DI-DIDDLE DIDDLE- DUM-DE DUM
SAY- I'M HALF GOOFY OVER LOSING MY TEN MILLION - YOU LOST THE SAME AMOUNT AND YOU SING - TELL ME WHY: YOU TELL ME!
AW. WHAT'S TEN MILLION ?!
YOU GOTTA BE BROAD MINDED, HAM, SURE - YOU GOTTA BE WIDE WITTED
I CAN'T DOPE IT! I'VE HEARD OF PEOPLE COMMITING SUICIDE OVER TWENTY DOLLARS - AND HERE HE LOSES TEN MILLION AND LIKES IT - MAYBE HE'S A BIGGER MAN INSIDE THAN ME
8-13
SEGAR

THIMBLE THEATER
NOW SHOWING—THE LAUGHING HYENA
Tomorrow—The Awful Truth

MAW- WE OUGHT TO BE PROUD OF CASTOR HE'S UNUSUAL- HE'S GOT QUALITIES
WHY, PAW ?
LOOK AT HAM. THERE HE'S WORRYING WITH ALL HIS MIGHT- HE'S ALL SHOT!
DOGGONE!
AND LOOK AT OLIVE. HER LOSS HAS ALL BUT PUT'ER TO BED - SHE'S A WRECK
DERN
TRA- LA-LA OOH-LE-OOH LAY-EEE-WHOO
SEE THAT — IS HE DOWN-HEARTED? HE LOST TEN MILLION JUST LIKE HAM AND OLIVE DID
NO!
I'M TELLIN' YOU, MAW, THAT BOY'S BIG INSIDE - HE'S A MAN - THERE AIN'T MANY PEOPLE WHO CAN LOSE TEN MILLION AND LAUGH IT OFF
8-14
SEGAR

THIMBLE THEATER
NOW SHOWING—THE AWFUL TRUTH
Tomorrow—Popeye's Verdict

WAIT TILL THE SUN SHINES NELLIE
EVERYBODY'S DOING IT- DO-INK-IT DOOINK IT
THERE HE GOES AGAIN- AND HE LOST TEN MILLION THE SAME AS ME AND OLIVE - HE SEEMS TO LIKE IT
I CAN'T DOPE HIM — BY ALL LAWS OF NATURE HE OUGHTA BE BEEFING, INSTEAD HE SINGS- THINK OF IT!
SAY!
SAY— MAYBE HE'S A HYPOCRICK
A WHAT?
I SAID — "MAYBE HE'S A HYPOCRICK"
AW. SHUT UP
BLOW ME DOWN I'LL BET THAT'S. WHAT HE IS. A HYPOCRICK
8-15
SEGAR

THIMBLE THEATER
NOW SHOWING—POPEYE'S VERDICT
Tomorrow—Is Castor Cuckoo?

HYPOCRICK!
TRA-LA-LA-LA LE-LA-LA LA-LA LA!
HYPOCRICK? HYPOCRICK? ? IS THAT A NOUN OR A VERB?
WHAT'S A "VERB"?
POPEYE- DO YOU MEAN TO STAND THERE AND TELL ME THAT YOU DON'T KNOW WHAT A VERB IS?
DON'T HIGHHAT ME - I ASKS YOU, WHAT'S A VERB?
A VERB IS THAT PART OF SPEECH WHICH ASSERTS-DECLARES OR PREDICATES SOMETHING THAT'S WHAT A VERB IS
?
?
?
SURE!
HE AIN'T NO HYPOCRICK - HE'S JUST PLAIN CRAZY!
BLOW ME DOWN!
© 1929, King Features Syndicate, Inc., Great Britain rights reserved.
8-16
SEGAR

THIMBLE THEATER
NOW SHOWING—IS CASTOR CUCKOO?
Monday—Conscience-Stricken

CASEY JONES MOUNTED TO THE CABIN - TE DIDDLE DUM DIDDLE-TE DIDDLE DUM DEE
JUST GOT ROBBED OF TEN MILLION AND HE'S HAPPY AS A LARK
I CAN'T DOPE YOU AT ALL
OH, DON'T MIND ME
NO SENSE IN WORRYING. WHY DON'T YOU BE LIKE ME? AM I DOWN HEARTED? NO!
HYPOCRICK
YOU'VE EITHER GOT SO MUCH BRAINS THAT YOU'RE ABLE TO CONTROL YOURSELF OR ELSE YOU'RE TOO DUMB TO WORRY!
SURE - THAT'S IT!
WHAT'S A "HYPOCRICK" POPEYE?
BLOW ME DOWN BUT YOU'RE IGGERANT!
8-17
© 1929, King Features Syndicate, Inc., Great Britain rights reserved.
SEGAR

THIMBLE THEATER
NOW SHOWING—CONSCIENCE-STRICKEN
Tomorrow—Self-Accusation

WEALTH!
MY FIRST CROOKED DEED
I AM A THIEF
AND A HEART WRECKER
SHE LOVED ME
IF I WAS CERTAIN THAT I WOULD GO TO HEAVEN, I'D END IT ALL RIGHT NOW
WHAT WAS THAT?! STRANGE - I'VE HEARD MORE NOISES THE LAST TEN MINUTES THAN I'VE HEARD DURING MY ENTIRE LIFE
NERVES, NERVES, THAT'S IT!
SEGAR
8-19

THIMBLE THEATER

NOW SHOWING—SELF-ACCUSATION

Tomorrow—Still on Her Mind

STEALING IS EASY- BATTLING WITH THE INNER VOICE IS HARD -
NOT ONLY DID I STEAL FOR COMMON GAIN - I WRECKED A HEART - THE HEART OF A HOMELY GIRL - BUT HOMELY GIRLS ARE HUMAN - AND SHE LOVED ME
I LOVE HIM! AND I HATE HIM
LOVE AND HATE AT THE SAME TIME - IT'S MADDENING!
BUSTIN' THE HEART OF A GOOD GAL - A PURE GAL LIKE OLIVE - JUST LEMME GET AHOLT OF THAT SWAB - BLOW ME DOWN -
JUST LEMME !
SNIFF
WAH
THE LAST OF THE HERRINGBONES A THIEF! THIEF! COMMON THIEF!
THIEF
THIEF
SEGAR
8-20

THIMBLE THEATER

NOW SHOWING—STILL ON HER MIND

Tomorrow—Not Ventriloquism

A COMMON THIEF - WHY DID I DO IT? I WAS NOT BORN A CRIMINAL!
WHISPERING - WHO'S WHISPERING? ANYBODY IN THIS ROOM?
ANYBODY IN THIS ROOM? SPEAK!
AW, IT WAS NOTHING - NERVES THAT'S ALL JUST NERVES - I'M SAFE - NOBODY KNOWS WHERE I LIVE — SAFE JUST NERVES
WHAT ON EARTH WAS THAT? NOTHING NOTHING OF COURSE
THE BRANCHES OF A TREE SCRAPING A WINDOW - NERVES! I'M SAFE! THEY WON'T GET ME!
THIEF THOUGH HE IS I CAN'T FORGET HIM - I WONDER IF HE'S ENJOYING THAT MONEY?
8-21
SEGAR

THIMBLE THEATER

NOW SHOWING—NOT VENTRILOQUISM

Tomorrow—The "Ham" Actor

A COMMON THIEF - WHY DID I DO IT? I WAS NOT BORN A CRIMINAL!
WHISPERING - WHO'S WHISPERING? ANYBODY IN THIS ROOM?
ANYBODY IN THIS ROOM? SPEAK!
AW, IT WAS NOTHING - NERVES THAT'S ALL JUST NERVES - I'M SAFE - NOBODY KNOWS WHERE I LIVE — SAFE - JUST NERVES
WHAT ON EARTH WAS THAT? NOTHING NOTHING OF COURSE
THE BRANCHES OF A TREE SCRAPING A WINDOW - NERVES! I'M SAFE! THEY WON'T GET ME!
THIEF THOUGH HE IS I CAN'T FORGET HIM - I WONDER IF HE'S ENJOYING THAT MONEY?
Great Britain rights reserved.
© 1929, King Features Syndicate, Inc.
8-21
SEGAR

THIMBLE THEATER

NOW SHOWING—THE "HAM" ACTOR

Tomorrow—Out of Control

I CAN IMAGINE MY FINGERS AROUND HIS SOFT WHITE THROAT!
?
HERRINGBONE YOU ARE DOOMED— IN MY FINGERS IS THE STRENGTH OF TEN DEMONS-STIMULATED BY RIGHTEOUS RAGE!
AND NOW I WILL SQUEEZE YOUR NECK - I WILL SQUEEZE AND SQUEEZE AND SQUEE
EEEEZE!
HOW YOU LIKE IT HERRINGBONE? HOW YOU LIKE THAT?
POW! YOU'RE DEAD!
BLOW ME DOWN! WHERE'LL WE BURY HIM?
!
SEGAR
8-R3

THIMBLE THEATER

NOW SHOWING—OUT OF CONTROL

Monday—No Dollars-No Sense

NO, HERRINGBONE, I WON'T LET GO OF YOUR NECK! STEAL OUR MONEY WILL YOU!
BLOW ME DOWN, I DON'T KNOW WHAT TO MAKE OF THAT EGG?
CURSE YOU- TAKE THAT!
AND THAT
HEY- SAVE SOME FOR TOMORROW! - YOU FOGGY? WHAT MAKES YOU BE LIKE THAT??
IT'S JUST MY IMAGINATION POPEYE - I CAN'T CONTROL IT- SURE I'M ALL RIGHT
YEAH, YOU'RE ALL RIGHT. YA' LOOK SWELL
WHEN I THINK OF HERRINGBONE ENJOYING HIMSELF ON OUR MONEY I NEARLY GO WILD
A DISGRACE TO THE FINE OLD HERRINGBONE FAMILY— THE LAST OF THE FAMILY A THIEF WHY DID I TAKE IT?
8-R4
SEGAR

THIMBLE THEATER

NOW SHOWING—NO DOLLARS; NO SENSE

Tomorrow—The Kissing Bug

YOU SEE, HERRINGBONE, I HOLD YOU HIGH BY THE NECK HA! YOU DIDN'T THINK I WAS SO STRONG, DID YOU? WELL, I AM!
THERE HE IS, DOCTOR
HE'S PERFECTLY SANE, JUST A CASE OF "IMAGERETIS" HIS IMAGINATION RUNS WILD- CAN'T CONTROL IT: NOTHING SERIOUS
THANK GOODNESS IT ISN'T SERIOUS!
YEAH, I'M GLAD OF THAT
POW
CRASH
BAM!
OH, NO - IT ISN'T SERIOUS - BUT WHO'S GOING TO PAY FOR THE FURNITURE?
CURSE YOU, HERRINGBONE, YOU CAN'T ESCAPE ME THIS TIME - NO! I WON'T LET GO! YOU'RE COOKED
8-R6
SEGAR

THIMBLE THEATER

NOW SHOWING—THE KISSING BUG

Tomorrow—A Satisfied Sheik

POW! HOW DO YOU LIKE MY UPPERCUT, HERRINGBONE?
DON'T TRY TO DUCK!
MY GOSH! I BELIEVE OLIVE'S IMAGINATION IS BEGINNING TO WORK LIKE HAM'S
SMACK
OH, EXCUSE ME, POPEYE - I IMAGINED YOU WERE MY LOVER
!
BLOW ME DOWN!
THUMP
8-27

THIMBLE THEATER

NOW SHOWING—A SATISFIED SHEIK

Tomorrow—A Rough Diamond

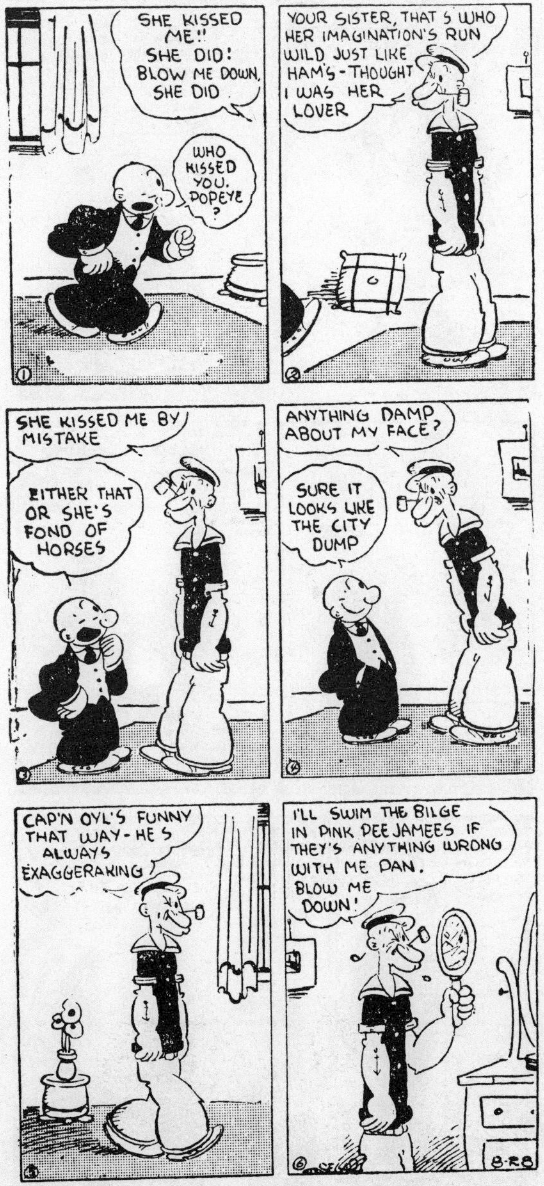
SHE KISSED ME!! SHE DID! BLOW ME DOWN, SHE DID
WHO KISSED YOU, POPEYE ?
YOUR SISTER, THAT'S WHO HER IMAGINATION'S RUN WILD JUST LIKE HAM'S - THOUGHT I WAS HER LOVER
SHE KISSED ME BY MISTAKE
EITHER THAT OR SHE'S FOND OF HORSES
ANYTHING DAMP ABOUT MY FACE?
SURE IT LOOKS LIKE THE CITY DUMP
CAP'N OYL'S FUNNY THAT WAY - HE'S ALWAYS EXAGGERAKING
I'LL SWIM THE BILGE IN PINK PEE JAMEES IF THEY'S ANYTHING WRONG WITH ME PAN. BLOW ME DOWN!
8-28

THIMBLE THEATER

NOW SHOWING—A ROUGH DIAMOND

Tomorrow—A Fair Exchange

YOU SHOULDN'T KID POPEYE LIKE THAT, ESPECIALLY AT A SERIOUS TIME LIKE THIS! YOU OUGHTA BE WORRYING OVER THE LOSS OF OUR MONEY
OLD POPEYE HE'S THE RESULT OF REVERSE EVOLUTION
HEY POPEYE. YOU'VE GOT A NIGHTMARE SKINNED A MILE
LISTEN. YOU AIN'T SO HOT - YA GOTTA WOOD HEAD AND A "BILLARD" BALL NOSE. THAT'S WHAT YOU LOOK LIKE - YEAH - LIKE SOMETHIN' THE CATS DRUGGED UP!
NOW ME. THEY'S SOMETHIN' TO MY FACE - I GOT PERSONALIKY. YOU DON'T SEE MANY FACES LIKE MINE
THAT'S RIGHT, YA DON'T
I'LL LOSE MY RESPECK FOR HIM YET - I'M JUST A DUMB SAILOR BUT I GOT SENSITIVITY
GOOD OLD POPEYE - HE'S O.K. SURE A DIAMOND IN THE ROUGH
BLOW ME DOWN

THIMBLE THEATER

NOW SHOWING—A FAIR EXCHANGE

Tomorrow—The Prodigal's Back

ARE WE GOING TO LET HERRINGBONE GET AWAY WITH OUR MONEY WITHOUT DOING A THING? LET'S CALL EVERY COP IN THE COUNTRY
THIEF THOUGH HE IS, I LOVE HIM STILL
BLOW ME DOWN, SHE LOVES HIM YET — I CAN'T FIGGER WOMEN
AND YOU SIT THERE LIKE A SILLY SAP AND GRIN JUST AS THOUGH NOTHING HAD HAPPENED
SURE- I'M BROAD MINDED
I CAN'T STAND THIS ANY LONGER. PEACE OF MIND IS WORTH MORE THAN ALL THE MONEY IN THE WORLD
I'LL DO IT! I'LL TAKE THE MONEY BACK
8-30

© 1929, King Features Syndicate, Inc., Great Britain rights reserved.

THIMBLE THEATER

NOW SHOWING—THE PRODIGAL'S BACK

Monday—The Philanthropist

IT BEATS ME! CASTOR LOSES MILLIONS AND SEEMS TO LIKE IT - SMILES LIKE A SAP ALL THE TIME
KNOCK KNOCK
GO SEE WHO'S AT THE DOOR, CASTOR
WHY, HELLO JULIUS, OLD KID, HOW'S EVER'THING? COME RIGHT IN
8-31

THIMBLE THEATER

NOW SHOWING—THE PHILANTHROPIST

Tomorrow—Stung!

I HAVE BROUGHT YOUR MONEY BACK - I WAS NOT BORN TO BE A THIEF - I'VE NEVER EVEN OPENED THE BAG
CONSCIENCE HURTS EH?
YOU SAY YOU'VE NEVER LOOKED INTO THE BAG?
IT'S NOT BEEN OPENED
YOU'RE NOT GOING TO TOUCH HIM - HE BROUGHT THE MONEY BACK ISN'T THAT ENOUGH?
LEMME GET ME HOOKS ON 'IM! LEMME! JUST LEMME!
YOU WENT TO A LOT OF TROUBLE MR HERRINGBONE. SO WE'RE GIVING YOU THE BAG AND ITS CONTENTS
ARE YOU CRAZY?! WHAT'SA IDEA?!
9-2

Great Britain rights reserved © 1929, King Features Syndicate, Inc.

THIMBLE THEATER
NOW SHOWING—STUNG!
Tomorrow—A Crushed Fin

CASTOR OYL, ARE YOU IN YOUR RIGHT MIND?
I MOST CERTAINLY AM!
DID YOU SAY THAT YOU ARE GIVING ME THIS?
THAT'S RIGHT
SURE THE CONTENTS IS ALL YOURS— OPEN IT UP AND SEE HOW RICH YOU ARE
?
IF THEY COMES ANY GOOFIER'N THAT EGG I AIN'T SEEN 'EM
SNAKES!
YEAH- SNAKES- WHAT DID YOU THINK WAS IN THERE, MONEY?
9-3
SEGAR

THIMBLE THEATER
NOW SHOWING—A CRUSHED FIN
Tomorrow—The Book Worm

YES, MR. HERRINGBONE, YOU STOLE A BAG OF SNAKES. IT'S A WONDER YOU DIDN'T GET WISE TO MY TRICK. BUT I SUPPOSE YOUR CONSCIENCE WAS KEEPING YOU BUSY
NOW, POPEYE, YOU'RE NOT GOING TO STRIKE MR. HERRINGBONE - HE'S HAD HIS LESSON
BLOW ME DOWN, I JUST WANT TO SHAKE HANDS WITH HIM
SHAKE, HERRINGFISH, OLD TOP - I AIN'T MADATCHER
9-4
SEGAR

THIMBLE THEATER
NOW SHOWING—THE BOOK WORM
Tomorrow—A "Checked" Exit

SAY CASTOR IF HERRINGBONE DIDN'T STEAL OUR MONEY THEN WHERE IS IT?
WHY IT'S RIGHT WHERE IT BELONGS IN THE BANK AND IT'S BEEN THERE FOR WEEKS
AND YOU KNEW IT WAS SAFE ALL THE TIME AND WOULDN'T TELL US. I OUGHTA KNOCK YOU ONE!
WHY DIDN'T YOU TELL US? WHY'D YOU LET US WORRY?
I'M FUNNY LIKE THAT JUST ONE OF MY PECULIARITIES
YOU CAUSED US A LOT OF GRIEF, CASTOR
Great Britain rights reserved. © 1929, King Features Syndicate, Inc.
HERE'S YOUR BANK BOOKS THERE'S TEN MILLION IN EACH ACCOUNT- I'M THE GUY WHO MADE YOU RICH. AND IF YOU CAN'T TAKE A JOKE YOU CAN GO SOAK YOUR HEADS
9-5
SEGAR

THIMBLE THEATER

NOW SHOWING—A "CHECKED" EXIT

Tomorrow—A Fly in the Molasses

NOTHING - ABSOLUTELY NOTHING TO LIVE FOR - I'M A PERFECT FLOP - OH, WELL - ONE LITTLE BULLET WILL FIX ALL THAT
THE LAST OF THE HERRINGBONES - GOING - GOING
!
KNOCK
KNOCK
HERRINGBONE, I'M GOING TO RETURN GOOD FOR EVIL - I KNOW THAT YOU ARE COMPLETELY OUT OF LUCK - SO PLEASE ACCEPT THIS LITTLE CHECK
$100,000.
SURE. 'SALL RIGHT SURE
H-M-M - BIG HEARTED CASTOR
9-6
SEGAR

THIMBLE THEATER

NOW SHOWING—A FLY IN THE MOLASSES

Monday—An Uncle and an "Ante"

WELL EVERYTHING'S TOTSY HOOTSY - NOTHING TO WORRY ABOUT MEAT ON THE TABLE AND MONEY IN THE BANK.. TEN MILLION ON ICE!
CAP'N OYL, YOU'RE THE FINEST GENTLEMAN IN THE WORLD! I MEANS IT!
YOU GOT BRAINS AND GENEROSIKY. BIG HEARTED, THAT'S YOU CAP'N
YOU OUGHTER BEEN PRESIDENT I'D VOTE FOR YOU ANY DAY. I MEANS IT!
?
?
BLOW ME DOWN. WILL YOU LEND ME A MILLION DOLLARS ?
Great Britain rights reserved.
© 1929, King Features Syndicate, Inc.,
9-7
SEGAR

THIMBLE THEATER

NOW SHOWING—UNCLE AND "ANTE"

Tomorrow—Popeye's "Stroke" of Luck

AW, CAN'TCHER LEMME HAVE A MILLION. CAP'N OYL ?
POPEYE, I GAVE YOU A MILLION JUST AFTER WE CAME BACK FROM DICE ISLAND - WHAT DID YOU DO WITH IT ?
A DAME TALKED ME OUT OF IT SHE WANTED THE MONEY FOR HER UNCLE, HE WAS SICK
DID YOU FALL FOR THAT? WHAT WAS THE MATTER WITH HER UNCLE?
HE HAD 'INFLAMMABLE' RHEUMATISM
HAD WHAT ?!
INFLAMMABLE RHEUMATISM. HA! HA! AND I SUPPOSE HE NEEDED THE MONEY TO BUY FIRE EXTINGUISHERS
HA! HA!
!
WHAT'S FUNNY ABOUT RHEUMATISM? I'LL BET YOU'D LAUGH AT A DEAD CORP. YEAH - AT A FOOMERAL
OLD POPEYE'S GOT TO HAVE SOME EDUCATION I THINK I'LL HIRE A TUTOR FOR HIM - I CAN AFFORD IT -
BLOW ME DOWN:
WHIFFLE
Great Britain rights reserved.
© 1929, King Features Syndicate, Inc.,
SEGAR

THIMBLE THEATER

NOW SHOWING—POPEYE'S "STROKE" OF LUCK

Tomorrow—The Tutor Shoulda "Noun" Better

AFTER ALL I DONE FOR HIM TOO — I ASKS FOR THE LOAN OF A MILLION AN'E SAYS NO! BLOW ME DOWN!
RUB RUB
POPEYE, WHAT YOU NEED IS EDUCATION. I THINK I'LL HIRE A TUTOR FOR YOU
WHAT I NEEDS IS CASH— SHOOT TWO BITS
LISTEN, HORSE IN THE FACE, I'LL SHOOT YOU CRAPS TILL THE COWS COME HOME. I'LL TAKE YOU QUICK
SAYS YOU
WHY YOU DISHED-FACED HUNK OF CHEESE YOU GOT ME FOR TWO THOUSAND DOLLARS
INSTEAD OF TAKIN' ME, YA GOT TOOKEN DIDN'TCHER, CAP'N OYL'
SAY-HAVE YOU BEEN RUBBING THE WHIFFLE FOR LUCK ?
I AIN'T TOUCHED YOUR WHIFFLE HEN- DON'T YOU TRUSK ME?
I'LL BET ANYTHING THAT HE'S BEEN RUBBING THE WHIFFLE
WHIFFLE
9-10
SEGAR

THIMBLE THEATER

NOW SHOWING—THE TUTOR SHOULDA "NOUN" BETTER

Tomorrow—"Grammar" Is Just Grandpa's Wife

POPEYE, YOU'RE AN AWFUL THING. BUT I LIKE YOU ANYWAY- I'VE HIRED A TUTOR FOR YOU- STEP RIGHT UP AND GET EDUCATED
WHAT'S A VERB?
ASK ME SUMPIN' HARD
A BIRD IS ANYTHING WHAT HAS WINGS EXCEPT AEROPLANES AND FLYING FISH
I DIDN'T SAY "BIRD" I SAID VERB- WHAT'S A VERB?
OH. VERB. OH, I SEE VERB
SAY, DO YOU KNOW WHAT A "GOOFIS" IS?
NO. I DON'T
WELL- I DON'T KNOW WHAT A VERB IS— SO THAT MAKES IT EVEN
WHIFFLE
9-11
SEGAR

THIMBLE THEATER

NOW SHOWING—"GRAMMAR" IS JUST GRANDPA'S WIFE

Tomorrow—A Beastly Trick

HERE'S YOUR TUTOR, POPEYE.. NOW PAY ATTENTION. YOU DIDN'T DO SO WELL YESTERDAY- AND I WANT YOU TO HAVE AN EDUCATION
OKE
WHAT'S A VERB?
ARE YOU STILL HARPIN' ON THAT?
ANSWER ME. WHAT'S A VERB?
IT'S A VEGETABLE
WRONG!
IT'S A FRUIT
GO OVER AND SIT ON THAT STOOL
AYE AYE SIR.
?
BLOW ME DOWN
9-12
SEGAR

THIMBLE THEATER

NOW SHOWING—A BEASTLY TRICK

Tomorrow—Accidental Mathematics

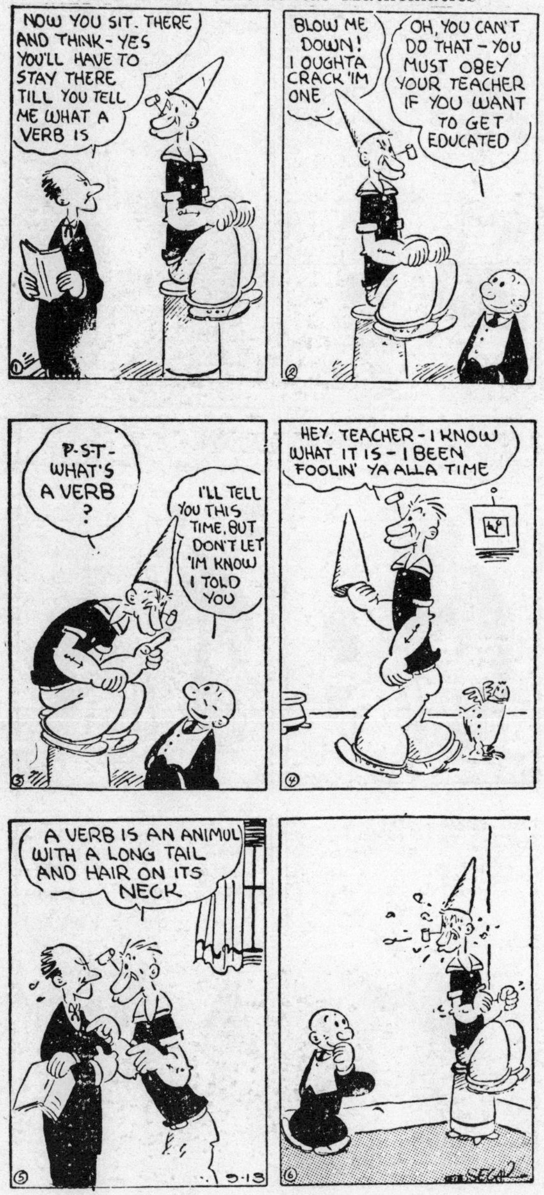

NOW YOU SIT. THERE AND THINK - YES YOU'LL HAVE TO STAY THERE TILL YOU TELL ME WHAT A VERB IS
BLOW ME DOWN! I OUGHTA CRACK 'IM ONE
OH, YOU CAN'T DO THAT - YOU MUST OBEY YOUR TEACHER IF YOU WANT TO GET EDUCATED
P-S-T- WHAT'S A VERB ?
I'LL TELL YOU THIS TIME, BUT DON'T LET 'IM KNOW I TOLD YOU
HEY. TEACHER - I KNOW WHAT IT IS - I BEEN FOOLIN' YA ALLA TIME
A VERB IS AN ANIMUL WITH A LONG TAIL AND HAIR ON ITS NECK
5-13
SEGAR

THIMBLE THEATER

NOW SHOWING—ACCIDENTAL MATHEMATICS

Monday—Copy Cat

THIS EDJACATION BUSINESS IS HOOEY
IT IS NOT. GO IN THERE AND GET BUSY. YOUR TUTOR IS WAITING
TO DAY I AM GOING TO TEST YOU AT MENTAL MULTIPLICATION
QUICK. HOW MUCH IS 6½ x 656 ? QUICK!
4,264
RIGHT!
BLOW ME DOWN!
ANYBODY WHAT CAN GUESS LIKE THAT DON'T NEED NO EDJACATION
!
?
SEGAR
5-14

THIMBLE THEATER

NOW SHOWING—COPY CAT

Tomorrow—Stop Straining Your Ears!

I WILL NOW TEST YOU AT SPELLING
DO YOUR BEST, POPEYE, I'M PAYING YOUR TUTOR FANCY WAGES
OKE
HOW DO YOU SPELL CAT ?
K-A-T
WRONG
HOW DO YOU SPELL DICTIONARY ?
D-I-C-T-I-O-N-A-R-Y
RIGHT!
DICTIONARY
HE CAN'T SPELL SMALL WORDS LIKE "CAT" BUT DID YOU HEAR HIM SPELL DICTIONARY ?
YEAH I SAW HIM SPELL IT
5-16
SEGAR

THIMBLE THEATER

NOW SHOWING—STOP STRAINING YOUR EARS!

Tomorrow—When a Wrong Word's Correct!

I WILL NOW TELL YOU A STORY AND I WANT YOU TO PAY ATTENTION
ALL RIGHT, TEACHER
A STORY WITH A MORAL - ONCE UPON A TIME THERE WAS A VERY WISE MAN - ETC
BLA-BLA-
NOW YOU TELL ME A STORY
IF YOU HEARD THIS ONE STOP ME
ONCE UPON A TIME THERE WAS TWO IRISHMEN -
?
PST-PST PST-PST-PST PST-PST-
!
5-17
SEGAR

THIMBLE THEATER

NOW SHOWING—WHEN A WRONG WORD'S CORRECT!

Tomorrow—A Hookey-Player Hooked

WHAT'S AN ADJECTIVE?
SEARCH ME
THINK - CAN'T YOU THINK! WHAT HAVE YOU A BRAIN IN YOUR HEAD FOR?
BALLAST
TELL ME A WORD THAT CAN BE USED AS AN ADJECTIVE
RIGHT!
5-18
Great Britain rights reserved.
© 1929, King Features Syndicate, Inc.
SEGAR

THIMBLE THEATER

NOW SHOWING—A HOOKEY-PLAYER HOOKED

Tomorrow—Popeye Wasn't on That Boat

MR. POPEYE! OH, MR. POPEYE! GOOD HEAVENS, WHAT WILL I EVER DO WITH A PUPIL LIKE HIM?
SLIPPED OUT WHEN MY BACK WAS TURNED
WELL, GET ON HIS TRAIL I'M PAYING YOU FANCY WAGES TO EDUCATE HIM, AND YOU'VE GOT TO KEEP BUSY!
YES, MR. OYL
I'LL HIDE OUT IN THE MOUNTAINS — EDJACATION IS HOOEY - I'D RATHER WORK THAN THINK ANY DAY
YA DON'T GOTTER HAVE EDJACATION TO SCRUB DECKS NOHOW
PEACE! BLOW ME DOWN! PEACE AT LAST!
NOW FOR A SNOOZE
WHAT'S A VERB ?
!
5-19
SEGAR

THIMBLE THEATER

NOW SHOWING—POPEYE WASN'T ON THAT BOAT

Tomorrow—The Sandman's Lullaby

HOW CAN I TEACH MR. POPEYE WHEN HE RUNS AWAY ALL THE TIME?
WELL, CHASE HIM—I'M PAYING YOU TO EDUCATE HIM AND YOU'VE GOT TO DO IT!
STOP! STOP! STOP! STOP! STOP! STOP! STOP! STOP! STOP! STOP! STOP! STOP!
WE'LL HELP YOU CATCH HIM, MISTER
WHAT'D HE DO MURDER SOME-BODY?
STOP! STOP! STOP! STOP! STOP
GRAB 'IM
DON'T LET HIM GET AWAY!
WE GOT 'IM, MISTER!
WHAT DO YOU WANT HIM FOR?
WHO DISCOVERED AMERICA?
5-20
SEGAR

THIMBLE THEATER

NOW SHOWING—THE SANDMAN'S LULLABY

Monday—Knowing His Worth

I HAVE HIRED AN EX PRIZE FIGHTER TO HELP ME WITH MY UNRULY PUPIL—I CAN'T HANDLE HIM MYSELF
GOOD IDEA! POPEYE MUST GET AN EDUCATION
WATCH HIM, MR. BOPPER, WHILE I GET MY BOOKS
IF HE MOVES ONE TENTH OF AN INCH, I'LL MURDER HIM
YOU AND WHO ELSE
WHAT IN THU— WHY I'LL BREAK—
HOW'S YOUR CORNS, MR. BOPPER
WHAM
WHY—WHAT'S THE MATTER WITH MR. BOPPER?
SAID HE NEEDED A NAP—WUZ OUT LATE LAST NIGHT
5-21
SEGAR

THIMBLE THEATER

NOW SHOWING—KNOWING HIS WORTH

Tomorrow—The Professor's No Magician

I CAN'T HANDLE YOU MYSELF, SO I'VE HIRED A BIG BRUTE TO PUNISH YOU WHEN YOU DISOBEY ME
YA HAS, HAS YA?
COME IN, MR. HOGAN
WHERE'S DE GUY YOUSE WANTS PUNISHED?
POPEYE!
YAS, POPEYE!
WHAT! YOU FEAR HIM?
I SEEN 'IM IN ACTION DOWN AT DE DOCKS—I DON'T WANT NO PART OF DAT BABY
MERCY! WHAT SORT OF A MAN ARE YOU?!
I'M A
GOOD MAN
5-23
SEGAR

THIMBLE THEATER
NOW SHOWING—THE PROFESSOR'S NO MAGICIAN

Tomorrow—Hospitable Mr. Blabber

I'M SORRY, BUT I CAN DO NOTHING WITH MR. POPEYE. HE'S A NATURAL BORN ROUGHNECK
I GUESS YOU'RE RIGHT
WHO'S A ROUGHNECK?!
YOU ARE! NOW FADE OUT I WANT TO TALK TO THE PROFESSOR
I WANT TO ASK YOUR ADVICE. OLIVE, HAM AND I HAVE THIRTY MILLION BETWEEN US - WOULD YOU ADVISE US TO INVEST IT OR NOT?
THIRTY MILLION DOLLARS WORKING FOR YOU WOULD SOON TURN INTO A BILLION. BY ALL MEANS INVEST IT - BUT - INVEST IT WISELY
DON'T LISTEN TO HIM - HE AINT SO HOT - JUSTA FLOP HE AIN'T SMART!
WHAT'S EATIN' YOU?
YOU'LL NOTICE HE GIVED UP. HE COULDN'T LEARN ME NOTHIN'

THIMBLE THEATER
NOW SHOWING—HOSPITABLE MR. BLABBER

Tomorrow—Straight as a Corkscrew

I'VE BEEN TALKING TO THE PROFESSOR AND HE ADVISES US TO INVEST OUR MONEY
WHY DON'TCHER BUY A SWELL SHIP AND LEMME BE CAPTAIN?
THAT'S OUT - NOW SHUT UP!
IT WONT HURT A THING TO GO DOWN TOWN AND LOOK AROUND
IF WE CAN RUN OUR CAPITAL UP TO A BILLION WHY NOT?
SURE
LET'S GO IN HERE AND SEE WHAT THEY HAVE
GLIBB AND BLABBER INVESTMENTS OF ALL KINDS
WELL—— WHAT DO YOU WANT?
WE HAVE THIRTY MILLION DOLLARS TO INVEST
OH, FOR HEAVEN'S SAKE! HAVE A CHAIR - MAKE YOURSELVES AT HOME!
MR. BLABBER

THIMBLE THEATER
NOW SHOWING—STRAIGHT AS A CORKSCREW

Tomorrow—Two of a Kind

HOW LONG HAVE YOU BEEN IN THIS INVESTMENT BUSINESS, MR. BLABBER?
YES, WE'D LIKE TO KNOW - WE MUST NOT TAKE RISKS WITH OUR THIRTY MILLION
TWO HUNDRED YEARS - WE ARE THE DESCENDANTS OF THE FOUNDERS, GLIBB AND BLABBER
TWO HUNDRED YEARS WITHOUT A LOSS TO OUR PATRONS
WE'LL GO HOME AND THINK IT OVER - WE GOTTA THINK IT OVER YOU KNOW
BY ALL MEANS THINK IT OVER A LONG TIME AND BRING YOUR MONEY HERE IN THE MORNING SURE
DO YOU THINK THEY HAVE THIRTY MILLION? THEY LOOK LIKE THIRTY CENTS TO ME
SURE THEY HAVE! I'LL BET THEY HAVE, I'LL BET YOU TEN DOLLARS
SAY - WHERE'D YOU GET TEN DOLLARS - YOU BEEN HOLDING OUT ON ME?
WELL, DIDN'T YOU HOLD OUT ON ME LAST WEEK? YOU CROOK!

THIMBLE THEATER

NOW SHOWING—TWO OF A KIND

Tomorrow—Popeye Lacks Humor

YES, MR. BLABBER, WE HAVE $30,000,000 TO INVEST
WHAT SORT OF INVESTMENT WOULD YOU LIKE?
SOMETHING PROFITABLE WOULD SUIT US
MR. BLABBER
FOOLISH OF ME! HA! HA! WHY I KNEW JUST WHAT YOU WANTED BEFORE YOU TOLD ME- YOU WANT ROCK BOTTOM PROFITABLE INVESTMENTS - AND WE GOT 'EM!
MR. BLABBER
BEFORE WE HAVE ANY DEALINGS - WE'LL HAVE TO ASK A FEW QUESTIONS. ARE YOU HONEST? WE WON'T DEAL WITH CROOKS, WE'RE PARTICULAR ABOUT THAT
I WANT TO INTRODUCE MY PARTNER, MR. GLIBB HE'S THE MOST HONEST MAN IN THE WORLD - FAIR AND SQUARE, THAT'S GLIBB!
HOWD'Y
FINE- HONESTY ALWAYS PAYS
9-27
SEGAR

THIMBLE THEATER

NOW SHOWING—POPEYE LACKS HUMOR

Monday—Hook, Line and Sinker

CAP'N OYL, WILL YOU LEND ME A MILLION DOLLARS?
NO! I'M GOING TO INVEST THE WHOLE WORKS
BY THE WAY POPEYE - YOU CUT YOURSELF A LOT WHEN YOU SHAVE DON'T YOU?
NO I DON'T
I DON'T NEVER CUT MYSELF
BUT HOW ON EARTH CAN YOU SHAVE AND LAUGH AT THE SAME TIME?
BLOW ME DOWN, I DON'T LAUGH WHEN I SHAVE
YA DON'T !!?
SAY- DO YOU MEAN TO TELL ME THAT YOU CAN LOOK INTO A MIRROR AND NOT LAUGH?!
?!
ME PAN'S O.K. AND BESIDES I GOT MORE PERSONALIKY THAN YOU GOT BRAINS AND THAT AIN'T SO MUCH EITHER!
I GUESS THAT'LL HOLD HIM
9-28
SEGAR

THIMBLE THEATER

NOW SHOWING—HOOK, LINE AND SINKER

Tomorrow—Money to Burn

CASTOR, YOU GO LEARN SOMETHING MORE ABOUT "GLIBB + BLABBER" INVESTMENTS
WE'LL LEAVE IT TO YOU
WHAT DO YOU WANT? OIL WELLS, GOLD MINES, OR WHAT?
ANYTHING THAT'S SAFE
NOW, PARTNER, IF ANY OF THAT BUNCH COME AROUND TODAY YOU KNOW WHAT TO DO
I OUGHT TO, I INVENTED ALL OUR TRICKS
GOOD MORNING, MR. OYL, I'M GLAD TO SEE YOU — I SUPPOSE YOUR TIME IS VERY VALUABLE SO LET'S GET DOWN TO BUSINESS
HOW'S THINGS, MR. BLABBER?
MR. BLABBER
MR. MORGAN WISHES TO SEE YOU ABOUT A VERY IMPORTANT MATTER
TELL HIM I'M BUSY
!
MR. BLABBER
9-30
GOSH! IF MR. MORGAN WANTS TO SEE YOU I CAN WAIT
HE PROBABLY WANTS TO BORROW A FEW MILLION, LET HIM WAIT
MR. BLABBER
SEGAR

THIMBLE THEATER
NOW SHOWING—MONEY TO BURN
Tomorrow—Gas Bags Need Filling

IT'S VERY NECESSARY THAT WE MAKE AN IMPRESSION UPON MR. OYL
WASTE BASKET
$5,000,000
HERE, WILLIE - DO YOUR STUFF WITH THIS BAG OF WASTE PAPER - SAME OLD STUNT
OKE
$5,000,000
MRS JONES SENT OVER FIVE MILLION FOR INVESTMENT WHAT'LL I DO WITH IT
WILLIE YOU'RE GOING TO LOSE YOUR JOB IF YOU'RE NOT CAREFUL
$5,000,000
HOW MANY TIMES MUST I TELL YOU NOT TO BOTHER ME WITH TRIFLES WHEN I'M BUSY!
YESSIR
YOU THINK FIVE MILLION IS A TRIFLE ?
SURE - WE DON'T BOTHER WITH ANYTHING UNDER THAT
WHEN ARE YOU GONNA PAY ME MY WAGES MR. GLIBB?
NOW WILLIE DON'T BE LIKE THAT - BE A GOOD KID AND WE'LL TAKE YOU INTO THE FIRM
10-1
SEGAR

THIMBLE THEATER
NOW SHOWING—GAS BAGS NEED FILLING
Tomorrow—Silence Is Golden

NO, MR. BLABBER, I DON'T THINK WE'D BE INTERESTED IN LEAD MINES
WHAT'S THE MATTER WITH LEAD MINES ?
MR. BLABBER
WE MIGHT CONSIDER INVESTING IN A FEW GOLD MINES THOUGH
A DOLLAR'S WORTH OF GOLD IS WORTH NO MORE THAN A DOLLAR'S WORTH OF LEAD
MR. BLABBER
LEAD MINES ARE ALL RIGHT - I'VE MADE $50,000,000. OUT OF THE FOUR I OWN THIS YEAR - NOT SO BAD
YEAH?!
MR. BLABBER
I'LL THINK OVER YOUR PROPOSITION. YOU KNOW IT'S A GOOD IDEA TO PROCEED SLOWLY
DON'T WAIT TOO LONG - I WANT YOU TO GET IN ON THE EASY MONEY
HEY, WILLIE, GOT ANY MONEY?
SURE - I'VE ALWAYS GOT MONEY
LEND ME TWO BITS, I'VE GOT TO HAVE HOT DOGS AND COFFEE - I'M FAMISHED
THIS'LL MAKE "ONE SIXTY FIVE" YOU OWE ME - AND DON'T FORGET IT
10-2
SEGAR

THIMBLE THEATER
NOW SHOWING—BOUGHT AND PAID FOR
Monday—The "Oreful" Truth

BE A GOOD SPORT WILLIE LEND ME FIFTY CENTS - IF YOU DON'T - WE'LL HAVE TO LOOK FOR A NEW OFFICE BOY
GO ON GIMME DE GATE WHAT DO I CARE! I BEEN HERE TWO MONTHS AND AIN'T GOT NO WAGES YET
GO ON - CAN ME! I DON'T MIND WORKIN' FOR NOTHIN', BUT DARN IF I'M GONNA SUPPORT YOU TWO EGGS - I AIN'T PAYIN' TO WORK NO PLACE! YOU BIRDS NICKEL AND DIME ME TO DEATH - AND NOW IT'S FOUR BITS !
COME ON, WILLIE, LEND ME FIFTY CENTS
!
P-S-T P-S-T
OH, HELLO MR. OYL, I WAS JUST TRYING TO BORROW HALF A BUCK FROM WILLIE TO BUY A CIGAR - I HAVE A POCKET FULL OF THOUSAND DOLLAR BILLS BUT NO CHANGE
HA! HA! GOOD JOKE ON YOU
SAY, MR. GLIBB. YOU GOT A SLICK PARTNER - DID YOU HEAR HIM GET AWAY WITH THAT CRACK ABOUT THE THOUSAND DOLLAR BILLS ?
S-S-H WILLIE, DON'T LET OUR CUSTOMER HEAR YOU - AND IF WE PUT OVER OUR LITTLE DEAL WE'LL PAY YOU YOUR BACK WAGES
OKE!
10-3
SEGAR

THIMBLE THEATER

NOW SHOWING—HUSH MONEY

Tomorrow—Bought and Paid For

SURE WILLIE. IF WE MAKE THIS DEAL WITH MR OYL YOU'LL GET YOUR BACK PAY AND THE FOUR DOLLARS AND THIRTY CENTS MR. BLABBER AND MYSELF OWE YOU
IN THAT CASE I'LL HELP YOU OUT
GOOD MORNING, MR OYL SAY, IF YOU WANT TO MAKE SOME MONEY JUST LET GLIBB AND BLABBER INVEST YOUR MONEY FOR YOU - AND THEY'RE HONEST TOO - YES SIR!
THANKS SON, HERE'S TEN BUCKS FOR THE INFORMATION
GEE MISTER. MUCH OBLIGED!
LOOK, MR GLIBB, HE GAVE ME TEN DOLLARS
LET ME SEE IT - I'LL TELL YOU WHETHER IT IS COUNTERFEIT OR NOT
YES, IT'S GOOD - THANKS WILLIE - I'LL INVEST IT FOR YOU - TEN DOLLARS IS TOO MUCH FOR YOU TO CARRY AROUND
YOU'RE GONNA WHICH ?!
YOU GIMME THAT OR I'LL GO TELL'IM YOU'RE A COUPLA CROOKS
OH WELL- TAKE IT IF YOU'RE GOING TO BE LIKE THAT
SEGAR
10-4

THIMBLE THEATER

NOW SHOWING—SILENCE IS GOLDEN

Tomorrow—Hush Money

MR BLABBER, WE'VE COME TO MAKE THE INVESTMENT WHICH YOU AND I TALKED OVER YESTERDAY
FINE - I HAVE EVERYTHING ALL FIXED UP
MR. BLABBER
HERE ARE THREE CHECKS FOR TEN MILLION DOLLARS EACH
CORRECT
HERE IS THE DEED TO THE HUNDRED ACRES OF FINE LAND, AND THE MINE IS RIGHT IN THE CENTER OF IT
MR. BLABBER
WELL, WE'VE GOT OUR MONEY INVESTED AT LAST
YES, OUR THIRTY MILLION DOLLARS IS WORKING FOR US
IT'LL MAKE US RICH
WHIFFLE
SEGAR
10-5

THIMBLE THEATER

NOW SHOWING—THE OREFUL TRUTH

Tomorrow—Down to Brass Tacks

WELL, NO MORE WORRIES FOR US - WE CAN SIT BACK AND COLLECT THE RETURNS ON OUR INVESTMENT
?
SAY- HAVE YOU INVESTED YOUR THIRTY MILLION DOLLARS?
SURE WE HAVE, DAD
WHAT DID YOU BUY?
WE BOUGHT A BRASS MINE
A BRASS MINE!!
BRASS MINE!
YES, A BRASS MINE
BRASS MINE! BRASS MINE! BRASS MINE! BRASS MINE:
HEY! WHAT'S WRONG WITH YOU, DAD?
SEGAR
10-7

THIMBLE THEATER
NOW SHOWING—DOWN TO BRASS TACKS
Tomorrow—Paw "Smelt" a Rat

WHAT DO YOU SUPPOSE IS WRONG WITH DAD? HE'S BEEN ACTING GOOFY EVER SINCE WE TOLD HIM OF OUR INVESTMENT
HE BEATS ME
CATCH ME, MAW - I THINK I'M GOING TO FAINT
!
WHAT'S THE MATTER WITH YOU, PAW? SNAP OUT OF IT!!
OUR KIDS - OUR KIDS AND THAT SAP HAM GRAVY INVESTED THEIR THIRTY MILLION IN A BRASS MINE
WELL - WHAT'S WRONG WITH THAT? BRASS IS AN IMPORTANT METAL, ISN'T IT?
SAY - DID YOU EVER HEAR OF A BRASS MINE?
WELL - NO - BUT THERE ARE LOTS OF THINGS I'VE NEVER HEARD OF

THIMBLE THEATER
NOW SHOWING—PAW "SMELT" A RAT
Tomorrow—The Brass Monkey

PAW - WHAT'S THE IDEA? I THINK YOU'RE JUST TRYING TO BE OBSTINATE
I KNOW WHAT I'M TALKING ABOUT - I WASN'T BORN YESTERDAY - YOU'RE A PACK OF DUMB-BELLS, ALL OF YOU!
LISTEN HERE, PAW - YOU'LL ADMIT THAT THERE ARE GOLD, SILVER, COPPER, IRON AND LEAD MINES - WELL, THEN WHY NOT BRASS MINES?
BECAUSE THERE AIN'T NO SUCH THINGS AS BRASS MINES THAT'S WHY - YOU SHE-SAP!!
HAR! HAR! NO BRASS MINES! HA! HA!
IF THERE WERE NO BRASS MINES THEN HOW COULD WE BUY ONE HA! HA
SURE! HA! HA! I SUPPOSE YOU THINK BRASS GROWS LIKE WHEAT OR BANANAS HA! HA!

THIMBLE THEATER
NOW SHOWING—THE BRASS MONKEY
Tomorrow—A Fool There Was

DAD, YOU SAY THERE'S NO SUCH THINGS AS BRASS MINES BUT YOU'RE WRONG - THE FELLOWS WE BOUGHT OUR MINE FROM ARE HONEST - THEY EVEN TOLD US ABOUT THE DIFFICULTIES OF BRASS MINING
I'M TELLIN' YOU THERE AIN'T NO BRASS MINES AIN'T! AIN'T! AIN'T!
THERE IS! IS! IS!
WHAT DID THEY SAY ABOUT THE DIFFICULTIES OF BRASS MINING?
THEY SAID IT WAS HARD TO MINE THE BRASS ON ACCOUNT OF THE GOLD
GOLD ?!
YEAH, THEY SAID THE GOLD WAS SO THICK THAT IT MADE IT HARD TO GET AT THE BRASS
!
FOR HEAVENS SAKE MAW - QUICK! BRING WATER! WATER!

THIMBLE THEATER

NOW SHOWING—A FOOL THERE WAS

Tomorrow—Somebody's Wrong

AND I SAY THERE AIN'T NO SUCH THINGS AS BRASS MINES
THE FACT THAT WE BOUGHT A BRASS MINE PROVES THAT THERE ARE BRASS MINES NOW DON'T IT?
NO, IT DON'T
LISTEN HERE, DAD - EVEN THOUGH I AM YOUR SON I'VE GOT BRAINS - GOTTA GOOD HEAD FULL OF SENSE
YEAH? WELL - DO YOU REMEMBER THE INVESTMENT YOU MADE A FEW YEARS AGO?
YOU BOUGHT THE MUNICIPAL BRIDGE OF THIS CITY AND TRIED TO MAKE PEOPLE PAY TO CROSS ON IT
AW, WHY DIG THAT UP?!
WHIFFLE
10-11
SEGAR

THIMBLE THEATER

NOW SHOWING—SOMEBODY'S WRONG

Monday—That Metal Badge

POPEYE AND MYSELF ARE GOING DOWN TO THE BEEZARK MOUNTAINS AND LOCATE OUR BRASS MINE
GOOD IDEA
MY DAD SAYS THERE AIN'T NO BRASS MINES
I'M GOING TO ASK THIS STRANGER AND SEE WHAT HE SAYS ABOUT IT
EXCUSE ME, MISTER, BUT DID YOU EVER HEAR OF SUCH A THING AS A BRASS MINE?
OF COURSE NOT
GEE - BUT YOU'RE DUMB!
SURE - DIDN'TCHER NEVER GO TO SCHOOL? BLOW ME DOWN
SEGAR
10-12

THIMBLE THEATER

NOW SHOWING—THAT METAL BADGE

Tomorrow—Within The Law.

CASTOR AND POPEYE ARE ON THEIR WAY DOWN TO THE BEEZARK MOUNTAINS TO LOCATE OUR BRASS MINE
YOU MAKE ME SICK
WELL HERE WE ARE IN BEEZARK CENTER NOW TO INQUIRE ABOUT OUR BRASS MINE
HELLO STRANGER SAY WHERE ARE THE BRASS MINES LOCATED?
LUNATIC!
YOU HEARD ME, I SAID YOU WAS A LUNATIC
WELL, BLOW ME DOWN!
LISTEN BIG BOY WHO YOU CALLIN' LUNAKICK? IN JUST ABOUT A MINUTE I'M GO'NER TAKE YA APART - YA BIG HICK!
YOU AND WHAT ARMY? WELL, I'M WAITIN' - COMMENCE!
NIX, POPEYE, LAY OFF HERE'S THE LAW
10-14
SEE TOMORROW
SEGAR

THIMBLE THEATER

NOW SHOWING—WITHIN THE LAW.

Tomorrow—That Copper's Got Too Much Brass

WE ASKS YOU WHERE THE BRASS MINES WAS AND YOU INSULK US - YOU CALLS US LUNAKICKS - MISTER I'M GO'NER BUST UP YOUR HATCHES
YOU UGLY RUNT! I'LL SMASH YOU UP
CUT IT OUT. POPEYE - THE VILLAGE COP IS HERE -
TAKE THAT!
CRACK
AND YOU'RE NOT GOING TO ARREST MY FRIEND? SAY DO YOU ALLOW STREET FIGHTS DOWN HERE?
BLOW ME DOWN!
THAT WARN'T NO FIGHT - PETE WENT OUT THE FIRST POP
© 1929, King Features Syndicate, Inc., Great Britain rights reserved.
SEGAR 10-15

THIMBLE THEATER

NOW SHOWING—THAT COPPER'S GOT TOO MUCH BRASS

Tomorrow—Brass Knuckles

I LON'T KNOW WHAT THE ARGYMENT WAS BUT YOU KNOCKED OUT PETE HAWKINS. SO YOU BETTER LEAVE TOWN - HE'LL GETCHA WHEN HE WAKES UP
I COMES WHEN I LIKES AND I GOES WHEN I PLEASES AND I DON'T TAKE NOTHIN' FROM NOBODY, NO TIME. BLOW ME DOWN!
YOU SURE SMACKED HIM GOOD POPEYE
SURE OFFICER, ALL WE DID WAS ASK THIS FELLOW WHERE THE BRASS MINES OF THE BEEZARK MOUNTAINS WERE LOCATED, AND HE CALLED US LUNATICS
BRASS MINES !!!
HEH! HEH! HEH! HEH!
BE CAREFUL HOW YOU LAUGH, COP. WE'RE TOUCHY ABOUT BRASS MINES. ONE MORE SNICKER OUTTER YOU AND I'LL EATCHER UP
FOR CRYIN' OUT LOUD! DON'T START ANYTHING WITH THE LAW — COME ON, POPEYE. YOU'LL GET ARRESTED
BETTER WATCH OUT - I'M THE CITY MARSHAL
© 1929, King Features Syndicate, Inc., Great Britain rights reserved.
SEGAR 10-16

THIMBLE THEATER

NOW SHOWING—BRASS KNUCKLES.

Tomorrow—The Mine "Mule."

G'WAN, YA HICK! I'LL CLEAN HOUSE ON YA IN ABOUT A MINUTE
STOP SQUABBLING! LET'S GO ASK THIS FELLOW IF HE KNOWS WHERE OUR BRASS MINE IS
WHY YOU SILLY SAP - THERE AIN'T NO BRASS MINES!
TAKE THAT BACK
STRANGER, I FEEL SORRY FOR YOU! YOU AIN'T GOT LONG TO LIVE
POPEYE, CAN'T YOU BEHAVE?!
CRACK
SOCK
BIFF
BETTER WATCH OUT. I'M THE CITY MARSHAL
HE CAN'T INSULK CAP'N OYL. BLOW ME DOWN HE CAN'T!
AW, POPEYE, LAY OFF
SEGAR 10-17

THIMBLE THEATER

NOW SHOWING—THE MINE "MULE."

Tomorrow—Brass Buttons.

YOU POOR NITWIT! THAR AIN'T NO SUCH THINGS AS BRASS MINES
THERE IS TOO! BESIDES YOU DON'T NEED TO GET SORE ABOUT IT
STEP ASIDE. I'LL TAKE 'IM THE SWAB
THERE AIN'T NO BRASS MINES
NIX POPEYE. YOU'LL LAND US BOTH IN JAIL
THERE IS TOO BRASS MINES!
THERE AIN'T!
CRACK
HEY THERE! STOP THAT! STOP IT! STOP IT! HEY THERE!
SOCK
BIFF
SAY! I'M THE CITY MARSHAL, HEY!
SURE THERE'S BRASS MINES! SURE THERE IS!
YA DERN TOOTIN' THERE IS!
YA DERN TOOTIN' THERE IS
10-18
SEGAR

THIMBLE THEATER

NOW SHOWING -BRASS BUTTONS.

Monday—The Property Man.

SAY YOU'D BETTER STOP YOUR FIGHTING AND QUIT TEASING THAT COP OR YOU'LL GET INTO SERIOUS TROUBLE
CAP'N OYL - I LIVES ME OWN LIFE AND DON'T NEVER FORGET THAT
HEY THERE! YOU'VE BEEN DISTURBING THE PEACE AROUND HERE LONG ENOUGH. YOU'RE UNDER ARREST - AND DON'TCHA HIT ME EITHER
YOU BETTER GET THE FIRE DEPARTMENT TO HELP YOU POP
GOOD NIGHT!
!
YOU AIN'T A REAL OSSIFER I'LL BET YOU'LL BE PLAYING COW BOY TO MORROW
SHUT UP. POPEYE!
YOU CAN'T FOOL WITH ME, I'M THE CITY MARSHAL!
BLOW ME DOWN!
SEE - I TOLD YOU YOU'D GET INTO TROUBLE
SEE!
10-19
SEGAR

THIMBLE THEATER

NOW SHOWING—THE PROPERTY MAN

Tomorrow—Who's Peeling Those Onions?

S'WAN - YOU COULDN'T HIT NOTHIN'
YOU SEE, POPEYE, WHAT YOUR FIGHTING DID - YOU'VE GOT THAT COP SHOOTIN' AT US!
BANG
BANG
HE AIN'T GOT NO RIGHTS TO SHOOT AT US - I'M GOIN' BACK AND MAKE HIM EAT THAT GUN
OH, NO YOU'RE NOT, YOU BIG SAP
CAN'T I GO CRACK 'IM JUST ONCE ?
NO — WE'VE GOT TO LOCATE THE HUNDRED ACRES AND SEE IF THERE'S A BRASS MINE ON IT
ACCORDING TO THIS MAP WE ARE NOW STANDING UPON THE LAND WHICH HAM, OLIVE AND MYSELF PAID $30.000.000 FOR
MISTER, I SEE YOU'RE LIVING ON MY LAND
SO YOU BOUGHT THESE ACRES FROM THEM SWINDLERS DIDJA?
YES SWINDLERS - I TRADED 'EM THIS LAND FOR A MILLION DOLLARS WORTH OF NO GOOD OIL STOCK. I WAS BORND HERE TOO - IT'LL BE HARD TO LEAVE THE OLD PLACE BUT I RECKON YOU'LL PUT ME OFF
10-21
SEGAR

THIMBLE THEATER
NOW SHOWING—WHO'S PEELING THOSE ONIONS?
Tomorrow—A Soft-Hearted Landlord

HEY POPEYE THIS MAN SAYS THAT THE MEN WHO BOUGHT THIS LAND FROM HIM AND SOLD IT TO US WERE CROOKS
WELL, BLOW ME DOWN! BLOW ME DOWN!
I RECKON YOU'LL TAKE THE PLACE. THE OLD HOME WHERE I WAS BORND
I DON'T KNOW WHAT TO DO
LIFE SURE IS HARD ON POOR FOLKS - I'VE GOT NINETY ACRES OF ONIONS GROWIN' HERE AND IF I DON'T GET 'EM RAISED I'LL BE BROKE - BUT IF YOU SAY GO - WHY WE'LL GO
GEE - THIS LAND IS ALL I OWN IN THE WORLD
THEN TAKE IT MISTER - I AIN'T ASKIN' NO FAVORS
YA AIN'T GO'NER DO IT, CAP'N OYL. YA AIN'T GO'NER KICK 'IM OFF'N THE OLD FARM WHERE HE WAS BRUNG UP - THE ONLY HOME HE EVER KNOW'D - YA AIN'T GONER, IS YA CAP'N OYL?
SNIFF
SEGAR 10-22

THIMBLE THEATER
NOW SHOWING—A SOFT-HEARTED LANDLORD
Tomorrow—The Mob Scene

CAP'N OYL - YOU'RE A MAN AIN'TCHER? THEN GIVE HIM THE LAND THEM CROOKS SNITCHED OFF'N HIM
THEY TOOK ME TOO POPEYE
THEY TOOK ME FOR A LOT OF MONEY - THIS FARM IS ALL I OWN IN THIS WORLD - I CAN'T HELP IT IF THEY BEAT HIM OUT OF IT
YEAH, AND MAYBE HE'S GOT KIDS TOO - LITTLE BABIES AND THINGS
!
YOU GOT CHILDREN, MISTER?
KIDS - THAT'S THE ONE THING I AIN'T SHORT ON
WELL - IF YOU'VE GOT CHILDREN - IF YOU'VE GOT LITTLE KIDS - I COULDN'T PUT YOU OFF - I COULDN'T PUT LITTLE KIDS OUT OF THEIR HOME
NOW DONTCHER WORRY, MATE, CAP'N OYL AIN'T GO'NER PUTCHER OFF - BLOW ME DOWN HE AIN'T GO'NER
SEGAR 10-23

THIMBLE THEATER
NOW SHOWING—THE MOB SCENE
Tomorrow—A Sentimental Sailor

I KNOW'D YOU WAS A MAN CAP'N OYL BLOW ME DOWN I DID!
YES - I'LL DO IT
MISTER, THIS HUNDRED ACRES COST ME A LOT OF MONEY - I OWN A THIRD OF IT - MY SISTER AND A FRIEND OWN THE REST
GLIB AND BLABBER BEAT YOU OUT OF THIS FARM AND SOLD IT TO US - BUT I'M GOING TO FIX IT SO YOU CAN HAVE IT BACK
COME ON UP TO THE HOUSE AND GET ACQUAINTED WITH MY FAMILY
I COULDN'T PUT LITTLE KIDS OUT OF THEIR HOME I COULDN'T DO THAT
SALLY, I WANT YOU TO MEET TWO FRIENDS OF MINE
HI POP
BLOW ME DOWN
SEGAR 10-24

THIMBLE THEATER

NOW SHOWING—A SENTIMENTAL SAILOR

Tomorrow—The Smack He Can't Forget

MY GOSH! HOW MANY KIDS HAS HE GOT ANYWAY?
I BEEN TRYIN' TO COUNT 'EM BUT I AIN'T MUCH ON 'RITHMATIC
SALLY, THESE GENTS ARE GOING TO GIVE US OUR LAND BACK
REALLY! OH, I CAN'T BELIEVE IT!
I'VE JUST GOT TO GIVE THEM A KISS!
'SALL RIGHT WITH ME. IF THEY DON'T MIND
SMACK
!
SMACK
BLOW ME DOWN! EVER' TIME A WOMAN KISSES ME I FALLS IN LOVE! BLOW ME DOWN!
S-S-S-H YOU BIG SAP DON'T LET 'EM HEAR YOU TALKIN' LIKE THAT!
©SEGAR
10-25

THIMBLE THEATER

NOW SHOWING—THE SMACK HE CAN'T FORGET

Monday—The End of Her Rope

WHAT AILS THE SAILOR? HE AIN'T ACTIN' NATURAL, IS HE?
I'LL TELL YOU WHAT IT IS— YOU KNOW YOUR WIFE KISSED US BECAUSE WE'RE GIVING YOUR FARM BACK
WELL- POOR OLD POPEYE ISN'T ACCUSTOMED TO BEING KISSED- HE'S UGLY AND ALL THAT BUT HE'S HUMAN AND SENSITIVE-
HE'S IN LOVE WITH YOUR WIFE
I DON'T BLAME HIM- SALLY'S A MIGHTY FINE WOMAN
BUT HE MEANS NO HARM- WHY HE'D MURDER ANY GUY WHO'D SUGGEST THAT HE STEAL YOUR MISSUS
WE'LL GO AWAY AND I'LL FORGET ALL ABOUT YOU FOLKS. BUT POPEYE—HE'LL REMEMBER
HE'LL REMEMBER HER KISS TILL HE CASHES IN
HE STRIKES ME AS BEING A FINE BIG-HEARTED MAN
YES, HE HAS THE BIGGEST HEART— AND INCIDENTLY THE HARDEST FIST
10-26
©SEGAR

THIMBLE THEATER

NOW SHOWING—THE END OF HER ROPE

Tomorrow—According to Webster

YES, MR. WEEDLE, I'VE SENT PAPERS TO THE OTHER OWNERS TO SIGN AND HIRED AN ATTORNEY- HE'LL FIX THINGS AND YOU'LL GET YOUR FARM BACK
I DON'T KNOW HOW TO THANK YOU— I CAN'T FIND WORDS
BY THE WAY- HOW COME YOU GOT SO MUCH FAMILY?
SOME FLOCK !!
WELL, THERE WAS TRIPLETS THREE TIMES AND TWINS TWICE BESIDES THE SINGLES
HOW MANY HAVE YOU, MR. WEEDLE?
DANGED IF I KNOW. I AIN'T COUNTED 'EM THIS YEAR
MY NEIGHBOR'S GOT ABOUT AS MANY AS US- SOMETIMES THEY GET ALL MIXED TOGETHER, AND IF IT WASN'T FOR BOILS AND SORE TOES WE'D HAVE A HECK OF A TIME SORTIN' 'EM OUT
THE MISSUS SAYS SHE DON'T WANT ANY MORE ON ACCOUNT OF IT BEING SO DARNED HARD THINKIN' UP NAMES
!
10-28
©SEGAR

THIMBLE THEATER

NOW SHOWING—ACCORDING TO WEBSTER

Tomorrow—A "Minor" Detail

WHY DON'T YOU ASK MR. WEEDLE IF THERE'S A BRASS MINE ON THIS LAND?
I'M THROUGH ASKING THAT QUESTION, POPEYE
HAVE YOU A DICTIONARY, MR. WEEDLE?
YEAH, BUT THE KIDS WORKED ON IT TILL THERE'S NOTHIN' LEFT BUT THE "B'S"
THAT'S O.K. THE WORD I WANT BEGINS WITH "B"
I'LL GET IT
B-BR-BRA-BRAS-"BRASS" "AN ALLOY OF COPPER AND ZINC. WELL I'LL BE-!
POPEYE-CAN YOU IMAGINE MY EMBARRASSMENT. THERE AIN'T NO SUCH THINGS AS BRASS MINES
THERE AIN'T?!
BRASS IS MADE FROM COPPER AND ZINC
WELL BLOW ME DOWN
10-29 SEGAR

THIMBLE THEATER

NOW SHOWING—A "MINOR" DETAIL

Tomorrow—The Copper and Lead

WELL, SO LONG, MR. WEEDLE, WE WISH YOU LUCK
GOOD BYE, MR OYL. THANKS FOR PUTTING AN END TO MY TROUBLES
AND SAY MR WEEDLE, DON'T LET ANY SLICKERS TAKE YOU FOR YOUR LAND AGAIN
DON'T WORRY I WONT !!
THAT OLD FARMER NEEDS A GUARDIAN AND THAT'S A FACT!
JUST A HICK THAT'S ALL
POPEYE CAN YOU IMAGINE A FELLOW TRADING HIS FARM FOR A BUNCH OF NO GOOD OIL STOCK? HA! HA! SOME DUMB-BELL
YEAH-AND CAN YOU 'MAGINE A GUY PAYING THIRTY MILLION DOLLARS FOR A BRASS MINE?
!
10-30 SEGAR

THIMBLE THEATER

NOW SHOWING—THE COPPER AND LEAD

Tomorrow—Gun Play

POPEYE, WE WANT TO CATCH A TRAIN FOR HOME TO-MORROW, AND YOU'VE GOT TO PROMISE NOT TO FIGHT ANY MORE YOU KNOW THAT HICK COP IS AFTER US
I PROMISE
SAY-YOU'RE THE GUY WHO SOCKED ME DAY BEFORE YESTERDAY AIN'T YOU?
YEAH, I'M THE GUY WHAT SOCKED YA DAY BEFORE YESTERDAY
CRACK
AND I'M THE GUY WHAT SOCKED YA TO-DAY, TOO
HEY THERE-YOU'RE UNDER ARREST AND DON'TCHA HIT ME EITHER
BLOW ME DOWN!
NOW SEE! SEE! YOU BIG SAP-WHAT'D I TELL YOU!
SEGAR 10-31

THIMBLE THEATER

NOW SHOWING—GUN PLAY

Tomorrow—The One-Man Bucket Brigade

YA DERN TOOTIN' IT'S LOADED! AND YOU'RE UNDER ARREST, BETTER LOOK OUT
G'WAN I'LL BET IT AIN'T LOADED
POPEYE, BE CAREFUL
HEY! YOU WATCH OUT!
LEMME HAVE THAT GUN - I WANT TO SEE IF IT'S LOADED
BANG
BANG
BANG
!
HERE'S YOUR GUN YOU WIN - SHE WAS LOADED
YA DERNED FOOL YA SHOT OFF ALL MY BULLETS!
WELL BLOW ME DOWN - THINKA THAT!
SEGAR
11-1

THIMBLE THEATER

NOW SHOWING—THE ONE-MAN BUCKET BRIGADE

Monday—That Jailer's No Postage Stamp

YOU BIG RUFFIAN SEE WHAT YOUR FIGHTING DID! YOU GOT US IN BAD WITH THE LAW
WE WONT BE ABLE TO GET OUT OF THIS COUNTRY - THAT COP WILL NOTIFY ALL THE RAILROADS - THE BEST THING FOR US TO DO IS LET HIM ARREST US
COME ON - LET'S GET IT OVER - AND I HOPE THIS WILL BE A LESSON TO YOU.
ALL RIGHT, ORFICER, COME ON - ARRESK US
THERE ISN'T A HOTEL IN THIS TOWN SO WE'RE GOING TO LET YOU TAKE US TO JAIL
WELL, IT'S A GOOD THING YA GIVE UP - BECAUSE I'VE GOT THE FIRE DEPT. TO HELP RUN YA DOWN
BY HECK!
SEGAR
11-2

THIMBLE THEATER

NOW SHOWING—THAT JAILER'S NO POSTAGE STAMP

Tomorrow—Ask and You Shall Receive

IT'S A GOOD THING FOR YOU THAT YOU GIVE UP. I'M WAS GETTIN TIRED OF FOOLIN WITH YOU SCALLYWAGS!
YOU AND YOUR WHOLE TOWN COULDN'T ARRESK ME IF I DIDNT WANT YOU TO CAP'N OYL INSISKS THAT WE LET YOU TAKE US
COME ON, COP TAKE US TO JAIL AND SHUT UP
DON'T GIMME NO DIRTY LOOKS COP I MAY SMACK YA ONE YET
YOU BE CAREFUL THERE!
POPEYE, WILL YOU SHUT UP!
JAILER, HERE'S A COUPLA CRIMINALS I CAPTURED ONE OF 'EM'S BAD DON'T LET 'EM ESCAPE
BAD EH?
SAY - I CAN LICK YOU!
!!
WHAT'S THAT!
POPEYE ARE YOU CRAZY ?!
SEGAR
11-4

THIMBLE THEATER

NOW SHOWING—ASK AND YOU SHALL RECEIVE

Tomorrow—The "Crack-Pot"

GET INTO THAT CELL BEFORE I SLAP YOU DOWN! I WON'T STAND NO MONKEY BUSINESS
I GOT A GOOD IDEAR TO TAKE YA APART - I OUGHTA CLEAN HOUSE ON YA
POPEYE, STOP IT! YOU HEAR ME!
YA WILL - WILL YA?
FOR CRYIN' OUT LOUD LAY OFF!
YAS I WILL!
HIT ME! GO ON, HIT ME!
POPEYE YOU CAN'T HIT A JAILER, IT'S AGAINST THE LAW
COME ON, HIT ME! HIT ME! LESSEE YA HIT ME - COME ON HIT ME - HIT ME!
CRACK
SEGAR 11-5

THIMBLE THEATER

NOW SHOWING—THE "CRACK-POT"

Tomorrow—The Fresh-Air Fiend

POPEYE, WHAT'D YOU DO THAT FOR? DON'T YOU KNOW IT'S AGAINST THE LAW TO HIT A JAILER!
BLOW ME DOWN HE DARED ME TO CRACK 'IM AND I CRACKS 'IM!
FIGHTING! ALWAYS FIGHTING! WHAT KIND OF AN EGG ARE YOU, ANYWAY?
I YAM WHAT I YAM AND THAT'S WHAT I YAM
SO YOU WENT AND HIT THE JAILER, EH? SAY - IM GONNA TELL THE SHERIFF - HE'LL FIX YOU DERN SCALLYWAGS
TELL THE ARMY
COME ON NOW, BOYS - GET INTO THAT CELL AND NO MORE FOOLISHNESS
DON'T CROWD ME - I'LL TAKE A CRACK AT YOU TOO IN A MINUTE
POPEYE, KEEP YOUR MOUTH SHUT

THIMBLE THEATER

NOW SHOWING—THE FRESH-AIR FIEND

Tomorrow—"The Firebug"

WELL, I HOPE YOU'RE SATISFIED - YOU GOT US PUT IN JAIL YOU FUNNY LOOKIN' SHIPWRECK
SAY - I CAN BUST OUT OF THIS EGG-CRATE ANYTIME
POPEYE! FROM NOW ON YOU WATCH YOUR STEP! YOU'RE THE LIMIT! I NEVER IN ALL MY LIFE SAW A RASCAL LIKE YOU -
ROUGH-HOUSING! ALL THE TIME ROUGH-HOUSING! GOOD NIGHT
CRACK
CREEK
THEY AIN'T ENOUGH VENTERLATION IN HERE SO I TOOK THESE BARS OUT
SEGAR 11-7

THIMBLE THEATER

NOW SHOWING—THE FIREBUG

Tomorrow—Barnum Was Right!

POPEYE YOU'RE GOING TO GET US INTO SERIOUS TROUBLE. YOU CAN'T TAKE LIBERTIES LIKE THAT WHEN YOU'RE IN JAIL -
I'M GO'NER TAKE THIS JAIL APART
PUT THOSE BARS BACK PUT 'EM BACK!
ALLA TIME SOWING WILD OATS. YOU'RE OLD ENOUGH TO KNOW BETTER - NOW PUT THOSE BARS BACK INTO THE WINDOWS
ALL RIGHT THEN I'LL BE GOOD
TROUBLE! ALWAYS A LOT OF TROUBLE TO WORRY ABOUT
HEY! CAP'N OYL I GOT A BIG IDEAR!
WHAT IS IT POPEYE ?
I'M GO'NER SET THE JAIL ON FIRE - THEN THEY'LL HAVE TO TURN US OUT- BLOW ME DOWN!
STOP!
SEGAR
11-8

THIMBLE THEATER

NOW SHOWING—BARNUM WAS RIGHT!

Monday—The Hunting Grounds

CAP'N OYL - WHAT DID THEM BIRDS LOOK LIKE WHAT SOLD YOU A BRASS MINE FOR THIRTY MILLION BUCKS?
DON'T NEVER MENTION BRASS MINE TO ME AGAIN. I'M TRYING TO LIVE THAT DOWN!
AND WHAT'S MORE, YOU NITWIT, IF YOU HADN'T GOT US CHUCKED INTO JAIL WE COULD HUNT THOSE SWINDLERS DOWN. YOU SILLY LOOKIN' SHIPWRECK IN THE FACE!
I DON'T MIND GETTIN' CUSSED OUT ONCT IN A WHILE CAP'N OYL - BUT INSULKS - BLOW ME DOWN. I DON'T LIKE INSULKS!
TO THINK THAT A FEW WEEKS AGO WE HAD THIRTY MILLION DOLLARS - THEN WE WERE HELD UP! DARN CRIMINALS!! WE'LL NEVER FIND ANOTHER SOFT SNAP LIKE CASTOR OYL
THE WOODS IS FULL OF 'EM - WE'LL BUY SOME OF THIS CHEAP LAND AND STICK SOME OTHER SUCKER
GLIBB AND BLABBER" ARE BACK LOOKING FOR LAND BARGAINS NEAR BEEZARK CENTER
WOULDN'T IT BE HOT IF POPEYE GOT HIS MITTS ON 'EM ?
© 1929, King Features Syndicate, Inc., Great Britain rights reserved
SEGAR
11-9

THIMBLE THEATER

NOW SHOWING—THE HUNTING GROUNDS

Tomorrow—"Sound" Advice

CASTOR OYL IN JAIL - THINK OF IT! I'M DISGRACED! AND IT'S ALL YOUR FAULT, YOU DISH-FACED SHIPWRECK!
STOP INSULKING ME - SAY, AIN'T YOU NEVER BEEN IN JAIL BEFORE ?
?
POPEYE, I'M TELLING YOU FOR THE LAST TIME - IF YOU WANT TO BE MY FRIEND YOU'VE GOT TO STOP FIGHTING!
WHIFFLE
ALL RIGHT - I PROMISE NEVER TO FIGHT NO MORE. BLOW ME DOWN - NOW ARE YOU SATCHISFIED ?
?
WE'VE GOT TO BE CAREFUL DOWN HERE - CASTOR OYL MAY BE AROUND THIS SECTION.
WELL - WE'VE GOT TO PICK UP SOME LAND - AND THIS IS THE BEST SPOT FOR BARGAINS. BLABBER, YOU'RE TOO JUMPY TO BE A GOOD SWINDLER
11-11
SEGAR

THIMBLE THEATER

NOW SHOWING—"SOUND" ADVICE

Tomorrow—Copping an Earful

BLOW ME DOWN! WHAT'RE WE STICKIN' IN THIS JAIL FOR? LE'S US PULL THEM BARS OUT AND EXCAPE
NO! WE'LL DO NOTHING LIKE THAT
DO YOU THINK I WANT A PACK OF BLOOD HOUNDS CHASING ME? WELL I DON'T!
DORGS DON'T MEAN NOTHIN' TO ME - I JUST AS SOON CRACK A BLEED HOUND AS A HOOMAN
THERE YOU GO - THINKING ABOUT ROUGH HOUSING - ALWAYS THINKING ABOUT SOWING WILD OATS - POPEYE, YOU'LL NEVER AMOUNT TO A THING
LISTEN BLABBER, THE THING FOR US TO DO IS FIND SOME POOR WIDOW AND CHEAT HER OUT OF HER FARM
YEAH, I GETCHA
11-12
SEGAR

THIMBLE THEATER

NOW SHOWING—COPPING AN EARFUL

Tomorrow—The Invited Guests

REMEMBER, YOU PROMISED ME THAT YOU'D QUIT FIGHTING
SURE - I'M THROUGH - I'LL NEVER SOCK NOBODY AGAIN AS LONG AS I LIVES
BEANS - ALLA TIME BEANS! WHY DON'TCHER GIVE US STEAKS AND GRAVY?
BEANS IS GOOD ENOUGH FOR BUM JAIL BIRDS
I DON'T TAKE INSULKS!
CRACK
SAY! YOU JUST NOW PROMISED TO QUIT FIGHTING!
ALL RIGHT THEN. BLOW ME DOWN, I'LL NEVER FIGHT NO MORE AGAIN - I PROMISE
GLIB, OLD BOY. IF YOU'LL LOCATE SOME POOR DUMB WIDOW WITH A FARM - I'LL CHEAT HER OUT OF IT QUICK!
LEAVE IT TO ME, BLABBER
WELL I'LL BE DERNED - !! CHEAT A POOR WIDOW! I'LL BET THEY'RE A COUPLA CROOKS
11-13
SEGAR

THIMBLE THEATER

NOW SHOWING—THE INVITED GUESTS

Tomorrow—They Get the Point

I WONDER IF I'LL EVER RUN INTO THOSE TWO CROOKS, GLIB AND BLABBER?
IF YA EVER DO JUST LEMME KNOW! JUST LEMME KNOW IF YA EVER DO!
THERE'S AN OFFICER FOLLOWING US - DO YOU THINK HE KNOWS ANYTHING?
THAT HICK COP DOESN'T KNOW HE'S LIVING
BY CRACKY! I'M NOT GOIN' TO LET THEM FELLERS ESCAPE - HEY, THERE!
HEY, THERE!
HEY, THERE!
HEY!
?
?
HEY, THERE - YA DERN CROOKS, I HEARD WHAT YA SAID ABOUT BEATIN' SOME POOR WIDOW OUT OF HER FARM! YOU'RE UNDER ARREST - COME ON GO TO JAIL - COME ON!
!
!
11-14
SEGAR

THIMBLE THEATER

NOW SHOWING—THEY GET THE POINT

Tomorrow—Company's Comin'

POPEYE, I MADE YOU PROMISE TO QUIT ROUGH-HOUSING - BUT IF WE EVER RUN ACROSS GLIB AND BLABBER I WANT YOU TO GIVE 'EM THE WORKS!
I GOTTA SOCK WHAT I USES ON SPECIAL EXTER ENEMIES. I'LL GIVE 'EM IT.
YOU HEAR ME? I SAID YOU'RE GOING TO JAIL AND DON'T GIMME NO SLICK TALK EITHER
G'WAN-COP- WE HAVEN'T TIME TO PLAY NOW. RUN ALONG
BESIDES YOU HAVEN'T A THING ON US, YOU HICK
THINK I'M PLAYIN' EH? SEE THIS PISTOL? THERE AIN'T NO NOTCHES ON THE HANDLE BUT I SURE LOVE TO WHITTLE
ALL RIGHT, WE'LL GO TO JAIL
YA DERN TOOTIN' YOU'RE GOIN' TO JAIL- YA CAN'T FOOL WITH ME- I HAD MY EYE ON YA EVER SINCE YA COME
11-15

THIMBLE THEATER

NOW SHOWING—COMPANY'S COMIN'

Monday—Dangerous Carves Ahead

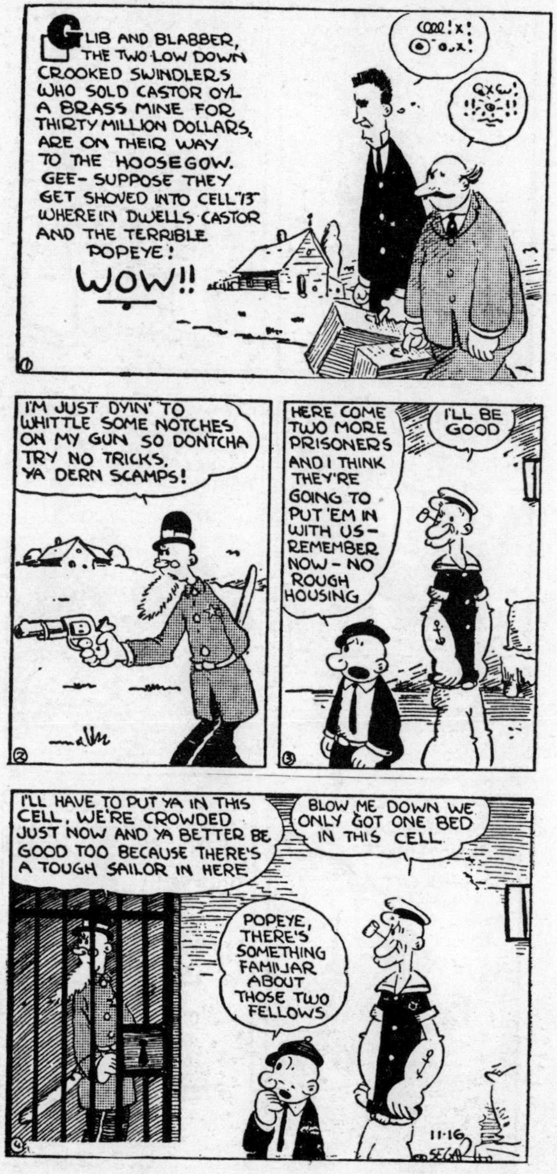
GLIB AND BLABBER, THE TWO LOW DOWN CROOKED SWINDLERS WHO SOLD CASTOR OYL A BRASS MINE FOR THIRTY MILLION DOLLARS, ARE ON THEIR WAY TO THE HOOSEGOW. GEE- SUPPOSE THEY GET SHOVED INTO CELL "13" WHEREIN DWELLS CASTOR AND THE TERRIBLE POPEYE!
WOW!!
I'M JUST DYIN' TO WHITTLE SOME NOTCHES ON MY GUN SO DONTCHA TRY NO TRICKS, YA DERN SCAMPS!
HERE COME TWO MORE PRISONERS AND I THINK THEY'RE GOING TO PUT 'EM IN WITH US- REMEMBER NOW- NO ROUGH HOUSING
I'LL BE GOOD
I'LL HAVE TO PUT YA IN THIS CELL, WE'RE CROWDED JUST NOW AND YA BETTER BE GOOD TOO BECAUSE THERE'S A TOUGH SAILOR IN HERE
BLOW ME DOWN WE ONLY GOT ONE BED IN THIS CELL
POPEYE, THERE'S SOMETHING FAMILIAR ABOUT THOSE TWO FELLOWS
11-16

THIMBLE THEATER

NOW SHOWING—DANGEROUS "CARVES" AHEAD

Tomorrow—A Buried Weapon

GENTS. WE WAS IN THIS CELL FIRST AND THE BED OVER THERE IS OURS. YOU BIRDS CAN SLEEP ON THE FLOOR
GET FRESH WITH US AND YOU'LL BE SLEEPING ON YOUR EAR
YOU CAN SLEEP ANY PLACE YOU LIKE - EXCEPT ON THE BED
WAIT A MINUTE, POPEYE - I KNOW 'EM. THEY'RE MR. GLIB AND BLABBER THE CROOKS WHO SWINDLED ME OUT OF $30,000,000 — SOLD ME A BRASS MINE
IT'S CASTOR OYL!!
DO YA JUST WANT ME TO CRIPPLE 'EM FOR LIFE, OR DO YA WANT A REAL JOB?
LOOK OUT, POPEYE, BLABBER'S GOT A KNIFE
11-18

THIMBLE THEATER
NOW SHOWING—A BURIED WEAPON

Tomorrow—A Point from Popeye

GLIB AND BLABBER WERE ARRESTED BY THE LOCAL COP AND THROWN INTO THE SAME CELL WITH CASTOR AND POPEYE. POPEYE IS GETTING READY TO WORK ON 'EM AND SWEARS THAT HE'LL KNOCK 'EM COLD——— BLABBER HAS A KNIFE
STAY OUT OF THIS GLIB, I'LL SETTLE HIS HASH WITH THIS PIG STICKER
IF YOU FAIL, I'LL STEP IN AND FINISH HIM
BETTER BE CAREFUL WITH THAT KNIFE, YA MIGHT FALL ON IT AFTER I POPS YA
HERE HE COMES. LOOK OUT!
CAREFUL NOW - DON'T STICK YOURSELF
CAN'TCHER GETCHER KNIFE OUTTER THE FLOOR? BLOW ME DOWN! NOW AIN'T THAT TOUGH?
11-19
SEGAR

THIMBLE THEATER
NOW SHOWING—A POINT FROM POPEYE

Tomorrow—A Broken Wing

GLIB AND BLABBER WERE THROWN INTO THE SAME CELL WITH CASTOR AND POPEYE POPEYE BEGAN CLEANING HOUSE ON BLABBER—— BLABBER STARTED A TERRIFIC OVERHAND SWING WITH HIS WICKED KNIFE— BUT POPEYE DUCKED BETWEEN HIS LEGS TRIPPING HIM— AND THE KNIFE BURIED ITSELF 4¾ INCHES INTO THE FLOOR
POPEYE, YOU SAP! CRACK 'IM WHILE HE'S TRYING TO PULL HIS KNIFE OUT OF THE FLOOR!
I AIN'T BEEN BRUNG UP TO POP 'EM WHEN THEY AIN'T LOOKIN'
YOU'RE WASTIN' TIME, YOU'LL NEVER GET IT OUT
YA WEAK? IT WASN'T IN TIGHT - YA OUGHTER EAT MORE BEEF
!
HERE - AND MIND YA DON'T FALL ON IT WHEN I POPS YA
POPEYE! DON'T GIVE IT BACK TO HIM!
G-R-R
G-R-R
11-20
SEGAR

THIMBLE THEATER
NOW SHOWING—A BROKEN WING

Tomorrow—Capital Punishment

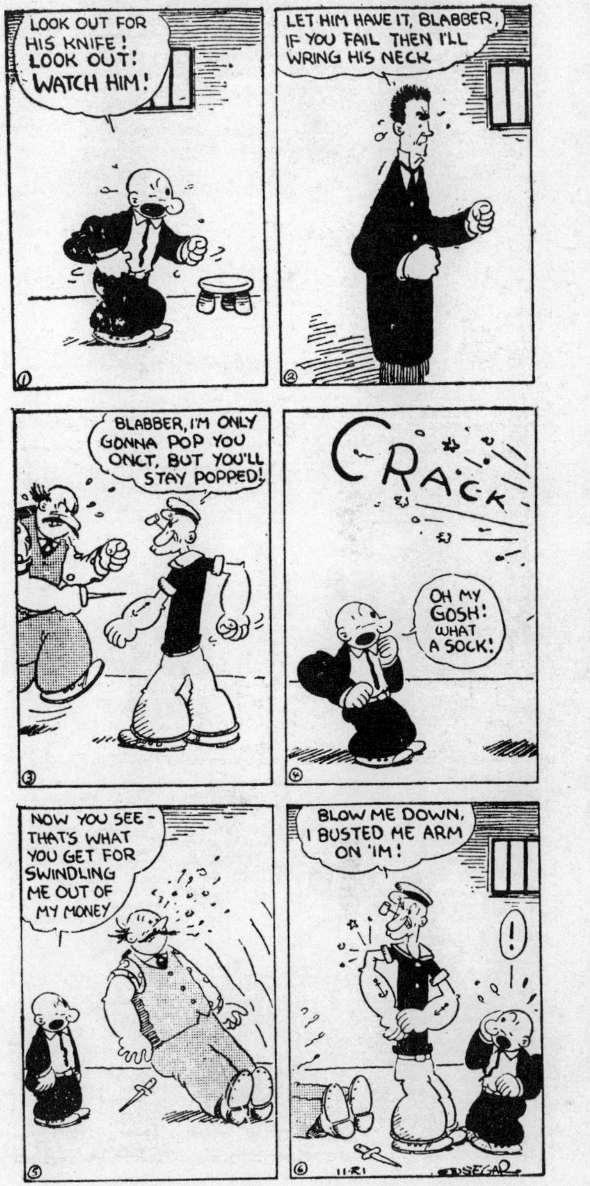
LOOK OUT FOR HIS KNIFE! LOOK OUT! WATCH HIM!
LET HIM HAVE IT, BLABBER, IF YOU FAIL THEN I'LL WRING HIS NECK
BLABBER, I'M ONLY GONNA POP YOU ONCT, BUT YOU'LL STAY POPPED!
CRACK
OH MY GOSH! WHAT A SOCK!
NOW YOU SEE - THAT'S WHAT YOU GET FOR SWINDLING ME OUT OF MY MONEY
BLOW ME DOWN, I BUSTED ME ARM ON 'IM!
!
11-21
SEGAR

THIMBLE THEATER
NOW SHOWING—CAPITAL PUNISHMENT
Tomorrow—A Heath Hint

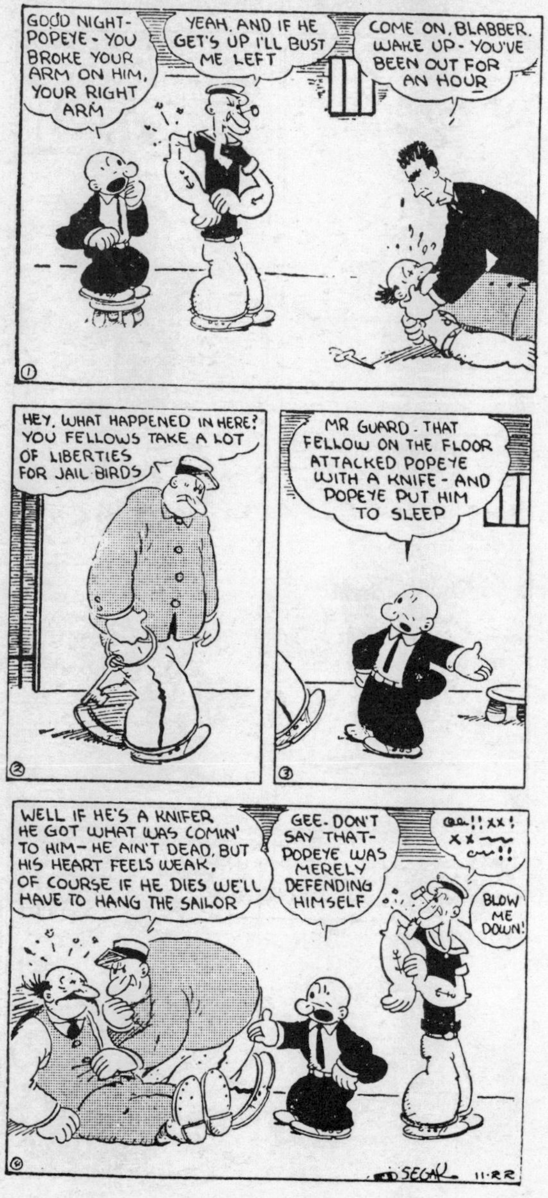

GOOD NIGHT- POPEYE - YOU BROKE YOUR ARM ON HIM, YOUR RIGHT ARM
YEAH, AND IF HE GET'S UP I'LL BUST ME LEFT
COME ON, BLABBER. WAKE UP - YOU'VE BEEN OUT FOR AN HOUR
HEY, WHAT HAPPENED IN HERE? YOU FELLOWS TAKE A LOT OF LIBERTIES FOR JAIL BIRDS
MR GUARD - THAT FELLOW ON THE FLOOR ATTACKED POPEYE WITH A KNIFE - AND POPEYE PUT HIM TO SLEEP
WELL IF HE'S A KNIFER HE GOT WHAT WAS COMIN' TO HIM- HE AIN'T DEAD, BUT HIS HEART FEELS WEAK, OF COURSE IF HE DIES WE'LL HAVE TO HANG THE SAILOR
GEE- DON'T SAY THAT- POPEYE WAS MERELY DEFENDING HIMSELF
BLOW ME DOWN!
SEGAR 11-22

THIMBLE THEATER
NOW SHOWING—A HEALTH HINT
Monday—The Left-Handed Champ

POPEYE, YOU SHOULDN'T HAVE HIT BLABBER SO HARD - IT WASN'T NECESSARY TO PUT HIM AWAY WITH ONE PUNCH. NOW WHAT ARE YOU GOING TO DO WITH A BROKEN ARM?
QUIT BAWLIN' ME OUT- BUSTED WINGS AIN'T NOTHIN- I CAN STAND IT
AND BESIDES I PUT THAT CROOK IN THE HOSPITAL DIDN'T I? THAT'S WHERE YOU WANTED HIM PUT, AIN'T IT?
YEAH, BUT SUPPOSE HIS PARTNER OVER THERE DECIDES TO TAKE YOU APART? WHAT COULD YOU DO WITH A BUSTED FIN?
TAKE HIM APART IS EXACTLY WHAT I'M GOING TO DO
DON'T FORGET- ME LEFT FLIPPER IS IN GOOD HEALTH- BLOW ME DOWN!
SEGAR 11-23

THIMBLE THEATER
NOW SHOWING—THE LEFT-HANDED CHAMP.
Tomorrow—Cheated Cheaters.

LET 'IM COME, CAP'N OYL, I CAN TAKE 'IM EVEN WITH A BUSTED FLIPPER - BLOW ME DOWN I CAN
STAND BACK, YOU COWARDLY CROOK! SURELY YOU WOULDN'T HIT A MAN WITH A BROKEN ARM: GLIB, YOU'RE EVEN LOWER THAN I THOUGHT
HE'LL HAVE MORE'N A BROKEN ARM IN ABOUT A MINUTE
I'LL GIVE YOU ALL I'VE GOT AND END IT!!
SOCK
ZAT ALL YA GOT?
YOU SHRIMP, I'LL TEAR—
GET UP AND I'LL THROW THIS IN YOUR FACE

THIMBLE THEATER

NOW SHOWING—CHEATED CHEATERS.

Tomorrow—Time to "Flea."

POPEYE- YOU'RE A WONDER! YOU LICKED 'IM WITH ONE ARM BROKEN
BLOW ME DOWN, I LIKES 'EM TALL- DIDN'T HE FALL PERTY?
I GUESS THAT'LL TEACH HIM A LESSON. WELL - WE GOT REVENGE- BUT THAT DOESN'T GET OUR MONEY BACK
WHY DON'T YA ASK HIM WHAT HE DID WITH YOUR MONEY?
HEY GLIB. WHAT DID YOU DO WITH OUR THIRTY MILLION DOLLARS?
BLABBER AND I CASHED YOUR CHECKS INTENDING TO SAIL FOR EUROPE - BUT WE WERE HELD UP - LOST EVERY CENT - THAT'S WHY WE'RE DOWN HERE AGAIN. WE WANTED TO SWINDLE SOME DUMB WIDOW OUT OF HER FARM
YOU'LL NEVER GO TO HEAVEN IF YOU CHEAT WIDOWS
11-26
SEGAR

THIMBLE THEATER

NOW SHOWING—TIME TO "FLEA."

Tomorrow—Tough Meat

HALF INCH PIPE DON'T MAKE GOOD BARS FOR A JAIL- A KID COULD BUST OUT OF THIS CHICKEN COOP LE'S GO
S-S-H, POPEYE
S-S-H
Z-Z Z-Z Z-Z
WE'RE IN LUCK! NOBODY SAW US. NOT EVEN THAT NOSEY COP
A CLEAN EXCAPE
WHIFFLE
I WISH NOW THAT WE'D STAYED IN JAIL. WE ARE FUGITIVES. FLEEING FROM THE LAW
APPLESAUCE!
POPEYE - WHAT WAS THAT?
OOOUUW
BLEED HOUNDS !!
OOUUW
OOUW
11-27
SEGAR

THIMBLE THEATER

NOW SHOWING—TOUGH MEAT

Tomorrow—Their Master's Voice

OOOOUW
A BUNCH OF BLOODY BLEED HOUNDS, BLOW ME DOWN!
OOUW
HURRY, POPEYE, OR THEY'LL TEAR US TO SHREADS!
THE BLOOD HOUNDS ARE UPON US —! I FEEL LIKE ELIZA CROSSING THE DELAWARE!! OR WAS IT THE HUDSON?
I RUNS FROM NO MAN SO WHY SHOULD I RUN FROM DORGS? I AIN'T GONNA RUN NO MORE
BUT POPEYE, YOU HAVE A BROKEN ARM THEY'LL EAT YOU UP!
SEGAR
11-28

THIMBLE THEATER

NOW SHOWING—THEIR MASTER'S VOICE.
Tomorrow—Face Value.

I RUNS FROM NO MAN, AN' I RUNS FROM NO DORG - AN' I'LL FIGHT 'EM TILL THE MARY ANN STOPS ROLLIN' - BLOW ME DOWN!
OUW OOOUW OOUW OOOUW
I WISH YOU LUCK, BUT I'M MOVING
OOUW OOUW OOUW
!
!
G-R-R
G-R-R
?
SEGAR 11-28

THIMBLE THEATER

NOW SHOWING—FACE VALUE.
Monday—Two's Company, Three's a Crowd.

POPEYE SHOULDN'T HAVE WAITED FOR THOSE BLOOD HOUNDS HE CAN'T FIGHT A PACK OF DOGS
I'D BETTER GO BACK AND SEE IF HE GOT KILLED OR ANYTHING - HEY POPEYE! YOU O.K.?
HOTSY TOTSY
CAP'N OYL, THEM DORGS RUNS LIKE CHICKENS WHEN THEY SEES ME
BUT BLOW ME DOWN, I DON'T KNOW WHY
YOU MEAN TO SAY THE BLOOD HOUNDS RAN WHEN THEY SAW YOU?
SURE - THEY TURNS AROUND AN' BEATS IT - AN' ALL I DONE WAS STICK ME FACE AT 'EM LIKE THIS AN' SAY - G-R-R-R
OH, I SEE— BUT I DON'T THINK THE "G-R-R-R" HAD ANYTHING TO DO WITH IT
11-30 SEGAR

THIMBLE THEATER

NOW SHOWING—TWO'S COMPANY, THREE'S A CROWD
Tomorrow—The Cliff's No Bluff

POPEYE - THEY'VE SLIPPED UP ON US! I'M SURE THERE'S SOMEONE BEHIND THAT BUSH
IT'S YOUR 'MAGINATION, WE LOST 'EM
MAYBE SO - WE DID ENOUGH CIRCLING TO THROW 'EM OFF OUR TRAIL
?
SAY - THERE'S SOMETHING FUNNY ABOUT THAT BUSH
MY GOSH, LOOK! LOOK AT THAT BUSH!
BLOW ME DOWN IT'S MOVIN'!
MOVING !!
12-2 SEGAR

THIMBLE THEATER

NOW SHOWING—THE CLIFF'S NO BLUFF

Tomorrow—The Welcome Bushwhacker

POPEYE, I KNOW WHY THAT BUSH IS MOVING TOWARD US – THERE'S A MAN BEHIND IT – HE'S USING IT AS A BLIND
LET'S GO!
WE'RE COOKED!
A FIFTY FOOT DROP TO THE OCEAN
TRAPPED!!
HEY THERE!!
HEY THERE!
12-3
SEGAR

THIMBLE THEATER

NOW SHOWING—THE WELCOME BUSHWHACKER

Tomorrow—A Gain and a Loss

COME ON. LET'S DIVE INTO THE OCEAN, CAP'N OYL, IT'S ONLY FIFTY FEET
POPEYE, YOU SAY THE SILLIEST THINGS
YOU MAY NOT CARE ABOUT YOUR OWN LIFE – BUT ME – I'M A NICE YOUNG MAN, AND I GOT SOMETHING TO LIVE FOR
WE'RE TRAPPED, AND WE'LL HAVE TO WAIT HERE AND SEE WHO'S SLIPPING UP ON US USING A TREE FOR A DISGUISE – WHAT A MESS WE'RE IN!
LOOK, WHO IT IS – IT'S ONLY THAT HICK COP
WHO'S A' HICK!?
TAKE THAT BACK! GO ON, TAKE IT BACK: WELL, ANYWAY, YOU'RE UNDER ARREST – DON'TCHA TRY NO TRICKS AND DON'TCHA HIT ME EITHER
SEGAR 12-4

THIMBLE THEATER

NOW SHOWING—A GAIN AND A LOSS

Tomorrow—The Powerful Samson

OFFICER, YOU'VE GOT US TRAPPED – BUT YOU CAN'T ARREST US – BECAUSE YOU ARRESTED US A MONTH AGO – AND YOU CAN'T ARREST THE SAME PEOPLE TWICE – I KNOW
I CAN, TOO!
AND I'LL PROVE IT, TOO – I'LL GET OUT MY BOOK OF RULES AND PROVE IT TO YOU
NOW YOU SEE RIGHT HERE IT SAYS – "AN OFFICER CAN ARREST A MAN AS OFTEN AS IS NECESSARY."
WELL, DOGGONE
THAT'S RIGHT YOU WIN
HEY THERE!!!
12-5
SEGAR

THIMBLE THEATER

NOW SHOWING—THE POWERFUL SAMSON

Tomorrow—The Officer Does His Duty

GIMME MY GUN - YA HAD NO RIGHT TO TRICK ME OUT OF IT NOHOW
ALL RIGHT, TAKE IT
!
YA DANGED FOOL THAT WAS A GOOD GUN COST "14^{60}" THIRTY YEARS AGO AND I NEVER EVEN SHOT IT YET
DERN THE LUCK! NOW I AIN'T GOT NO FORTITUDE
SEGAR 12-6

THIMBLE THEATER

NOW SHOWING—THE OFFICER DOES HIS DUTY

Monday—An Air-Minded Sailor

GO ON HOME, COP, YOU CAN'T ARREST US WITHOUT A GUN
YOU FELLERS BREAK JAIL AND WHEN I CAPTURE YOU - YOU WON'T GO BACK WITH ME - YA MAKE ME SICK
DON'T TRY TO STOP US
WE CAN'T STAY HERE ALL DAY - STEP ASIDE, COP
HEY THERE, SHERIFF! I GOT 'EM CAPTURED COME GET 'EM
12-7
SEGAR

THIMBLE THEATER

NOW SHOWING—AN AIR-MINDED SAILOR

Tomorrow—The Dead Rise

POPEYE, WE'RE TRAPPED— THE SHERIFF AND HIS MEN ARE UPON US!
COME ON, SHERIFF, HERE THEY ARE - I'VE GOT 'EM CAPTURED
I HELD 'EM SINGLE HANDED AND I WANT MY WAGES RAISED
BY HECK!
DON'T MOVE - PUT UP YOUR HANDS
BLOW ME DOWN THEY AIN'T GOT US YET— AND WE MAY NOT GET KILLED!
HEY, THERE!!
SEGAR

THIMBLE THEATER

NOW SHOWING—THE DEAD RISE

Tomorrow—Paid in Full

DON'T BE SCARED, CAP'N OYL, OLD POPEYE'S GOT AHOLT OF YA!
!
S P L A S H
THEY'VE BEEN UNDER TEN MINUTES
DERN IT! AND AFTER I HAD 'EM CAPTURED, TOO!
THEY AIN'T UP YET— I'LL BET THEY GOT STUCK IN THE MUD
LE'S GO HOME. THEY'RE DEAD
S-S-H- DON'T MAKE NO NOISE
SEGAR

THIMBLE THEATER

NOW SHOWING—PAID IN FULL

Tomorrow—Alone at Last

SAY, FISHERMAN, HOW MUCH YA WANT FOR THIS ROWER BOAT?
TWENTY BUCKS. BUT I WON'T SELL TO YOU BIRDS- YOU LOOK LIKE THOSE JAIL BREAKERS AND THE SHERIFF'S A FRIEND OF MINE.
YOU DON'T LOOK SO HEALTHY AND YOU COULDN'T FIGHT WITH A BROKEN ARM SO I'LL TAKE YOU BACK TO JAIL
GOT IT ALL FIGERED OUT, AINTCHA?
CAREFUL- POPEYE- DON'T BUST YOUR OTHER ARM
COME ON! LET'S GO FROM HERE!
HERE'S TWENTY DOLLARS- SO DON'T SAY WE STOLD YOUR TUB
SEGAR 12-11

THIMBLE THEATER

NOW SHOWING—ALONE AT LAST

Tomorrow—The Floating Sound

I CAN'T ROWER IT WITH A BUSTED WING SO I'LL HAVE TO SCULL'ER
JUST SO WE KEEP MOVING
AT SEA, IN AN OPEN BOAT!
AN' NO FOOD
WELL ANYWAY WE ESCAPED THE LAW
BLOW ME DOWN WE DID!
HEY, THERE !
SEGAR 12-12

THIMBLE THEATER

NOW SHOWING—THE FLOATING SOUND

Tomorrow—That Bloodhound's a Water Spaniel

GOOD HEAVENS, POPEYE! WE HAVE NO DRINKING WATER!
SURE WE AIN'T. DID YA THINK THIS WAS A FLOATIN' HOTEL?
AND WE AIN'T GOT NO FOOD AND NO NAPKINS OR TOWELS. IN FACK ANYTHING YOU NAME WE AIN'T GOT
BUT WE OUTWITTED THE LAW, AND THAT'S SOMETHING. WHERE YOU HEADIN' FOR, POPEYE?
I'M HEADIN' TO SEA IN A OPEN BOAT. WE'RE FOOLS !!
I THOUGHT I HEARD A VOICE
YA DON'T HEAR VOICES ON THE HIGH SEAS - BLOW ME DOWN, YA DON'T!
HEY, THERE!
HEY, THERE!
HEY, THERE!
HEY, THERE
SEGAR 12-13

THIMBLE THEATER

NOW SHOWING—THAT BLOODHOUND'S A WATER SPANIEL

Monday—Throw Him an Anchor!

I KNOW WHAT'S THE MATTER WITH YA, CAP'N OYL - YA GOT SEA FEVOR. YOU'RE OUTTER YOUR HEAD
POPEYE, I'M IN MY RIGHT MIND - AND I'M TELLING YOU. I HEARD A VOICE
BLOW ME DOWN, YA GONE NUTTY !
YA DON'T HEAR VOICES ON THE HIGH SEAS! IT AIN'T NATURAL!
I WON'T ARGUE WITH YOU - BUT I KNOW WHAT I KNOW!
HEY, THERE! YOU'RE UNDER ARREST! DON'T TRY NO TRICKS AND DONTCHA HIT ME NEITHER
!
!
SEGAR 12-14

THIMBLE THEATER

NOW SHOWING—THROW HIM AN ANCHOR

Tomorrow—The "Buoy" They Left Behind Them

SEE - I TOLD YOU I HEARD A VOICE - THERE'S THAT COP AND ONLY A HUNDRED YARDS BEHIND US
BLOW ME DOWN !
WELL LAY ME IN A SCUPPER IF I AIN'T A LUBBER FOR NOT NOTICIN' THIS OLD PIECE OF CANVAS BEFORE
A SAIL, POPEYE! WE CAN RIG A SAIL!
HEY THERE !!
WHEN WE GETS OUR SAIL RIGGED WE'LL LEAVE YOU BEHIND LIKE A TELEPHOME POST
IN THE NAME OF THE LAW OF BEZARK CENTER I DEMAND THAT YOU GIVE YOURSELVES UP!
WHIFFLE
SEGAR 12-16

THIMBLE THEATER

NOW SHOWING—THE "BUOY" THEY LEFT BEHIND THEM

Tomorrow—Along the Horizon

IT'S LUCKY WE FOUND THAT OLD PIECE OF CANVAS —
ALL SHIP SHAPE AND READY TO LAY TO THE WIND
HEY. THERE
STOP! PULL DOWN THAT SAIL - HOW MANY TIMES MUST I TELL YOU. YOU'RE UNDER ARREST
SAYS YOU
GOOD-BYE, COP
WHERE ARE WE GOING, POPEYE?
NAME IT, CAP'N OYL, BLOW ME DOWN! JUST NAME YOUR PORT!
DERN!
SEGAR
12-17

THIMBLE THEATER

NOW SHOWING—ALONG THE HORIZON

Tomorrow—The Mystery Ship

OUTWITTED ME! GOT CLEAN AWAY! AND ME, AN OFFICER WHO ALWAYS GETS HIS MAN — DERN!
LOST! LOST ON THE HIGH SEAS! AND NO COMPASS - HOW'LL I GET TO SHORE? — MARIA WILL KILL ME IF I AIN'T HOME TO SUPPER
DERN!
WE FOOLED THAT COP - THIS SAIL YOU RIGGED WORKS GREAT
I FEELS SORRY FOR THE LUBBER - I HOPES HE ROWERS HIS BOAT T'WARD LAND
CAP'N OYL WE AIN'T SO LUCKY! NO FOOD! NO WATER! AND THIS ORNERY TUB AIN'T SEA WORTHY BLOW ME DOWN
POPEYE, DON'T TALK LIKE THAT! YOU MAKE ME FEEL TERRIBLE
A SHIP!
AN' NOT A SHEET TO THE WIND!
12-18
SEGAR

THIMBLE THEATER

NOW SHOWING—THE MYSTERY SHIP

Tomorrow—Not a Lady's Man

OF COURSE WE'LL GO ABOARD THIS SHIP - YELL TO 'EM SO THEY CAN DROP A LADDER
I AIN'T YELLIN' TO NOBODY YET - THERE'S SOMETHING STRANGE ABOUT SHIPS IN FAIR WEATHER WITHOUT A SHEET TO THE WIND. I'M TRYIN TO SEE HER NAME
BLOW ME DOWN! IT'S THE BLACK BARNACLE!
WELL - WHAT OF IT?
YOU TALK LIKE YOU'RE AFRAID TO GO ABOARD, POPEYE
I'VE HEARD TALES ABOUT HER - SAILORS SPEAK OF THE BLACK BARNACLE IN WHISPERS LIKE AS IF EVIL SPIRIKS WAS LIS'NIN'
SEGAR
12-19

THIMBLE THEATER

NOW SHOWING—NOT A LADY'S MAN

Tomorrow—Shadows of the Sea

YOU TALK AS THOUGH YOU THINK IT'S A MYSTERY SHIP— BUT THERE'S FOOD ON HER AND I'M HUNGRY— WE CAN'T STAY IN THIS OPEN BOAT
WE KNOWS OUR OPEN BOAT BUT WE DON'T KNOW WHAT'S WAITIN' FOR US ON THE DECKS OF THE "BLACK BARNACLE"
WE'LL— POPEYE— ARE WE GOING ABOARD OR NOT?
IF YOU SAYS CLIMB ON, WE CLIMBS ON, BUT IT'S AGAINST THE JUDGEMENT OF OLD POPEYE WHO KNOWS WHAT HE KNOWS
THE "BLACK BARNACLE" CAP'N OYL, BELONGS TO THE SEA HAG !!
SEA HAG ?
WHO'S SHE? SEA HAG! GEE, WHAT A CREEPY NAME!
I NEVER DID SEE HER AN' I HOPES I'LL NEVER LAY ME GOOD EYE ON A CREATURE LIKE I HEARD SHE IS— AN' IF I THOUGHT SHE'S ON BOARD I'D SET ME SAILS AND GO FROM HERE, BLOW ME DOWN
SEGAR 12-20

THIMBLE THEATER

NOW SHOWING—SHADOWS OF THE SEA

Monday—The Haunted Ship

THE "BLACK BARNACLE," SO POPEYE SAYS, IS A MYSTERY SHIP— QUEER TALES AND HORRIBLE THINGS HAVE BEEN TOLD BY SAILORMEN ABOUT THIS OLD HULK OF A SCHOONER AND THE "SEA HAG," ITS OWNER, SO THE RUMOR GOES, IS A HORRIBLE CREATURE SO TERRIBLE THAT EVEN THE BLOOD OF A FEARLESS MAN LIKE POPEYE RUNS COLD AT THE VERY MENTION OF HER— A WITCHLIKE CREATURE OF THE DEEP ——
YOU'VE LET YOUR SAILOR SUPERSTITIONS GET THE BEST OF YOU, POPEYE— I'LL BET THE SHIP'S O.K.
THERE AIN'T A SAILOR LIVIN' BUT WHAT WOULD DRUTHER LOSE A EYE THAN BOARD THE BLACK BARNACLE!
I'M NO COWARD— CAP'N OYL, AND WE'LL HOP ONTO HER— BUT IF THE SEA HAG IS ON'ER— ME HEART'LL STOP AN' THAT'S A FACK, BLOW ME DOWN!
I AIN'T NEVER FAILED TO GET MY MAN YET AND I AIN'T GONNA BEGIN FAILIN' NOW NEITHER
SEGAR 12-21

THIMBLE THEATER

NOW SHOWING—THE HAUNTED SHIP

Tomorrow—Shiver Me Timbers

THERE'S A ROPE HANGING OVER HER SIDE— STEER FOR IT— I'M GOING ON BOARD
WHEN YOU GET'S ON, DROP ME A ROPE LADDER. I CAN'T SCOOT UP A LINE WITH ME BUSTED FIN
HUH! THAT'S FUNNY! I DON'T SEE ANYBODY AROUND
SHE'S ABANDONED, POPEYE— IT'S A DESERTED SHIP!
"BLACK BARNACLE" THE SHIP OF HORRYBLE TALES— I FEELS CREEPY
WHAT'S THERE TO BE AFRAID OF? WE'RE ALONE
I FEELS LIKE THERE'S EVIL SPIRIKS ALL AROUN' ME— BLOW ME DOWN I DON'T LIKE THIS!
!
SEGAR 12-23

THIMBLE THEATER

NOW SHOWING—SHIVER ME TIMBERS

Tomorrow—That "Oarful" Noise

BELIEVE ME OR NOT, CAP'N OYL. BUT BEFORE WE COME ABOARD I SWEARS I HEARD THE SQUEEK OF A DONKEY ENGINE
POPEYE, YOU'RE TRYING TO MAKE A MYSTERY - YOU'RE ALL WET UNDER THE HAT
THERE'S NOBODY ON THIS SHIP BUT US. SHE'S BEEN ABANDONED, WE'RE ALONE
REMEMBER, WE'RE ON THE BLACK BARNACLE WHICH IS OWNED BY THE TERRIBLE SEA HAG - AND HORRYBLE TALES HAS BEEN TOLD ABOUT 'ER
THIS SHIP MAY HAVE A CREW OF GHOSTS! GHOSTS OF THE MEN WHAT'S BEEN MURDERED ON HER DECKS! EVIL SPIRIKS, TOO
DON'T BE LIKE THAT, YOU MAKE ME FEEL TERRIBLE
12-24 SEGAR

THIMBLE THEATER

NOW SHOWING—THAT "OARFUL" NOISE

Tomorrow—Through the Hatch

POPEYE - I WISH YOU'D STOP TELLING ME ABOUT THE "SEA HAG" WHO OWNS THIS SHIP, THE BLACK BARNACLE
YOU'VE GOT MY NERVES STANDING ON END! I JUMP EVERY TIME I HEAR THE SQUAWK OF A GULL
CAP'N OYL, I GOTTER HUNCH WE AIN'T ALONE ON THIS SHIP - I FEELS WE AIN'T - LIKE WE THOUGHT WE WAS
IT'S ONLY YOUR SAILOR SUPERSTITION WORKING ON YOU - WE'RE O.K.
WHAT WAS THAT ?!
KREEK
THEY CAN'T OUTWIT ME, BY HECK - I'D ROW THIS BOAT TO CHINA TO CATCH THEM RASCALS
SEGAR 12-25

THIMBLE THEATER

NOW SHOWING—THROUGH THE HATCH

Tomorrow—The Topic of Conversation

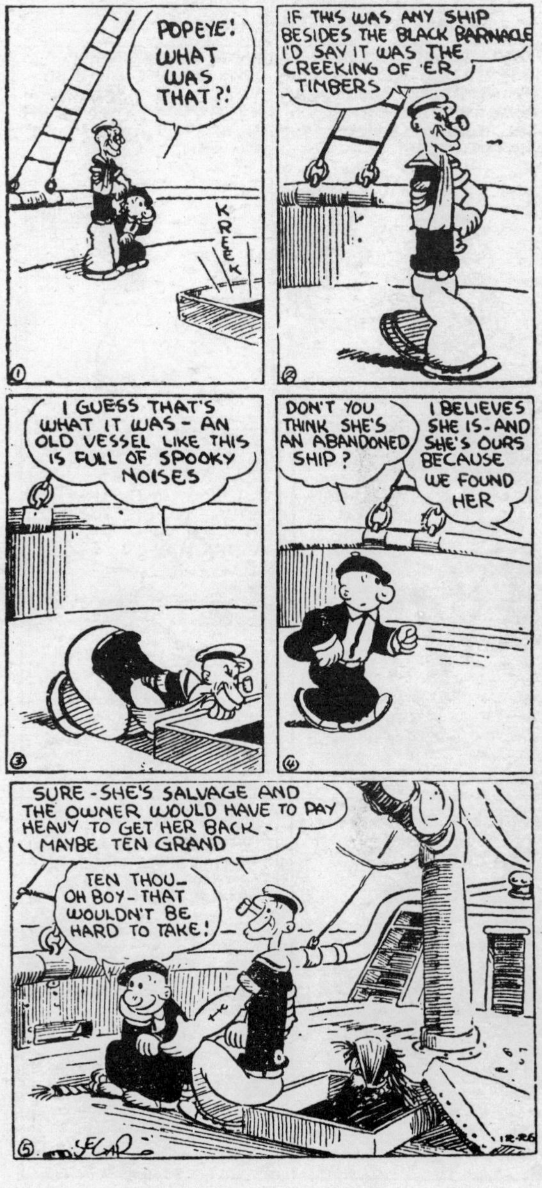
POPEYE! WHAT WAS THAT?!
KREEK
IF THIS WAS ANY SHIP BESIDES THE BLACK BARNACLE I'D SAY IT WAS THE CREEKING OF 'ER TIMBERS
I GUESS THAT'S WHAT IT WAS - AN OLD VESSEL LIKE THIS IS FULL OF SPOOKY NOISES
DON'T YOU THINK SHE'S AN ABANDONED SHIP?
I BELIEVES SHE IS - AND SHE'S OURS BECAUSE WE FOUND HER
SURE - SHE'S SALVAGE AND THE OWNER WOULD HAVE TO PAY HEAVY TO GET HER BACK - MAYBE TEN GRAND
TEN THOU - OH BOY - THAT WOULDN'T BE HARD TO TAKE!
SEGAR 12-26

THIMBLE THEATER

NOW SHOWING—THE TOPIC OF CONVERSATION
Tomorrow—Under Observation

POPEYE, I THINK THIS SHIP IS PERFECTLY O.K. AND THAT THE TALES YOU HEARD ABOUT HER ARE IMAGINARY THE RESULT OF SAILOR SUPERSTITION
CAP'N OYL, THIS SHIP IS OURS BECAUSE WE FOUND ER ADRIFT- SHE'S SALVAGE AND THE OWNER WOULD HAVE TO PAY TO GET 'ER BACK
BUT THE SEA HAG OWNS THE BLACK BARNACLE AND I AIN'T TRYIN' TO COLLECT ANYTHING FROM HER
YOU HAD ME SHAKEY AT FIRST WITH YOUR SEA HAG STORIES. BUT NOW I THINK THEY'RE MYTHS - I'LL BET THERE'S NO SUCH THING AS A SEA HAG
SHE'S REAL ALL RIGHT- I AIN'T TOLD YOU ALL ABOUT HER - I KNOWS MORE THINGS WORSE'N THE TALES I TOLD YOU
HOOMAN LIFE AIN'T NOTHIN' TO HER! SHE'S HORRYBLE AND THAT'S A FACK!
SEGAR

THIMBLE THEATER

NOW SHOWING—UNDER OBSERVATION
Monday—Three Is a Crowd

A SHIP! I'LL BET THEY'RE ON THAT SHIP!
POPEYE, I'M NEARLY STARVED- LET'S LOOK IN THE GALLEY, THERE MAY BE FOOD
I DON'T LIKE SNOOPIN' AROUND THIS TUB- WE MIGHT FIND SOMETHING HORRYBLE
WE MIGHT FIND BUMPED OFF MEN SITTING IN CHAIRS! I HEARD TALES ABOUT 'EM LIKE THAT ON THE BLACK BARNACLE
I'M NOT A BIT HUNGRY
POPEYE, I'VE GOT THAT FUNNY FEELING LIKE THERE WAS SOMEONE STARING AT ME
GHOSTS LOOKIN' AT US - GHOSTS OF THEM WHAT DIED ON THIS SHIP
SEGAR

THIMBLE THEATER

NOW SHOWING—THREE IS A CROWD
Tomorrow—The Ghost Ship

POPEYE, WE OUGHT TO LOOK THE SHIP OVER- AT LEAST WE SHOULD EXPLORE THE GALLEY. THERE MIGHT BE FOOD
I'M NOT HUNGRY ENOUGH TO SNOOP AROUND THIS SHIP. WE MIGHT FIND SOMETHING HORRYBLE, LIKE DEAD MEN SITTING IN CHAIRS
SAY, IF YOU DON'T LAY OFF THAT LINE OF TALK I'LL COLLAPSE! YOU GOT ME SCARED STIFF!
ALL YOU TALK ABOUT IS SEA HAGS - EVIL SPIRITS AND MYSTERY- I SAY THAT WE'RE ALONE AND SAFE ON THIS SHIP
HEY, THERE! YOU'RE UNDER ARREST! DON'T TRY NO TRICKS AND DON'TCHA HIT ME NEITHER
SEGAR 12-30

THIMBLE THEATER

NOW SHOWING—THE GHOST SHIP
Tomorrow—The Immortal One

YA DERN TOOTIN' I FOLLOWED YA—AND YOU'RE UNDER ARREST
I ALWAYS GET MY MAN!
WELL—NOW THAT YOU'VE GOT US, WHAT ARE YOU GOING TO DO WITH US?
TAKE YA TO BEEZARK CENTER AND PUTCHA BACK IN JAIL
WE GOT SOMETHING TO SAY ABOUT THAT
WHERE'S THE CAPTAIN? I'LL HAVE HIM TURN ABOUT AND TAKE US TO SHORE
THERE AIN'T NO CAPTAIN
THIS IS THE BLACK BARNACLE, A MYSTERY SHIP. NO CREW OR NOTHIN'—BUT THERE MAY BE PILES AND PILES OF BUMPED OFF MEN IN THE CABINS AND THERE'S EVIL SPIRIKS ALL 'ROUND US
WELL I SWAN!
SURE! AND MAYBE MEN WALKING AT NIGHT WITHOUT HEADS